THE
ARTS
ON
TELEVISION

Fifteen Years of
Cultural Programming

Supported by the
National Endowment
for the Arts

1976-
1990

ii

For sale by the U.S. Government Printing Office
Superintendent of Documents, Mail Stop: SSOP, Washington, DC 20402-9328
ISBN 0-16-035926-0

ACKNOWLEDGMENTS

Among the many careful readers who helped weed out inaccuracies and verify the spellings of hundreds of names were John Ligon and Georgia Gould, ALIVE FROM OFF CENTER; Diane Dufault and Susan Lacy, AMERICAN MASTERS; Janet Young, AMERICAN PLAYHOUSE; Judy Kinberg, DANCE IN AMERICA; Lauri Straney, LIVE FROM LINCOLN CENTER; Susan Erben, THE METROPOLITAN OPERA PRESENTS; Dora Lewis, P.O.V.; Margaret Tiberio, NEW TELEVISION; Deborah Nicholson, THE INDEPENDENTS; Melanie Parkhurst, WONDERWORKS.

Those who researched photos and lent them to us included: Suzanne Faulkner Stevens and Gloria Gottschalk, LIVE FROM LINCOLN CENTER; Allan Abrams, VOICES AND VISIONS; Mimi Johnson, Performing Arts Services; Deborah French, QED COMMUNI-CATIONS; Ellen Schneider, P.O.V.; Gary Clare, Bill O'Donnell, GREAT PERFORMANCES; Judy Kinberg, DANCE IN AMERICA; and the Public Broadcasting Service. Individuals who kindly supplied photos and/or granted us permission to use them include: John Huszar, William Struh, David Berger, Milt Hinton, Herbert Migdoll.

Leading the librarians who helped fill in gaps in information were Alice Wilder and Nancy Brine of the Public Broadcasting Service Library. Many were the public librarians who consulted reference books for us, clarifying the finest points. Joy Evans and Holly Tank of the National Endowment for the Humanities provided background information, advice and insight.

Among the Arts Endowment's staff who assisted in many capacities were Debra Thomas, Deborah Parker, Dirickson Nutt, Johnie Lewis, Joan La Rocca, Chris Morrison, Jeanne McConnell and Sue Coliton. Three Media Arts Fellows, Carol Ehler, Cathy Phoenix and Patti Bruck, conducted considerable research. This book could not have happened without the contributions of former Media Arts Program staff, Chloe Aaron, Catherine Wyler, Julia Moore, Susan Lively and Maria Goodwin; of the current managers of the Arts on Television program, Laura Welsh and La'Verne Washington; and of Media Arts staff members Rob McQuay and Cliff Whitham. Thanks go finally to Randolph McAusland for his cogent advice on the design of this book at a crucial stage in its genesis, and for his encouragement at every turn.

—R.K.

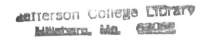

The Media Arts: Film/Radio/Television Program is one of 12 discipline programs in the National Endowment for the Arts, a federal agency. The media arts include documentary, experimental, animated and narrative works, as well as audio art. The basic aims of the program are fostered by the encouragement of new work by artists of exceptional talent; the distribution of that work through exhibition, broadcast, cable and cassette; and the preservation of the highly vulnerable heritage of this youngest of the arts. The program has a special interest in bringing the best of all the arts to the widest possible audience through the support of nationally-broadcast radio and television programs.

John E. Frohnmayer, Chairman
National Endowment for the Arts

Brian O'Doherty, Director
Media Arts Program

Compiled, researched and edited by Rebecca Krafft
Editorial supervision and introductory essays by Brian O'Doherty
Book design by Designlink, Bethesda, Md.

Published by Media Arts: Film/Radio/Television Program,
National Endowment for the Arts, Fall, 1991
Printed by the U.S. Government Printing Office

For further information contact:
Media Arts: Film/Radio/Television Program, Room 720
National Endowment for the Arts
1100 Pennsylvania Avenue, N.W.
Washington, DC 20506

Library of Congress Cataloging-in-Publication Data

The Arts on television, 1976-1990 : fifteen years of cultural programming supported by the National Endowment for the Arts / [compiled, researched and edited by Rebecca Krafft].
         p. cm.
         Includes index.
         1. Television and the performing arts—United States. 2. Television programs—United States. I. Krafft, Rebecca. II. National Endowment for the Arts.
PN1992.66.A78 1991
791.45'75'097309047—dc20   91-34045
                                                              CIP

CONTENTS

FOREWORD

John E. Frohnmayer
Chairman,
National Endowment for the Arts

Television is the main source of information and entertainment for most Americans. Television can also give all Americans, of all races, ages and locations their birthright: access to the highest quality art of this and prior generations.

As this volume makes abundantly clear, the National Endowment for the Arts has helped provide access to our heritage by its support of broadcasts on public television. Since 1976, the Endowment has supported over 1,000 television programs in 31 series. Viewers can see Baryshnikov dance, Seiji Ozawa conduct, Jessye Norman sing, Alan Lomax discourse on folk music, Pinchas Zukerman play, Georgia O'Keeffe reminisce, Max Roach play the drums. The programs detailed here show not only the range of formal arts—symphony, dance, theater and opera—but the vigorous profusion of informal, folk and vernacular arts throughout the country. The quality of these programs (and the talents of their originators) has been publicly acclaimed virtually everywhere honors are given.

Planning began for the Arts on Television in 1972 with the Endowment's second chairman, Nancy Hanks, and the Media Arts Program's founding director, Chloe Aaron. Responsibility for development of this major initiative was assigned to the Arts on Television section of the Media Arts Program. Each year since then, advisory panels have helped formulate policy and have recommended grant awards. These panels of citizens, drawn from several fields and every part of the nation, reevaluate ongoing series each year and carefully scrutinize plans for new ones. Their recommendations have been closely monitored by the National Council on the Arts, which in turn has shaped the Endowment's goal of broad dissemination of this quality work.

For those Americans who by reason of geography, economics or disability do not have access to symphony halls, opera houses, theaters and museums, the best of the arts has been brought into their homes. A quarter of the PBS audience lives in rural areas and small towns. For them Arts on Television has particular meaning.

Because the arts help us define who we are and what we value, broadcasts have frequently been supplemented by printed matter delivered to home and school. These performances have not just entertained, they have enhanced our perception, stimulated our thinking, broadened our knowledge.

No education in the arts can proceed without exposure to the art form itself. Literacy in the arts is something that every child has a right to expect during the course of his or her education; the Arts on Television have made that possible. And, the vast educational potential of the fifteen-year archive remains to be fully realized through cassette distribution. To give a sense of its potential, in 1990, eight major series supported by the Arts Endowment brought 125 hours of programming to a cumulative audience of 310 million people at a cost per viewer of 1.5 cents of taxpayers' money.

The Endowment's dedication to quality public television has encouraged adventurous private funders to make common cause in bringing the

> *"No education in the arts can proceed without exposure to the art form itself. Literacy in the arts is something that every child has a right to expect during the course of his or her education."*

arts to broadcast. Without such partners, these programs would not have been possible. Corporate and foundation executives have generously carried the major load, matching the Endowment's dollar three and sometimes up to six times. The contributions of the Corporation for Public Broadcasting, the Station Program Cooperative, the Public Broadcasting Service and its member stations have also been crucial.

The Endowment owes particular thanks to Congress and the Presidents who have supported our efforts. To paraphrase our enabling legislation, the government cannot call a great artist into being, but it can create the climate in which that artist can flourish. Nowhere is the success of that vision more apparent than in the pages you are about to read.

INTRODUCTION

Brian O'Doherty
Director, Media Arts: Film/Radio/
Television Program

Television's power is in its magnetic seductiveness, its chromatic virtuosity, its donation of iconic status to the banal, its blithe leveling of content, its moral neutrality, its ability to witness, and above all, in its processes. It is perfectly tractable to virtually any task; it will sell anything for you: ways of seeing and feeling, an ideology, a product, a person, an event. Even when the dead screen dimly reflects the world outside in its curved glass, it is a formidable potency. What happens to the arts when they inhabit our society's most ambiguous piece of furniture?

When the Endowment's Arts on Television enterprise began in 1972, the ecology of media was so different that it now looks like an archaic electronic age. The networks, uncontested in their monopoly, had a 90% share of the audience, and had just begun their decline to the low sixties. Their attitude to the arts was frequently enlightened and the classics of arts programming still rebuke much of today's product—CBS's *Omnibus*, the Toscanini concerts, *Playhouse 90*, Menotti's *Amahl and the Night Visitors*. High culture frequently slummed it on variety shows; on *The Ed Sullivan Show*, Marian Anderson might appear between Señor Wences and Peg Leg Bates (who in the welcome transactions between so-called high and low culture, now appears as an accredited American master on PBS).

The Public Broadcasting Service (PBS) was born out of the expiring body of National Educational Television in 1969. As Brian G. Rose points out in his pioneering book, *Television and the Performing Arts*, the growth of PBS absolved commercial stations from cultural quotas and the networks from residual guilt with respect to high culture, whose ratings were always comparatively low. The harsh imperatives of commerce pushed the arts off the networks' schedules, thereby withdrawing the arts' access to the networks' admirably mixed audience. PBS, politically disempowered in the 1970s through regulatory restrictions, for a time was generously hospitable to the arts. Two commercial ventures in the early 1980s, CBS Cable and the ABC/Hearst ARTS channel, tested whether the arts could generate revenue on the multiple-choice spectrum of cable television. The admirable CBS experiment failed quickly; ARTS merged with The Entertainment Channel and survived as the A&E Network, an interesting documentary, feature film and comedy channel. Bravo, which started up in 1980, became the most adventurous of the "arts channels," and remains so. However, since 1974, Endowment-supported arts programming has been linked to the vicissitudes of PBS and its constituent stations.

When Nancy Hanks, the Endowment's second Chairman, and Chloe Aaron, the Media Arts Program's founding director, sought ways of introducing regular arts programming to PBS in 1974, there were serviceable precedents. *Great Performances*, created by Jac Venza and WNET/Thirteen in New York, had been in place for a year and the Endowment had briefly funded *NET Playhouse* in the late 1960s. Much of public television's product was British. But American arts programming, insisting on its presence week after week, was missing. Hanks, Aaron and colleagues at the Ford Foundation, the Corporation for Public Broadcasting (CPB) and Exxon, established the ideal constellation of support for an arts series: a gifted production staff with suitable expertise in the art form, a host station, a welcoming PBS and CPB, foundation and corporate sponsors. And of course, the possibility of a significant audience, "significant" meaning an audience at least in the hundreds of thousands. But more

---

"Series could be watched or ignored, but at least, the cultural birthright was available amidst television's general pottage."

---

important was the notion of *access*— that if the art form were broadcast, choice was possible. The series could be watched or ignored, but at least, the cultural birthright was available amidst television's general pottage. Out of this first excursion came two series which still vigorously survive, *Live from Lincoln Center* and *Dance in America*.

These first ventures clarified how series were—and are—validated: the panel process. This process, indispensable to the Endowment's function, is still widely misunderstood. All applications eventually come to a diversely-composed, outside panel of peers, experts and laypersons, appointed by the Endowment's Chairman, which reviews the submitted written materials and sample films and videos. This panel's recommendations are submitted to the presidentially appointed National Council on the Arts, which meets quarterly, for its review. The National Council advises the Chairman, who alone, by law, is empowered to award grants. It is the integrity of this process—involving free discussion by continually changing groups of individuals whose actual and potential conflicts are scrupulously minimized—that gives the results conviction. Thus, hovering in the vicinity of every successful—and on occasion unsuccessful—series are the enabling contributions of serial panels over fifteen years, contributions remarkable for their cogency, argumentativeness and vision.

Insofar as this process is trusted, not just by applicants, participants, the Endowment, but by the public on the one hand, and by Congress on the other, the much-cited integrity of the process is maintained. A further criterion of success is how these panel results are perceived by other funders. The Arts on Television program's annual budget, which in the period of this report varied from $1.7 million to $6.1 million, is a useful tactical instrument for initiating series and supporting them modestly from year to year. Costs have climbed steadily, but the Endowment's budget has not. In 1974, an hour program could be produced, on an average, for $250,000; that cost has more than doubled. The Endowment must be deeply grateful to other funding partners who usually carry the main burden of support. Any report on the arts on television must also note the way in which the National Endowment for the Humanities, in fulfilling its own legislative mandates, has made common cause on several series.

"It is the integrity of this [the panel] process—involving free discussion by continually changing groups of individuals whose actual and potential conflicts are scrupulously minimized—that gives the results conviction."

Now that the fiscal landscape is intimidatingly bare, the decade and a half reported on here looks, in retrospect, like an age, if not of gold, certainly of silver. The oil companies' fascination with public television reached its apogee as enlightened executives exercised a sophisticated taste in the arts. Exxon steadfastly funded *Live from Lincoln Center*, *Dance in America* and *Great Performances*. Mobil, wary of partners, forcefully developed its own esthetic preferences, particularly for *Masterpiece Theater*. Texaco preceded all others in its support for the Metropolitan Opera radio (1931) and television (1977) broadcasts, and its sponsorship remains after the others' has ceased. Alternative funding has not been readily forthcoming, and current economic travails have brought other social priorities to the top of many sponsors' agenda. At the end of the period reported in this book, the arts were learning that in times of economic crisis, they are unpleasantly vulnerable, leading to discomforting speculations on the public perception of the arts as indispensable to our culture.

Public television, during this period, suffered numerous vicissitudes. Prompted in part by the advent of commercial cablearts, it conducted exacting self-examinations. Chronically underfunded and administered through parallel systems (PBS/CPB) that encouraged misunderstandings and blurred decision-making, it remained friendly, nevertheless, to Endowment initiatives as developed by constituent stations. The introduction in 1979 of a prime-time schedule (8:00 to 10:00pm, Monday through Thursday) was a significant advance in defining PBS as a potential network with simultaneous carriage. As cable and cassette continued to multiply viewers' choices, public television shared the audience erosion suffered on a much larger scale by the networks, with which PBS is unequivocally in competition. This has forced public television to borrow some of the techniques and practices of commercial television, as well as develop the regular programming strands

> *"It is the particular glory of broadcast that it presents the work directly, without intervention, and indifferent to age and gender, across geographic, economic, ethnic and educational boundaries."*

that build an audience through an evening. Public television's most radical move was made in 1990, when its division of decision-making powers was concentrated in a single vice-president, Jennifer Lawson, who has sole responsibility in funding, programming and managing the weekly schedule. This has helped remove the somewhat Balkanized negotiations through which public television programs were funded. Ms. Lawson's openness and sympathies with the arts are a matter of record, but the fate of the arts on public television is impacted by several long-term developments.

For the arts must now compete for a place in the schedule with science and public affairs which, in this time of endemic crises, make strong claims on the public's attention. The arts do not generate comparable ratings, and ratings, for local stations which depend on viewer support for over half their budgets, become a matter of survival. Thus the long thirteen-part art series once launched regularly on public television is no longer welcome—in large part because its quality is unpredictable and may lock a station into a reluctant commitment for the duration. Public television now cherishes its mobility, its ability to shift schedules, and aggressively play to its strengths in soliciting the audience's attention. PBS's recent triumphs—*The Civil War* series and *The Ring Cycle* (see page 28)—have been impressive. Its daring has been commendable, though several of the system's individual stations may not be overly hospitable to forceful examinations of controversial issues, issues which the arts increasingly explore.

It is difficult for those devoted to the arts to accept that on television, the arts are just another special interest. While the rhetoric that "the arts provide a culture with its spiritual coordinates and ennoble and enlarge its participants" is still convincing to some, this perception of the arts and, crudely, how they sell themselves, may be out of date. The traditional view has been that from the beginning of the republic, the arts have not been intrinsic to the workings of the practical, empirical American mind. This view is also out of date. The period covered in this book witnessed the insertion of the arts into the mainstream discourse, a process powerfully augmented by television. With the passage of the modernist era, which insulated the arts within their conventional boundaries, each art now exists in a more urgent social context. This agency has been continually reminded that the arts have been projected into the national discourse and that the contribution the arts can make in responding to the major issues of the day is invaluable, if at times their mode of discourse is not couched in terms attractive to all.

It is intrinsic to broadcast that the audience is unselected—rather, self-selected—and is thus brought abruptly into theater and concert hall, or directly into the film or video work. Thus television decontextualizes the arts—a theme of post-modernism—exposing them to audiences uninstructed in their codes and methods. While this may lead to serious misinterpretations, it is the particular glory of broadcast that it presents the work directly, without intervention, and indifferent to age and gender, across geographic, economic, ethnic and educational boundaries. Such access is invaluable in areas of so-called high culture, where the codes of the art form are more widely shared. The Arts on Television enterprise has steadily supported, with its co-funders, the broadcast of the magnificent engines of high culture (Metropolitan Opera, Lincoln Center, American Ballet Theatre, L.A. Philharmonic, etc.), the existence of which is more fragile than is generally realized.

Broadcast has involved what Deborah Jowitt has called "translation," the re-presentation of the work—whether symphony, dance, or theater—on the television screen. The unsophisticated view holds that television, like some utensil, "carries" such arts to the audience. Since television is itself transformative, all television representation involves translation, translation that is the domain of the media artist/director. This is not the place to speculate on the nature of television's compressed space and smooth electronic time, but it is the place to point to the development of a brilliant cadre of television directors, particularly in opera and dance, in the fifteen years under discussion. Such pioneering figures as Merrill Brockway, the late Peter Weinberg, Brian Large, Kirk Browning, David Griffiths and several others developed, as Brian Rose discerned, perceptible styles. To the complex group art that performance always is, the further component of the television art itself comes into play. The resulting hybrid is itself a fusion art form.

Dance, for instance, is perhaps the most exacting of the arts in translation to television. Unlike opera, which is not known for quicksilver movement, dance is impossible to photograph live on stage. Frequently, *Dance in America* went to a large sound stage in Nashville, Tennessee, to re-enact its scenarios. But how to construct the space of the dance, to choose shots that enhance the choreographer's intent,

without cutting off hands and feet, the unforgivable error in televising dance? This demands profound advance knowledge of the choreographic "score"—of the music, of individual and group action—as the television "score"—angles, number of cameras, close-ups versus wide shots, where to truck and pan, etc.—is plotted. At all times, as Fred Astaire was the first to insist, the full figure in motion must not be compromised by over-interpretation or directorial self-indulgence. The development of these directorial skills in interpretation and translation is one of public television's finest achievements.

Media artists, however, have an even more ambitious agenda for television. Their aim is not to translate or witness formal art events. They make work that is inseparable from the television medium and which, like film, makes no concessions other than to the artistic imperatives of the medium itself. This ambition is fulfilled in several Endowment-supported series. When it began, the survival of *Alive from Off Center* (page 158) in the public television environment would have been accounted as, at the least, unlikely. Utterly uncompromising in its presentation, the series locates itself firmly in the precincts of what used to be called the avant-garde, or two avant-gardes: the most advanced international thinking on movement, theater and language on the one hand, and advanced video art on the other. The results, whether teledance or teletheater, have no existence apart

from their video presentation. In this high-risk area, three successive executive producers and their staffs have offered welcome difficulties amidst television's generally obliging excursions, and have colonized on public television a vivid ground for risk, experiment and sheer invention. Similarly, the individual vision of the video artists presented on *New Television* implicitly criticizes the weary conventions through which most television narratives jog to their appointed ends.

Documentary, non-fiction, or factual film/video has traditionally generated numerous debates on objectivity, balance and the vexed nature of "reality." In partnership with the Ford Foundation, the Endowment entered this field with *Non-Fiction Television*, first broadcast in 1979 (see page 194), with the late David Loxton as the exceptionally gifted executive producer. Media artists were commissioned and received full funding for their projects, avoiding the years of fund-raising that repeatedly stall independent productions. Three years after the demise of *Non-Fiction Television*, Marc N. Weiss and David M. Davis initiated the acquisition series *P.O.V.* (taken from the screenwriter's shorthand for "point of view"; see page 169). *P.O.V.*, along with WGBH/Boston's *Frontline*, are the windows through which the independent film/video artist projects his or her vision of the world and its events. A documentary magazine, with the video equivalents of editorial board, publisher and editor-in-chief, *P.O.V.* fulfills (twenty-five years after the development of technology that made video available to the individual) the dream of adding to broadcast the voices of individuals unheard during the era of network monopoly. Like the painter or writer, the film/video documentarian sees the world and its vicissitudes as potential subject matter. The documentarian's art frequently lies in presenting its overt subject in a way that leaves the viewer the responsibility of forming his or her opinion. As a form of enlight-

"Since children at a critical developmental stage acquire most of their information from television, literacy in media is at least as important as literacy in print."

ened witnessing, it avoids the coerciveness that compromises the viewer's independent judgment.

This touches on a matter intrinsic to all television viewing and which is high on the agenda of the Media Arts Program: educating the audience to decipher the covert messages implicit in the bewildering glut of programs that crowd the television spectrum. Many believe that in this century the electronic media compromised public discourse and transgressed every privacy; how important it is then, that the audience become aware of the modes of manipulation to which it is

subjected and, through such awareness, develop the capacity to filter and criticize what is presented to it as truth. The values intrinsic to much television entertainment require at least some ironic scrutiny; such entertainment favors effortless assimilation through predictable, indeed predetermined responses. Since children at a critical developmental stage acquire most of their information from television, literacy in media is at least as important as literacy in print. Within the period covered by this book, the Endowment engaged in an intense research and development project with a private funder to develop a series enabling children between the ages of eight and ten to become literate in media and in the arts. This will come to fruition in the 1990s. Programs in media literacy are also conducted by several media arts centers funded by the Endowment.

Fifteen years' support of arts programming has accumulated a panorama of productions that takes in important aspects of our culture. Preservation of and access to this material is the appropriate completion of this enterprise. Television, which consumes omnivorously, traditionally saw little utility in preserving its past. But the value, and shelf-life, of this fifteen-year archive is indubitable. It documents the presence and thinking of major artists whose image and substance would otherwise be lost; it shows the outstanding dance companies of the era in full performance; its

operatic record is—and will be—historically fascinating, particularly to those eager to compare performances widely separated in time; independent makers witness and present an extraordinary range of issues of national and personal import; some of the greatest actors of the period perform (often previous to their greater fame) in productions written by some of the country's outstanding writers; the art of video is followed up to and through the moment it achieved maturity; some of the era's signature musicians and performers, classical, jazz and folk, have been placed on the record, as have many of our finest orchestras and ensembles. The appendix on page 215 gives the distribution sources for individual programs. Several have already been released on cassette. Many of the dance and music programs are detained by rights negotiations which limit their circulation. The Endowment desires that all these programs be made available whenever possible; stations, producers and performers must, when necessary, proceed step by step through the difficult legal territory that retards their release.

Has this fifteen-year record been guided by a coherent policy or long-term plan? Under the rubric of "making the best available to the most," certain aspects of the record are obvious. Support has been weighted heavily towards the performing arts where the great companies' repertory and performers are immediately available; here, as pointed out previously, the issue is one of translation. Six of the eight ongoing series are thus drawn from the performing arts. In non-performing arts (photography, architecture and design, poetry, painting, sculpture) the approach—format, style, host, editorial direction—has to be invented. Several series, limited in length, have been offered in poetry, visual art, design, folk art, advanced music.

Any one discipline, however, can stand several investigations, and a single series in one area, for example design, cannot be assigned the responsibility of providing the definitive word. This would slight the diversity of talents, subjects, approaches and audiences available. Following the consistent advice of several panels, the Endowment undertook to bring each art to the national audience, including the contributions of media artists whose work continually redefines the conventions of film and television. Making a record of our major artists through documentary portraits was considered a high priority, which has been met. Programs should also reflect the diversity of the audience and of the creative community. An overall plan for the Arts on Television however is subject to numerous variables that inevitably compromise its reach. Implementing such a policy and plan depends on the passion of media artists and producers, the usual budgetary constraints, access to air-time, the consensus of panels and advisors, and, ultimately, on finding funding part-ners. In this last essential, as the list on page 204 makes clear, the Endowment has been most fortunate.

As one period ends, however, planning for the next is well underway. Series on the contributions of dance, American film and music in the twenti-eth century were funded in the period under review, and will reach broad-cast over the next few years. These series are part of a larger Arts on Television project for the 1990s re-peatedly endorsed by panels: the development of parallel series on each of the arts in this century. This is a magnificent theme: how have the arts responded to the great events of this tumultuous century? How have they transformed and irrevocably altered our perceptions? How have they con-tributed to our understanding of our past and present, and how do they position us to face the approaching horizon of the twenty-first century? While the Endowment can help formu-late such projects, their fulfillment depends on the graces of enlightened co-funders.

Since 1976 the media universe has been radically transformed. The in-creased choices offered by cable (60% of American homes are now cabled); more pay-per-view; the cassette revo-lution; satellite distribution; interac-tive television; virtual reality; a techni-cally sophisticated camcorder available to everyone; the decline in network audiences—all have reversed one of the most persistently held no-tions about television: that it reduces the exhilarating diversity of a society to a numb uniformity. We now know that media can define sub-groups, serve and enhance local and ethnic pride, encourage criticism and dia-logue. The arts, with their vivid con-stituencies, clearly have claims here. But nothing in media remains stable. The advance of technology is already pressing upon us, and new technolo-gies always alter the way information is delivered and perceived. The further multiplication of channels from around 40 to over 300 through fiber optics will call for more product for which funds are increasingly scanty; this will intensify the competition for the audience. Can the arts diversify their distribution across this new landscape? Will the development of a new generation of high-definition receivers, clarifying the ambiguities of television's space, enable the arts to extend their audience? Ten or fifteen years from now, when another publi-cation details the record on govern-ment support for the arts on television, we will see whether the gains made in the past fifteen years were sustained or, we hope, far surpassed.

Sources:

Brian G. Rose, *Television and the Performing Arts: A Handbook and Reference Guide to American Cultural Programming.* Westport: Greenwood Press. 1986.

Deborah Jowitt, "*Dance in America:* Some observations on its accomplishments, its self-imposed boundaries and a challenge for the future." October, 1978. Unpublished paper.

Chapter 1:
DANCE

American Ballet Theatre in La Bayadere. *Photo by Martha Swope.*

DANCE IN AMERICA

DANCE SPECIALS

DANCE IN AMERICA

At its inception in 1976, DANCE IN AMERICA was perceived by the dance community as partaking of a medium so degraded by commercial discourse that it was unsuitable for any self-respecting art. These suspicions have long vanished. The series' 58 programs in 15 seasons now constitute a glorious record of a golden age in American dance, as well as an indispensable archive for the future.

The original reservations were two in number, pertaining to audience and to space. It was thought that broadcast would depopulate the theaters. Nancy Hanks, the Endowment's second chairman, quickly discredited this perception by commissioning a study of The Joffrey Ballet that showed that television *increased* live attendance, and at a Senate hearing pointed out that football stadia had been filled, not emptied, by television. Dance in America's "stadium" is, however, occupied by some 1 to 2 million viewers each week.

The small screen—the most powerful of image-brokers—has been denigrated for its supposed inability to articulate the spaces in which group interaction takes place. If this is so, the success of broadcast football is hard to understand. The effect of miniaturization—the so-called fishbowl effect—is lessened by the automatic adjustment of perception to diminished scale, and by the increasing clarity of a new generation of television screens.

Television space is, however, notoriously labile and ambiguous, and choreographers became, through this series, well acquainted with the problems of constructing dances within it. George Balanchine, whose participation resulted in a dazzling record, adjusted some of his works to clarify them in television's concentrated space. His collaboration with Merrill Brockway, Emile Ardolino and Judy Kinberg, resulted in part from Exxon, the Endowment's funding partner's passion for the choreographer's work. The series developed directors, including for a time Edward Villella, gifted in establishing visual rhythms and pulses that mirror the dance's "narrative," however abstract. The results are among the most significant American contributions to the history of recorded dance.

Executive producer: Jac Venza
Awards: 1981 Peabody Award for Excellence in a Series
Additional funders include: Corporation for Public Broadcasting, Exxon
Corporation, Martin Marietta, Texaco, public television stations
A production of WNET/Thirteen

SEASON ONE, 1976

City Center Joffrey Ballet

A selection from The Joffrey Ballet's repertory: Gerald Arpino's rock ballet, *Trinity* (1970); a solo from Arpino's *Olympics* (1966); a scene from Robert Joffrey's *Remembrances* (1973), music by Richard Wagner; two scenes from Kurt Jooss's anti-war ballet, *The Green Table* (1932), and the *Conjurer's Solo* from Leonide Massine's *Parade* (1917), set and costumes by Pablo Picasso. Arpino, Joffrey, Jooss and Massine are interviewed. (January 21, 1976; 60 min.)

Director: Jerome Schnur
Producer: Emile Ardolino

Martha Graham in the 1935 production of her ballet, Frontier.

Sue's Leg/Remembering the Thirties

Twyla Tharp's *Sue's Leg* (1975) celebrates the music of Fats Waller and the dance of the 1930s—the big apple, marathon dancing, ballroom dancing, Busby Berkeley-style production numbers, the bump and grind. The principal dancers are Tom Rawe, Kenneth Rinker, Twyla Tharp and Rose Marie Wright. Costumes are by Santo Loquasto. The program includes *Remembering the Thirties*, a documentary film collage on social dancing of the 1930s. (March 24, 1976; 60 min.)

Director, producer: Merrill Brockway
Writer: Arlene Croce

Martha Graham Dance Company

Several works by Martha Graham: *Frontier* (1935), music by Horst; *Lamentation* (1930), music by Kodaly; *Appalachian Spring* (1944), music by Copland; *Diversion of Angels* (1948), music by dello Joio; *Adorations* (1975), which was created for the program, music by Albeniz, Cimarosa, Dowland and Frescobaldi, and *The Dance of Vengeance* from *Cave of the Heart* (1946), music by Barber. The dancers are Takako Asakawa, Jessica Chao, Mario Delamo, Janet Eilber, Diane Gray, Eivind Harum, Yuriko Kimura, Peggy Lyman, Daniel Maloney, Susan McGuire, Elisa Monte, Bonnie Oda Homsey, Peter Sparling, David Hatch Walker, Tim Wengerd and Henry Yu.

Appalachian Spring, *Frontier* and *Cave of the Heart* were designed by Isamu Noguchi. The host is Gregory Peck. (April 7, 1976; 90 min.)

Director: Merrill Brockway
Producer: Emile Ardolino
Writer: Nancy Hamilton

The Pennsylvania Ballet

Excerpts from five works: Hans van Manen's *Grosse Fugue* (1971) and *Adagio Hammerklavier* (1973), music by Beethoven; Balanchine's *Concerto Barocco* (1948), music by Bach; Benjamin Harkavy's *Madrigalesco* (1963), music by Vivaldi, and Charles Czarney's *Concerto Grosso* (1971), music by Handel. The dancers are Karen Brown, Alba Calzada, Joanne Danto, Marcia Darhower, Gregory Drotar, Tamara Hadley, Mark Hochman, David Jordan, Dane LaFontsee, Michelle Lucci, Edward Myers, Lawrence Rhodes, Janek Schergen, Jerry Schwender and Gretchen Warren. Documentary material and statements by Barbara Weisberger, the founder of the Pennsylvania Ballet and its director until 1982, give a short history of the company. (June 2, 1976; 60 min.)

Director: Merrill Brockway
Producer: Emile Ardolino
Writer: Tobi Tobias

SEASON TWO, 1976 - 1977

American Ballet Theatre

American Ballet Theatre makes its first appearance on the series with two works: Eugene Loring's *Billy the Kid* (1938), set to Aaron Copland's score, with principal dancers Terry Orr, Frank Smith, Marianna Tcherkassky and Clark Tippett; and Sir Frederick Ashton's *Les Patineurs (The Skaters)* (1937), music by Giacomo Meyerbeer, with Fernando Bujones, Karena

Brock, Kristine Elliott, Nanette Glushak and Charles Ward as principal dancers. Costumes for *Les Patineurs* designed by Cecil Beaton. The host is Paul Newman. (December 15, 1976; 60 min.)

Director: Merrill Brockway
Producer: Emile Ardolino
Writer: Tobi Tobias

Merce Cunningham Dance Company

The works performed are *Minutiae* (1954), incorporating sculpture by Robert Rauschenberg, and *Solo* (1973), both to music by John Cage; the early video/dance *Westbeth* (1974), with costumes by Jasper Johns; *Septet* (1953), costumes by Remy Charlip; *Sounddance*, set and costumes by Mark Lancaster; *Antic Meet* (1958), with a seven-armed sweater by Rauschenberg; *Scramble* (1967), set and costumes by Frank Stella; *RainForest* (1968), music by David Tudor, set and costumes by Andy Warhol; and a new piece created for the program, *Video Triangle*. The dancers are Karole Armitage, Karen Attix, Ellen Cornfield, Merce Cunningham, Morgan Ensminger, Meg Harper, Catherine Kerr, Robert Kovich, Chris Komar, Charles Moulton and Julie Roess-Smith. (January 5, 1977; 60 min.)

Director: Merrill Brockway
Producer: Emile Ardolino
Writer: Merce Cunningham

Dance Theatre of Harlem

Excerpts from the company's repertory: Louis Johnson's *Forces of Rhythm* (1972), music by Rufus Thomas and Donny Hathaway;

Balanchine's *Bugaku* (1965), music by Toshiro Mayuzumi; Lester Horton's *The Beloved* (1948), music by Judith Hamilton; Arthur Mitchell's *Holberg Suite*, music by Edvard Grieg, and Geoffrey Holder's Caribbean-inspired piece, *Dougla* (1974). The principal dancers are Lydia Abarca, Roman Brooks, Homer Bryant, Virginia Johnson, Gayle McKinney, Melva Murray-White, Ronald Perry and Paul Russell. Includes documentary material on Dance Theatre of Harlem's history and interviews with the company's founder, Arthur Mitchell. (March 23, 1977; 60 min.)

Director: Merrill Brockway
Producer: Emile Ardolino
Writer: Tobi Tobias

Pilobolus Dance Theater

Pilobolus dances *Monkshood's Farewell* (1974), music by Robert Dennis; *Ocellus* (1972), music by Moses Pendleton and Jonathan Wolken; *Ciona* (1975), music by Jon Appleton, and *Untitled* (1975), music by Robert Dennis. The principal dancers are Robby Barnett, Alison Chase, Martha Clarke, Moses Pendleton, Michael Tracy and Jonathan Wolken. All works are choreographed by Pilobolus. Documentary material on the company's history and its working method was recorded at Dartmouth College, where the original members met. (May 4, 1977; 60 min.)

Director: Merrill Brockway
Producers: Emile Ardolino, Judy Kinberg
Writer: Elizabeth Kendall

Trailblazers of Modern Dance

A documentary on the roots of American modern dance from the late 19th century to the 1930s, incorporating rare footage from the turn of the century and reconstructed versions of early works. Appearing on the pro-

gram are Lynn Seymour in *Five Brahms Waltzes in the Manner of Isadora Duncan* (1975), choreographed by Sir Frederick Ashton; Annabelle Gamson in versions of Duncan's choreography to *Etude* and *Mother*, music by Scriabin; the Joyce Trisler Danscompany in excerpts from *Spear Dance Japonesque* (1919) and *Soaring* (1919), originally by Denishawn, reconstructed by Klarna Plinska; and David Anderson, Michael Deane, Daniel Ezralow, Donlin Foreman, Clif de Raita and Tim Wengerd in Ted Shawn's *Polonaise* (1923), music by Edward MacDowell, reconstructed by Norman Walker. (June 22, 1977; 60 min.)

Director: Emile Ardolino
Producers: Merrill Brockway, Judy Kinberg
Writer: Elizabeth Kendall

SEASON THREE, 1977 - 1978

Choreography by Balanchine, Part One

The first of a series with the New York City Ballet in works by George Balanchine. Part one includes *Tzigane* (1975), music by Maurice Ravel, danced by Suzanne Farrell, Peter Martins and ensemble. The andante movement from Mozart's *Divertimento no. 15* (1956) is danced by Tracy Bennett, Merrill Ashley, Maria Calegari, Susan Pilarre, Stephanie Saland, Marjorie Spohn, Victor Castelli and Robert Weiss. *The Four Temperaments* (1946), music by Paul Hindemith, is performed by principal dancers Bart Cook, Merrill Ashley, Daniel Duell, Adam Luders and Colleen Neary. The host is Edward Villella. (December 14, 1977; 60 min.)

Director: Merrill Brockway
Producer: Emile Ardolino
Writer: Arlene Croce

Choreography by Balanchine, Part Two

Excerpts from the three parts of *Jewels* (1967). Karin von Aroldingen, Gerard Ebitz, Merrill Ashley and company dance in *Emeralds*, music by Faure; Patricia McBride and Robert Weiss dance in *Rubies*, music by Stravinsky; Suzanne Farrell and Peter Martins perform in *Diamonds*, music by Tschaikovsky. Also presented is *Stravinsky Violin Concerto* (1972), with principal dancers Bart Cook, Peter Martins, Kay Mazzo and Karin von Aroldingen. (December 21, 1977; 70 min.)

George Balanchine instructing the ballerina Merrill Ashley. Photo by Steven Caras.

Director: Merrill Brockway
Producer: Emile Ardolino
Writer: Arlene Croce

Paul Taylor Dance Company

Two works by Paul Taylor. *Esplanade* (1975), to Bach's *Double Violin Concerto in D*, and *Runes* (1975), music by Gerald Busby, designs by Gene Moore. Dancers are Carolyn Adams, Ruth Andrien, Elie Chaib, Thomas Evert,

Christopher Gillis, Nicholas Gunn, Bettie de Jong, Robert Kahn, Linda Kent, Susan McGuire, Monica Morris, Victoria Uris and Lila York. Includes commentary about the company written by Paul Taylor. (January 4, 1978; 60 min.)

Director: Charles S. Dubin
Producer: Emile Ardolino
Writer: Paul Taylor

San Francisco Ballet: Romeo and Juliet

Romeo and Juliet (1976) is choreographed by Michael Smuin to the original Prokofiev score introduced by the Kirov Ballet in 1940. Smuin's adaptation of Prokoviev's scenario features Jim Sohm in the role of Romeo, Diana Weber as Juliet and Attila Ficzere as Mercutio. The host is Richard Thomas. (June 7, 1978; 120 min.)

Director: Merrill Brockway
Producers: Emile Ardolino, Judy Kinberg
Writer: Tobi Tobias
Awards: Emmy Award: Best Set Design

Choreography by Balanchine, Part Three

Balanchine's *Prodigal Son* (1929), music by Prokofiev, set and costumes by Georges Rouault, features Mikhail Baryshnikov in the title role, Karin von Aroldingen and Shaun O'Brien. Also included is *Chaconne* (1976), performed by Suzanne Farrell and Peter Martins to the divertissement from Gluck's *Orpheus and Euridice*. The host is Edward Villella. (November 29, 1978; 60 min.)

Director: Merrill Brockway
Producers: Emile Ardolino, Judy Kinberg
Writer: Arlene Croce

SEASON FOUR, 1979

Choreography by Balanchine, Part Four

Karin von Aroldingen, Sean Lavery and ensemble in *Elegie* from Tschaikovsky's *Suite no. 3*; Patricia McBride and Mikhail Baryshnikov in *The Steadfast Tin Soldier* (1975), music by Bizet; Merrill Ashley, Robert Weiss and company in Verdi's *Ballo della Regina* (1978); Suzanne Farrell, Peter Martins and ensemble in Tschaikovsky's *Allegro Brillante* (1956) and Patricia McBride and Mikhail Baryshnikov in *Tschaikovsky Pas de Deux* (1960). (March 7, 1979; 69 min.)

Director: Merrill Brockway
Producers: Emile Ardolino, Judy Kinberg
Writer: Arlene Croce
Emmy Award: Outstanding Classical Program in the Performing Arts

The Feld Ballet

Excerpts from seven works by The Feld Ballet, choreographed by Eliot Feld: *Intermezzo* (1969), set to music by Brahms; *Danzon Cubano* (1978), music by Aaron Copland; *La Vida* (1978), music by Copland; *Excursion* (1975), music by Samuel Barber; *The Real McCoy* (1974), music by George Gershwin; *Santa Fe Saga* (1977), music by Morton Gould, and *Half-Time* (1978), music by Gould. The principal dancers are Helen Douglas, Eliot Feld, Alfonso Figuera, Kenneth Hughes, Michaela Hughes, Edmund LaFosse, Linda Miller, Gregory Mitchell, Christine Sarry, Jeff Satinoff and Gwynn Taylor. Copland and Gould discuss with Feld their attraction to vernacular source materials as inspiration for their work. (May 16, 1979; 60 min.)

Director: Emile Ardolino
Producer: Judy Kinberg
Writer: Tobi Tobias

Martha Graham Dance Company: Clytemnestra

Martha Graham's *Clytemnestra* (1958) derives from the *Oresteia* of Aeschylus as imagined by the wife of Agamemnon, the king who led the Greeks to victory in the Trojan War. Performing in the work are Christine Dakin, Mario Delamo, Janet Eilber, Diane Gray, Yuriko Kimura, Peggy Lyman, Lucinda Mitchell, Elisa Monte, Peter Sparling, Bert Terborgh, Tim Wengerd and George White, Jr. Music by Halim El Dabh; set by Isamu Noguchi; costumes by Halston. Christopher Plummer hosts the program. (May 30, 1979; 90 min.)

Director: Merrill Brockway
Producers: Emile Ardolino, Judy Kinberg

SEASON FIVE, 1980

American Dance Festival: Pilobolus

Four works created by Pilobolus, performed at the American Dance Festival. *Walklyndon* (1971), choreography by Robby Barnett, Lee Harris, Moses Pendleton and Jonathan Wolken, performed by Barnett, Wolken, Jamey Hampton and Michael Tracy. Pendleton performs his work *Momix. Alraune* (1975) is performed by the choreographers Pendleton and Alison Chase. *Molly's Not Dead* (1978), choreographed by Chase, Pendleton, Barnett and Wolken, is performed by Barnett, Chase, Hampton, Tracy, Wolken and Georgiana Holmes. Documentary material and interviews with members of Pilobolus and Charles Reinhart, director of the American Dance Festival, are included. (November 17, 1980; 60 min.)

Director: Emile Ardolino
Producer: Sidney J. Palmer
Writer: Elizabeth Kendall
A production of South Carolina ETV

Two Duets with Choreography by Jerome Robbins and Peter Martins

Two works are presented: *Other Dances* (1976), choreographed by Jerome Robbins, and *Calcium Light Night* (1977), the first ballet choreographed by Peter Martins. *Other Dances*, set to music by Chopin, created for and performed by Natalia Makarova and Mikhail Baryshnikov. *Calcium Light Night*, set to music by Charles Ives is danced by Heather Watts and Ib Andersen. Includes rehearsal footage and interviews with Robbins and Martins. (February 20, 1980; 60 min.)

Directors: Other Dances: Emile Ardolino; Calcium Light Night: Emile Ardolino, Kirk Browning
Producers: Emile Ardolino, Judy Kinberg
Writer: Tobi Tobias

Divine Drumbeats: Katherine Dunham and Her People

In the 1930s, Katherine Dunham began her exploration of the origins of black dance in the Americas, recreating and popularizing Afro-Caribbean dances in a series of highly popular revues and extravaganzas. Featured is a revival of one of Dunham's most important works, *Rites de Passage*, originally choreographed in 1941, and adapted from the puberty and fertility rites of African tribes with music based on a Haitian drum theme by Paquita Anderson, Georges Auric and Dunham. Members of Dunham's long-disbanded troupe and students from her East St. Louis school perform. Principal dancers include Norman Davis, Doris Bennett and Pearl Reynolds. James Earl Jones hosts the program. (April 16, 1980; 60 min.)

Director: Merrill Brockway
Producers: Merrill Brockway, Catherine Tatge
Writer: Glen Berenbeim

Beyond the Mainstream

A performance documentary on the work of prominent postmodern choreographers: excerpts from Trisha Brown's *Line-up* (1977) and *Glacial Decoy* (1978), with principal dancers Brown, Russell Dumas, Elizabeth Garren, Lisa Kraus, Nina Lundborg and Stephen Petronio; Steve Paxton's *Contact Improvisation* (1971 - 1975), danced by Paxton, Danny Lepkoff, Nina Martin, Lisa Nelson, Nancy Stark Smith and Randy Warshaw; Yvonne Rainer's *Trio A* (1966), performed by Frank Conversano, Bart Cook and Sara Rudner; Selections from David Gordon's *Chair* (1974) and *The Matter* (1972), performed by Gordon and Valda Setterfield; Kei Takei's *Light (Stone Fields)*, performed by Takei; Laura Dean's *Dance* (1978), performed by Dean, Angela Caponigro, Paul Epstein, Peter Healey, John Proto, Patty Shenker, Perry Souchuk and David Yoken. (May 21, 1980; 60 min.)

Director: Merrill Brockway
Producers: Merrill Brockway, Carl Charlson
Writer: Faubion Bowers

SEASON SIX, 1981

Nureyev and The Joffrey Ballet: In Tribute to Nijinsky

The Joffrey Ballet presents three re-creations from Diaghilev's Ballets Russes. Rudolf Nureyev performs Vaslav Nijinsky's historic roles. Stravinsky's *Petrouchka* (1911), choreographed by Michel Fokine, set and costumes by Alexander Benois, is danced by Nureyev, Denise Jackson, Christian Holder and Gary Chryst. Weber's *Le Spectre de la Rose* (1911), also choreographed by Fokine, is performed by Nureyev and Denise Jackson. Debussy's *L'Apres-Midi d'un Faune (Afternoon of a Faun)* (1912), choreographed by Nijinsky, is performed by Nureyev and Charlene Gehm. *Spectre* and *Faune* were designed by Leon Bakst. (March 9, 1981; 90 min.)

Director: Emile Ardolino
Producers: Emile Ardolino, Judy Kinberg
Writer: Dale Harris
A production of WNET/Thirteen in association with the BBC

The Tempest: Live with the San Francisco Ballet

Michael Smuin's adaptation of Shakespeare's *The Tempest* (1980) for the San Francisco Ballet, broadcast live from the War Memorial Opera House in San Francisco. Principal dancers are Evelyn Cisneros, Attila Ficzere, David McNaughton and Tomm Ruud. The original score by Paul Seiko Chihara, is based on Henry Purcell's 17th-century incidental music. Sets by Tony Walton; costumes by Willa Kim. (March 30, 1981; 120 min.)

Director: Emile Ardolino
Producers: Emile Ardolino, Judy Kinberg
Writer: Stephen Cobbett Steinberg
A production of WNET/Thirteen and KQED/San Francisco

L'Enfant et Les Sortileges (The Spellbound Child)

George Balanchine's adaptation of his 1925 work is set to Ravel's masterpiece, with a libretto by Colette. It tells of a rebellious boy and the wild animals who instruct him in compassion. Principal dancers from the New York City Ballet are Susan Freedman, Alexia Hess, Julie Kirstein, Francis Sackett, Mel Tomlinson and Karin von Aroldingen. The boy is played by Christopher Byars. The singers are Karen Hunt, Gary Glaze, Emily Golden, Elizabeth Pruett, Jane Shaulis, William Stone, Dan Sullivan, Carl Tramon and Ruth Welting. The puppeteers are Richard Ellis, Bruce Edward Hall, J.J. Kroupa, Roman Paska, Jim Rowland and Bryant Young. Puppets by Kermit Love; production design by David Mitchell. (May 25, 1981; 60 min.)

Director: Emile Ardolino
Producers: Emile Ardolino, Judy Kinberg

SEASON SEVEN, 1982

Paul Taylor: Three Modern Classics

The Paul Taylor Dance Company performs three works by Taylor: *Aureole* (1962), set to music by Handel and danced by Carolyn Adams, Ruth Andrien, Elie Chaib, Robert Kahn and Lila York. *Three Epitaphs* (1956), set to American folk music and danced by Thomas Evert, Daniel Ezralow, Linda Kent, Cathy McCann and Susan McGuire. *Big Bertha* (1970), music from the St. Louis Melody Museum's collection of band machines, is danced by Carolyn Adams, Thomas Evert, Bettie de Jong and Monica Morris. A retrospective of Taylor's career, from his controversial early works to such later successes as *Esplanade* (1975) is presented. (January 11, 1982; 60 min.)

Director: Emile Ardolino
Producers: Emile Ardolino, Judy Kinberg
Writer: Holly Brubach
A production of WNET/Thirteen in association with the University of North Carolina Center for Public Television; Big Bertha was originally produced by South Carolina ETV and the American Dance Festival

Paul Taylor: Two Landmark Dances

Two works by Paul Taylor. *Le Sacre du Printemps (The Rehearsal)* (1980) is performed to Stravinsky's two-piano version by Carolyn Adams, Ruth Andrien, Elie Chaib, Christopher Gillis, Bettie de Jong and Lila York. *Arden Court* (1981) is performed to the music of William Boyce by Carolyn Adams, Elie Chaib, Thomas Evert, Daniel Ezralow, Christopher Gillis, Robert Kahn, Susan McGuire, David Parsons and Lila York. Recorded live at the American Dance Festival in North Carolina. (April 12, 1982; 60 min.)

Director: Emile Ardolino
Producers: Emile Ardolino, Judy Kinberg
Writer: Holly Brubach
A production of WNET/Thirteen in association with the University of North Carolina Center for Public Television

Bournonville Dances, with Members of the New York City Ballet

Six works by the Danish choreographer August Bournonville (1805 - 1879): the ballabile and tarantella from *Napoli* (1842) and the pas de deux from *The Kermesse in Bruges* (1851), music by Holger Simon Paulli; the pas de trois from *La Ventana* (1854), music by Hans Christian Lumbye; the pas de deux from *William Tell*, music by Rossini, and the pas de deux from *Flower Festival in Genzano* (1858), music by Edvard Helsted.

The Joffrey Ballet performs Leonide Massine's The Green Table.

Stanley Williams, a former teacher with the Royal Danish Ballet, staged the works. The principal dancers are Ib Andersen, Merrill Ashley, Daniel Duell, Lisa Hess, Darci Kistler, Lourdes Lopez, Peter Martins, Stephanie Saland, Helgi Tomasson, Heather Watts and Robert Weiss. (May 24, 1982; 60 min.)

Director: Edward Villella
Producers: Judy Kinberg, Edward Villella
Writer: Tobi Tobias

SEASON EIGHT, 1982 - 1983

The Green Table with The Joffrey Ballet

Kurt Jooss's *The Green Table*, which premiered in 1932 during the final days of the Weimar Republic, was conceived as a response to the horrors of World War I and as a warning of coming dangers. It is considered the classic anti-war dance statement. Principal dancers in the Joffrey production are James Canfield, Gary Chryst, Mark Goldweber, Jerel Hilding, Philip Jerry, Valmai Roberts, Beatriz Rodriguez and Carole Valleskey. Staged by Jooss's daughter, Anna Markard. Also includes a documentary of Jooss's life and work including interviews with the late choreographer and archival film showing excerpts of his other three extant works: *Pavane on the Death of an Infanta*, *Big City* (1932) and *A Ball in Old Vienna* (1932). (December 13, 1982; 60 min.)

Director: Emile Ardolino
Producer: Judy Kinberg
Writer: Tobi Tobias

Balanchine Celebrates Stravinsky with the New York City Ballet

Recorded at the New York State Theater during the company's second Stravinsky Festival. The performance, created to mark the Stravinsky centennial, features three works choreographed by Balanchine to music of Stravinsky: *Agon* (1957) with principal dancers Heather Watts and Mel Tomlinson; *Variations* (1966) with Suzanne Farrell; and *Persephone* with Karin von Aroldingen, Mel Tomlinson, Vera Zorina and the chorus of the New York City Opera. (February 14, 1983; 90 min.)

Director: Emile Ardolino
Producer: Barbara Horgan
Writer: Nancy Goldner

A production of the New York City Ballet and Lincoln Center for the Performing Arts in association with WNET/Thirteen

The Catherine Wheel

The television adaptation of Twyla Tharp's ballet *The Catherine Wheel* (1981), with a score by David Byrne, integrates the performance with a computer-generated dancing figure, a variety of three-dimensional computer graphics and image modifications. Principal dancers are John Carrafa, Richard Colton, Katie Glasner, Raymond Kurshals, Tom Rawe, Sara Rudner, Christine Uchida, Shelly Washington and Jennifer Way. Documentary material is included. (March 28, 1983; 90 min.)

Director: Twyla Tharp
Producer: Alan Yentob
A production of Catherine Wheel, Inc., in association with WNET/Thirteen and the National Video Corporation
Source: HBO Video, HomeVision (home video)

The Magic Flute with the New York City Ballet

Peter Martins's narrative ballet, *The Magic Flute* (1981), is choreographed to music by Ricardo Drigo, with sets by David Mitchell. The work is performed by the New York City Ballet, plus a cast of 18 children from the company's School of American Ballet. The principal dancers are Ib Andersen and Heather Watts. Martins introduces the ballet. (April 25, 1983; 60 min.)

Director: Merrill Brockway
Producer: Judy Kinberg
Writer: Holly Brubach

SEASON NINE, 1984

San Francisco Ballet: A Song for Dead Warriors

The San Francisco Ballet in *A Song for Dead Warriors* (1979), choreographed by Michael Smuin to music by Charles Fox, examines the disparity between Native Americans' glorious past and their current reality. The work was inspired by the story of Richard Oakes, a leader of a group of young Native Americans who staged the takeover of Alcatraz Island in 1969. Principal dancers are Evelyn Cisneros, Antonio Lopez and Vane Vest. Includes a documentary explaining the origins of the ballet. (January 16, 1984; 60 min.)

Director: Merrill Brockway
Producer: Judy Kinberg
Writer: Holly Brubach
A production of WNET/Thirteen and KQED/San Francisco

A Choreographer's Notebook: Stravinsky Piano Ballets by Peter Martins

Four works set to Stravinsky piano pieces, choreographed by Peter Martins, danced by members of the New York City Ballet: *Concerto for Two Solo Pianos* (1980) with Heather Watts, Ib Andersen and Jock Soto; *Eight Easy Pieces*, performed by Stacy Caddell, Susan Gluck and Roma Sosenko; *Tango*, a duet with Heather Watts and Bart Cook; *Piano-Rag Music*, performed by Maria Calegari and four male dancers. With commentary by Martins. (February 13, 1984; 60 min.)

Director: Merrill Brockway
Producer: Judy Kinberg
Writer: Holly Brubach

American Ballet Theatre: Don Quixote (Kitri's Wedding)

Mikhail Baryshnikov's production of the classic ballet *Don Quixote* (1869) focuses on one of the lighter episodes in Cervantes's novel, Kitri's love affair with the poor barber Basil, with runaway lovers, a cross-country chase and a happy ending. Principal dancers are Baryshnikov, Cynthia Harvey, Frank Smith, Victor Barbee and Richard Schafer. Baryshnikov choreographed the work after Marius Petipa and Alexander Gorsky to the music of A.L. Minkus. Taped live at the Metropolitan Opera House. (March 5, 1984; 90 min.)

Director: Brian Large
Executive producer: Robin Scott
A production of the National Video Corporation
Source: HBO Video, HomeVision
(home video)

Balanchine: A Two-Part Documentary

A retrospective of George Balanchine's career, from its beginnings in Imperial Russia where he was trained as a dancer and musician, to its culmination with the New York City Ballet. Using rare footage and archival material spanning the 1920s to the 1980s, excerpts from virtually all Balanchine's major ballets are shown along with examples of his choreography for Broadway musicals and Hollywood films. Balanchine also discusses a wide variety of subjects. (May 28 and June 4, 1984; 120 min.—2 x 60 min.)

Director: Merrill Brockway
Producer: Judy Kinberg
Writer: Holly Brubach

SEASON TEN, 1984 - 1985

Baryshnikov by Tharp with American Ballet Theatre

The program combines Twyla Tharp's innovative choreography and Mikhail Baryshnikov's dance mastery. In *The Little Ballet*, choreographed to music by Glazunov, Baryshnikov performs with Diedre Carberry. *Sinatra Suite* is a series of duets performed by Elaine Kudo and Baryshnikov to songs by Frank Sinatra. The program concludes with the Tharp-Baryshnikov signature piece, *Push Comes to Shove* (1976), set to the rhythms of ragtime and the counterpoint of Handel. (October 5, 1984; 60 min.)

Directors: Don Mischer, Twyla Tharp
Producer: Don Mischer
Writers: Twyla Tharp, Peter Elbling
Don Mischer Productions in association with WNET/Thirteen
Source: Kultur International Films
(home video)

Martha Graham Dance Company: An Evening of Dance and Conversation with Martha Graham

Three dances choreographed by Martha Graham and accompanied by her commentary. Two of Graham's early "Greek" classics are presented: *Errand into the Maze* (1947), with sets by Isamu Noguchi and music by Gian Carlo Menotti, and *Cave of the Heart* (1946), a dance of jealousy and evil set to music by Samuel Barber. The third, more recent work, is *Acts of Light*, with music by the Danish composer Carl Nielson and costumes by Halston. (December 14, 1984; 60 min.)

Director, producer: Thomas Grimm
A production of the Martha Graham Center for Contemporary Dance, Danmarks Radio and WNET/Thirteen
Source: Video Artists International
(home video)

American Ballet Theatre at the Met

Three dances from American Ballet Theatre's repertory. *Les Sylphides* (1909), Michel Fokine's ballet from the original repertory of Ballet Theatre set to the music of Chopin, features the company's artistic director, Mikhail Baryshnikov, with Cheryl Yeager, Marianna Tcherkassky, Cynthia Harvey and ensemble. *Triad* (1972), choreographed by Kenneth MacMillan, music by Prokofiev, features Amanda McKerrow, Robert LaFosse and Johan Renvall. *Paquita*, staged by Makarova after Petipa to music by A.L. Minkus, is danced by Cynthia Gregory and Fernando Bujones and company. Taped live at the Metropolitan Opera House. (February 22, 1985; 90 min.)

Director: Brian Large
Producer: Robin Scott
A production of the National Video Corporation in association with WNET/Thirteen
Source: HBO Video, Home Vision
(home video)

Paul Taylor Dance Company: Recent Dances

In 1985, the Paul Taylor Dance Company turned 30 years old, a milestone for the company and its director, Paul Taylor, whose retirement from dancing ten years earlier marked the start of a brilliant new phase in his career as a choreographer. Three dances from this period are presented: an excerpt from *Mercuric Tidings*, set to the music of Franz Schubert; *Snow White*, a treatment of the fairy tale; and *Sunset* (1983), set to music by Edward Elgar. An interview with Paul Taylor is included. (March 29, 1985; 60 min.)

Director, producer: Pierre Morin
Producer: Judy Kinberg
A production of Societe Radio-Canada in association with WNET/Thirteen

SEASON ELEVEN, 1985 - 1986

Alvin Ailey American Dance Theater: Three by Three

Three dances from the repertory of the Alvin Ailey American Dance Theater: Ailey's classic *Blues Suite* (1958), set to traditional blues; *Fever Swamp* (1983), choreographed by Bill T. Jones with music by Peter Gordon; and

Donald McKayle's lyric folk-piece *Rainbow 'Round My Shoulder* (1959), set to traditional prison songs. Brief introductions to each piece follow a young boy as he watches rehearsals and hears the comments of each choreographer. (October 18, 1985; 60 min.)

Director: Pat Birch
Producers: Catherine Tatge, Ellis Haizlip
A production of Tatge Productions, the Ellis B. Haizlip Company, Polivideo and WNET/Thirteen

The San Francisco Ballet in Cinderella

The San Francisco Ballet's production of Prokofiev's *Cinderella* (1973), choreographed by Lew Christensen and Michael Smuin, stars Evelyn Cisneros as Cinderella, Alex Topciy as the Prince and Catherine Batcheller as the Fairy Godmother. Kermit the Frog and Miss Piggy act as host and hostess for the program. Taped in performance at the War Memorial Opera House. (December 7, 1985; 90 min.)

Directors: Emile Ardolino, Michael Smuin
Producer: Judy Kinberg
A production of WNET/Thirteen, KQED/San Francisco and the San Francisco Ballet

Dance Theatre of Harlem in A Streetcar Named Desire

Arthur Mitchell's Dance Theatre of Harlem performs the revival of Valerie Bettis's *A Streetcar Named Desire* (1952), featuring Virginia Johnson as Blanche. Set to a jazz-inspired film score by Alex North, it combines aspects of classical and modern dance. Mitchell also narrates an introduction to the company which includes selections from Frederick Franklin's *Sylvia* (1951) and Geoffrey Holder's *Bele*

Mikhail Baryshnikov from Baryshnikov by Tharp. *Photo © 1984 by Herbert Migdoll. Courtesy of photographer.*

(1955), examples of two other of the company's strengths—classical ballet and theatrical dance rooted in diverse cultures. (February 21, 1986; 60 min.)

Director: Thomas Grimm
Producers: Judy Kinberg, Thomas Grimm
A production of WNET/Thirteen, Danmarks Radio, Dance Theatre of Harlem, Channel Four/Britain and Antenne Deux

Choreography by Jerome Robbins with the New York City Ballet

Two ballets by Jerome Robbins recorded in performance at the New York State Theater. *Fancy Free* (1944), Robbins's first ballet, is the tale of three sailors on an eagerly anticipated shore leave, performed to a commissioned score by Leonard Bernstein. With principal dancers Joseph Duell, Florence Fitzgerald, Jean-Pierre Frohlich, Kipling Houston, Lourdes Lopez, Sean O'Brian, Stephanie Saland. *Antique Epigraphs* (1984), set to music by Claude Debussy, features a cast of 11 women and evokes an aura of classical Greece. Robbins is shown during rehearsals and in interviews. (May 2, 1986; 60 min.)

Director: Emile Ardolino
Producer: Judy Kinberg
A production of WNET/Thirteen and Jerome Robbins

SEASON TWELVE, 1986 - 1987

Mark Morris

An introduction to the early work of the choreographer and dancer Mark Morris: *Songs that Tell a Story (Robe of White)*, with music by the Louvin Brothers; *Prelude*, music by Cowell; *Love, You Have Won*, music by Vivaldi; *Dogtown*, music by Yoko Ono; *Jealousy*, a solo danced by

Morris, music by Handel; *The Tamil Film Songs in Stereo Pas de Deux*, set to an Indian film score; and Vivaldi's *Gloria*. An interview with Morris filmed in Seattle complements the performances. (October 10, 1986; 60 min.)

Director: Thomas Grimm
Producers: Judy Kinberg, Thomas Grimm
A production of WNET/Thirteen and Danmarks Radio

In Memory of. . . A Ballet by Jerome Robbins with the New York City Ballet

In Memory of. . . (1985), a ballet by Jerome Robbins set to Alban Berg's *Violin Concerto*, features Suzanne Farrell at the head of a large cast. Interviews with Robbins precede and follow the performance, in which he discusses Berg's music, the creative process and his working relationship with George Balanchine, from their Broadway days to their collaborations at the New York City Ballet. (January 16, 1987; 60 min.)

Director: Emile Ardolino
Producer: Judy Kinberg
A production of WNET/Thirteen and Jerome Robbins

Agnes: The Indomitable de Mille

By Agnes de Mille's own account, "This is the story of an American dancer, a spoiled, egocentric, wealthy girl, who learned with difficulty to become a worker. . ., to brace a Victorian sensibility to contemporary roughhousing, and who, with happy good fortune, participated. . .in a renaissance of the most ancient and magical of all the arts." This documentary chronicles de Mille's career—the landmark ballets such as *Rodeo* (1942), Broadway musicals such as *Oklahoma* (1943) and *Carousel* (1945) and the film versions, her collaborations and her widely felt influence.

Includes rare archival footage, an extensive interview and material from her autobiographies. (May 8, 1987; 60 min.)

Director: Merrill Brockway
Producer: Judy Kinberg
Awards: Emmy Award: Outstanding Informational Special

SEASON THIRTEEN, 1987 - 1988

David Gordon's Made in USA

Three works by David Gordon performed by American Ballet Theatre and David Gordon's Pick Up Company. *Made in USA*, is a dialogue-duet for American Ballet Theatre's Mikhail Baryshnikov and the Pick Up Company's Valda Setterfield. Combining dance and conversation, *Made in USA* traces the arrival in America of two very different performers—Baryshnikov from Russia and

Setterfield from England—who come from different countries and traditions with one common goal: to dance in America. The program also includes *Murder*, danced by Baryshnikov; and *TV Nine Lives*, a quintet for Baryshnikov and Pick Up Company. (October 23, 1987; 60 min.)

Director: Don Mischer
Producers: Don Mischer, Rhoda Grauer
A production of WNET/Thirteen and Don Mischer Productions

Roses and Last Look with the Paul Taylor Dance Company

The Paul Taylor Dance Company in two of Taylor's contrasting works: *Roses*, a dance for six couples set to music by Wagner, and *Last Look* (1985), a work at the opposite end of Taylor's spectrum, created in collaboration with the composer Donald York and the painter Alex Katz. (January 15, 1988; 60 min.)

Director: Thomas Grimm
Producers: Judy Kinberg, Thomas Grimm
Writer: Holly Brubach
A production of WNET/Thirteen and Danmarks Radio in association with NOS Television

Balanchine and Cunningham: An Evening at American Ballet Theatre

American Ballet Theatre performs works by two of America's greatest choreographers: *La Sonnambula* (1946) by George Balanchine features Mikhail Baryshnikov in the lead role, the Poet, who is first bewitched by the Sleepwalker, danced by Alessandra Ferri, and then betrayed by the Coquette, danced by Leslie Browne. *Duets* (1949), by Merce Cunningham, is a sequence of pas de deux for six couples set to John Cage's *Improvisation no. 3*. The dancers include Melissa Allen, Gil Boggs, Ricardo Bustamante, Wes Chapman, John Gardner, Robert Hill, Kathleen Moore, Amanda McKerrow, Amy Rose, Christine Spizzo, Clark Tippet and Jennet Zerbe. With on-camera commentary by Baryshnikov. (February 5, 1988; 60 min.)

Director: Thomas Grimm
Producers: Judy Kinberg, Thomas Grimm
Writer: Holly Brubach
A production of WNET/Thirteen and Danmarks Radio

Members of the American Indian Dance Theatre in The Grass Dance. *Photo by Don Perdue.*

SEASON FOURTEEN, 1989

Baryshnikov Dances Balanchine

Mikhail Baryshnikov dances the lead roles in two contrasting Balanchine ballets. *Apollo* (1928), the oldest Balanchine ballet still performed, is his first collaboration with the composer Igor Stravinsky. *Who Cares?* (1970) is a suite of dances set to songs by George Gershwin, including *I Got Rhythm* and *Embraceable You*. The principal dancers include Leslie Browne, Deirdre Carberry, Christine Dunham and Stephanie Saland. With on-camera commentary by Baryshnikov. (January 13, 1989; 60 min.)

Director: Thomas Grimm
Producers: Judy Kinberg, Thomas Grimm
Writer: Holly Brubach
A production of WNET/Thirteen and Danmarks Radio

Gregory Hines's Tap Dance in America

Gregory Hines celebrates tap, a distinctively American form which blends African, Irish, Dutch and English traditions, along with some of America's greatest tap dancers—old-time "hoofers" from tap's heyday in the early part of the century as well as contemporary practitioners: Honi Coles, Brenda Bufalino, Bunny Briggs, Buster Brown, Camden Richman, Diane Walker, Fred Strickler, Greg Burge, Hinton Battle, Jennifer Lane, Jimmy Slyde, Manhattan Tap, Sandman Sims, Savion Glover, Tommy Tune and the American Tap Dance Orchestra. (March 17, 1989; 60 min.)

Director: Don Mischer
Producers: David Goldberg, Rhoda Grauer
Don Mischer Productions in association with WNET/Thirteen

A Night at The Joffrey

Three works representing the principal aesthetic veins of The Joffrey Ballet's repertory are performed. Sir Frederick Ashton's *Monotones II* (1966), set to Erik Satie's *Gymnopedies*, is danced by two men and a woman on a bare stage. William Forsythe's *Love Songs* is set to songs sung by Aretha Franklin and Dionne Warwick. *Round of Angels*, set to the *Adagietto* from Gustav Mahler's *Fifth Symphony*, is choreographed by Gerald Arpino, Robert Joffrey's successor as artistic director. Includes interviews with each choreographer. (April 28, 1989; 60 min.)

Directed and produced by: Judy Kinberg, Thomas Grimm
A production of WNET/Thirteen and Danmarks Radio in association with Czechoslovak TV, the BBC, Polyphon, La Sept/France

La Sylphide with the Pennsylvania and Milwaukee Ballet

Peter Martins's staging of August Bournonville's romantic ballet *La Sylphide*, performed by the Pennsylvania and Milwaukee Ballet, starring Melissa Podcasy and Marin Boieru. *La Sylphide* has been a mainstay of the ballet repertory since its premiere in 1832 by the Paris Opera. An interview with Martins, who was trained in the Bournonville tradition in his native Denmark, is presented at intermission. Taped live at the Philadelphia Academy of Music. (March 24, 1989; 60 min.)

Director: Merrill Brockway
Producer: Judy Kinberg

SEASON FIFTEEN, 1990

The Search for Nijinsky's Rite of Spring

The Joffrey Ballet performs its reconstruction of the 1913 Vaslav Nijinsky ballet set to Igor Stravinsky's seminal ballet score, *Le Sacre du Printemps (The Rite of Spring)*. Although the music became a monument of 20th-century art, the choreography was performed only a few times and was believed lost. The history of the original production—which caused a riot at its premiere—and the detective-like story of its reconstruction by the art historian Kenneth Archer and the dance historian Millicent Hodson precede a performance of the complete work. (January 12, 1990; 60 min.)

Produced and directed by: Judy Kinberg, Thomas Grimm
A production of WNET/Thirteen and Danmarks Radio in association with Czechoslovak TV, the BBC, La Sept/France, NOS Television

The American Indian Dance Theatre: Finding the Circle

The American Indian Dance Theater, a three-year-old company of Native American dancers from more than a dozen tribes, performs the range of Native American dances, from a seasonal rain dance to a shawl dance to a sacred eagle dance. Company members discuss their art and its role in Indian life in segments taped at an intertribal pow-wow in Oklahoma and at the Zuni Pueblo in New Mexico. The tribes represented by the dancers include Apache, Cherokee, Chippewa, Comanche, Cree, Navajo, Sioux and Zuni. (February 2, 1990; 60 min.)

Director: Merrill Brockway
Producer: Catherine Tatge
A production of WNET/Thirteen in association with Tatge/Lasseur Productions
Source: WNET Videotakes (home video)

Judith Jamison interprets Cry in Alvin Ailey: Memories and Visions.

Bob Fosse: Steam Heat

The late Bob Fosse, one of Broadway's and Hollywood's most influential and successful directors and choreographers is the subject of this documentary profile. The hallmark Fosse style, with its syncopated, sophisticated and sensual movements, is seen in clips from *Cabaret* (1972), *Damn Yankees* (1955), *Pajama Game* (1954), *Pippin* (1972), *Liza with a Z* (1972) and *All That Jazz* (1979). The program includes clips from a 1987 tribute to Fosse featuring remembrances from E.L. Doctorow, Neil Simon and others, interviews with the late director and commentary by Gwen Verdon. (February 23, 1990; 60 min.)

Director, producer: Judy Kinberg
Writer: William Henry III
Emmy Award: Outstanding Informational Special

A Tudor Evening with American Ballet Theatre

Two classics by the choreographer Antony Tudor: *Dark Elegies* (1937), set to Mahler's song cycle *Kindertotenlieder (Songs on the Death of Children)*, and *Jardin aux Lilas (Lilac Garden)* (1936), set to music by Ernest Chausson. Principal dancers are Leslie Browne, Martine van Hamel, Ricardo Bustamante and Michael Owen. Tudor played an instrumental role in establishing American Ballet Theatre's dramatic character, creating dances in a psychological landscape never before imagined for the ballet stage. His contribution to dance is explored in a documentary that includes interviews with Agnes de Mille and Maude Lloyd, both members of the original cast. (April 13, 1990; 60 min.)

Directed and produced by: Judy Kinberg, Thomas Grimm
A production of WNET/Thirteen and Danmarks Radio

Dancing for Mr. B: Six Balanchine Ballerinas

The special relationship between George Balanchine and six acclaimed dancers who worked with him is the subject of this documentary. Through rare film footage of the ballerinas in rehearsal and performance and through their own recollections, the film profiles six New York City Ballet stars: Mary Ellen Moylan, Maria Tallchief, Melissa Hayden, Allegra Kent, Merrill Ashley and Darci Kistler. Through their eyes, the film offers insight into the great choreographer's impact, technique and psychology. Includes footage from such major works as *The Firebird* (1910), *The Four Temperaments* (1946), *Symphony in C* (1947) and *La Sonnambula* (1946). (March 30, 1990; 90 min.)

Directors: Anne Belle, Deborah Dickson
Producer: Anne Belle
A production of Seahorse Films in association with WNET/Thirteen
Source: Direct Cinema

DANCE SPECIALS

Alvin Ailey: Memories and Visions

Works by Alvin Ailey are performed by the members of the Ailey City Center Dance Theater, with comments by Ailey. Shown are *Cry* (1971), performed by Judith Jamison, and *A Song for You* (1972), performed by Dudley Williams, and excerpts from *Blues Suite* (1958), *The Lark Ascending* (1972), *Mary Lou's Mass* (1971), *Hidden Rites* (1973) and *Revelations* (1960). Principal dancers include Kelvin Rotardier, Judith Jamison, Sylvia Waters, Dudley Williams, Estelle Spurlock, Linda Kent, Donna Wood, Sara Yarborough, Clive Thompson and John Parks. (May 6, 1974; 60 min.)

Director: Stanley Lathan
Producers: Ellis Haizlip, Alonzo Brown, Jr.
Executive producer: Jac Venza
A production of WNET/Thirteen

American Ballet Theatre: A Close-up in Time

A unique record of the style, history and achievements of American Ballet Theatre. Several works from the company's repertory are presented, including Agnes de Mille's *Rodeo* (1942), music by Aaron Copland; Michel Fokine's *Les Sylphides* (1909), set to the music of Chopin, and Antony Tudor's *Pillar of Fire* (1942) to music by Arnold Shoenberg. (October 8, 1973; 90 min.)

Director: Jerome Schnur
Executive producer: Jac Venza
A production of WNET/Thirteen
Source: Arthur Cantor Films

Break

A dance work made for television by the choreographer Bill T. Jones, performed as a duet between Jones and Maria Cheng with a corps of dancers. Filmed in a rock quarry in Minnesota in 100-degree heat, *Break* examines the sexual and racial conflicts of the 1960s. (December 21, 1983; 30 min.)

Directed and produced by: Mark Lowry, Kathryn Esher
A production of the Walker Art Center and KTCA/St. Paul-Minneapolis

Conversations About the Dance

A combined performance and lecture on the history of dance. As the renowned choreographer Agnes de Mille traces the evolution of dance and American dance history, members of The Joffrey Ballet create the forms and dances, helping the viewer understand how movement and emotion are formulated by the varied forms of dance over the centuries. Recorded

live at Los Angeles's Greek Theatre. (January 28, 1979; 90 min.)

Director: Charles S. Dubin
Producer: Loring d'Usseau
Choreography: Agnes De Mille
A production of KCET/Los Angeles

Making Television Dance

The choreographer Twyla Tharp imaginatively merges dance into television's space. Several works conceived for television are shown in development and performance. Most make use of one or more special video effects; others use the television screen to convey an intimacy between dancers in space and the viewer. Dancing in four etudes are Shelley Washington in *Speed*; Tom Rawe in *Repetition*; Jennifer Way in *Focus*; and Christine Uchida in *Retrograde*. The four dancers and Tharp travel to the country where they perform to bluegrass music by Snuffy Jenkins and Pappy Sherrill. Tharp and Mikhail Baryshnikov are shown rehearsing and performing *One for the Road*. (October 4, 1977; 60 min.)

Director: Don Mischer
Producer: Twyla Tharp
A production of the Television Laboratory at WNET/Thirteen and the Twyla Tharp Dance Foundation
Source: Phoenix Films

Chapter 2:
OPERA AND MUSICAL THEATER

The entry of the gods into Valhalla in the final scene of Das Rheingold, part one of Richard Wagner's Ring of the Nibelung. *Photo by Winnie Klotz.*

THE METROPOLITAN OPERA PRESENTS

AMERICA'S MUSICAL THEATER

MUSICAL COMEDY TONIGHT

OPERA SPECIALS

THE METROPOLITAN OPERA PRESENTS

(Formerly LIVE FROM THE MET)

The Metropolitan Opera's broadcasts dissolved the walls of the theater into a continental arena, extending the audience to millions remote from the opera house at a cost of a few cents (of tax dollars) per viewer. On several occasions, its telecasts have been beamed by satellite to Europe. Despite increased competition on the public broadcasting schedule from science, politics and nature's fauna, opera's hold on the national audience has been firm. This was resoundingly demonstrated in June, 1990, when Wagner's Ring cycle was broadcast for seventeen hours on four consecutive evenings reaching an American audience of 12 million (8.1 million households). Texaco's sponsorship of the Met's broadcasts on radio (from 1931) and television (since 1977) is the longest media commitment to an arts institution by a major corporation. The Endowment has been a junior partner in this magnificent act of sustained patronage. And radio simulcast in stereo has enabled viewers to circumvent television's limited sound capability.

Broadcasts of operas by Puccini, Verdi, Donizetti, Mozart and others emphasize the Met's role as a distinguished curator in the museum of high culture. It has premiered for American audiences Berg's *Lulu* and Weill's *The Rise and Fall of the City of Mahagonny*. Its casts make up an honor roll of virtually every major figure in opera, and its stage and television productions have, despite increasing costs, frequently reinterpreted standard readings of the classic texts.

The Met's telecasts have incubated a small cadre of television directors remarkably sensitive to the small screen's reciprocal dialogue of intimacy and spectacle. Deeply versed in the art form, these directors skillfully establish a sense of place which, in its elimination of the proscenium, can offer a more convincing illusion than that available at the opera house. For the television analog to the live performance is in itself a creative artifact "conducted" by a director with a profound knowledge of score and spectacle.

Executive producer: Michael Bronson (1977 - 1986); Peter Gelb (1987 - present)
Awards: 1984 Peabody Award
Additional funders include: Texaco, Pioneer Electronic Corporation (1985 - 1988), Charles E. Culpeper Foundation, Mrs. Donald D. Harrington, Ailene B. and Pierre Claeyssens, Cynthia Wood
A production of the Metropolitan Opera Association and WNET/New York

SEASON ONE, 1977

La Bohème

The live telecast of *La Bohème* (1896), Giacomo Puccini's opera of 19th-century Paris and its penniless yet high-spirited artists, marks the premiere of LIVE FROM THE MET. Renata Scotto stars as Mimi, Luciano Pavarotti as Rodolfo, Maralin Niska as Musetta, Ingvar Wixell as Marcello and Paul Plishka as Colline. James Levine conducts the Metropolitan Opera Orchestra. Tony Randall hosts the program. (March 15, 1977; 195 min.)

Production by: Fabrizio Melano
Television director: Kirk Browning
Producer: John Goberman
Awards: Peabody Award

SEASON TWO, 1977 - 1978

Rigoletto

Giuseppe Verdi's tragic opera *Rigoletto* (1851) is the story of the hunch-backed court jester to the Duke of Mantua. At court, Rigoletto plays the cynical, sarcastic fool; yet at home he is a gentle and loving father to Gilda. Haunted by the curse of Monterone, Rigoletto's actions unwittingly contribute to Gilda's seduction and death. Cornell MacNeil sings the title role; Ileana Cotrubas sings the role of Gilda and Placido Domingo performs as the Duke of Mantua. The Metropolitan Opera's artistic director James Levine conducts. (November 7, 1977; 180 min.)

Production by: John Dexter
Television director: Kirk Browning
Producer: Christopher Sarson
Awards: Peabody Award

Don Giovanni

Don Giovanni (1787) by Wolfgang Amadeus Mozart is the classic story of Don Juan, the seducer of women whose conquests ultimately bring about his downfall. The production stars James Morris as Don Giovanni; Joan Sutherland as Donna Anna; John Brecknock as Don Ottavio; Julia Varady as Donna Elvira and John Macurdy as the Commendatore. Richard Bonynge conducts. At intermission the program host, Tony Randall, interviews the principal artists, and backstage scenes are shown. (March 16, 1978; 210 min.)

Production by: Herbert Graf
Television director: Kirk Browning
Producer: Christopher Sarson

Act II from Kurt Weill's The Rise and Fall of the City of Mahagonny. *Photo by James Heffernan.*

Cavalleria Rusticana and I Pagliacci

Cavalleria Rusticana (1890) and *I Pagliacci* (1892), two short operas traditionally performed on the same bill, are among the first operatic works to portray ordinary people and their lives. In Pietro Mascagni's *Cavalleria Rusticana*, Tatiana Troyanos sings Santuzza and Placido Domingo sings Turiddu. The cast also includes Isola Jones, Vern Shinall and Jean Kraft. In Ruggiero Leoncavallo's *I Pagliacci*, Nedda is sung by Teresa Stratas, Canio by Placido Domingo; Tonio by Sherrill Milnes and Silvio by Allan Monk. James Levine conducts both operas. (April 5, 1978; 185 min.)

Production, set and costume design by: Franco Zeffirelli
Television director: Kirk Browning
Producer: Christopher Sarson

SEASON THREE, 1978 - 1979

Otello

Giuseppe Verdi completed his tragic masterpiece *Otello* in 1887 at age 74, retelling Shakespeare's drama of doubt and jealousy. The production stars Jon Vickers in the title role; Renata Scotto as Desdemona; Cornell MacNeil as Iago and Jean Kraft as Emilia. James Levine conducts. (September 25, 1978; 230 min.)

Production and set design by: Franco Zeffirelli
Television director: Kirk Browning
Producer: Christopher Sarson

The Bartered Bride

The Bartered Bride (1870), the final work of the Czech composer Bedrich Smetana, is the story of love's triumph over a prearranged marriage. The work is a national cultural treasure of Czechoslovakia, considered the very best type of folk opera. The performance stars Teresa Stratas as Marenka; Nicolai Gedda as Jenik; Jon Vickers as Vasek and Martti Talvela as Kecal. James Levine conducts. (November 21, 1978; 150 min.)

Production by: John Dexter
Television director: Kirk Browning
Producer: Christopher Sarson

Tosca

In the late 1880s, Giacomo Puccini witnessed Sarah Bernhardt's performance in Victorien Sardou's play *La Tosca* in Paris. Though overwhelmed and inspired, some ten years passed before Puccini premiered his classic opera *Tosca* (1900). Set in Rome in 1800—the scene of political unrest and police brutality—*Tosca* is a story of loyalty and the heroic defiance of tyranny. Shirley Verrett sings the title role. Cavaradossi is sung by Luciano Pavarotti; Scarpia by Cornell MacNeil; Sacristan by Fernando Corena and Angelotti by John Cheek. James Conlon conducts. (December 19, 1978; 180 min.)

Production by: Tito Gobbi
Television director: Kirk Browning
Producer: Christopher Sarson

Luisa Miller

Giuseppe Verdi's opera *Luisa Miller* (1849), based on a play by Friedrich Schiller, is a tale of two doomed lovers: a peasant girl and a nobleman's son. In this production Luisa is sung by Renata Scotto; Rodolfo by Placido Domingo; Miller by Sherrill Milnes and Federica by Jean Kraft. James Levine conducts. (January 20, 1979; 210 min.)

Production by: Nathaniel Merrill
Television director: Kirk Browning
Producer: Christopher Sarson

SEASON FOUR, 1979 - 1980

Otello

Opening night of the Metropolitan Opera's 1979 - 1980 season features *Otello* (1887), Giuseppe Verdi's musical rendering of the tragedy by Shakespeare. Placido Domingo sings the role of Otello; Gilda Cruz-Romo is Desdemona; Sherrill Milnes is Iago; Shirley Love is Emilia and Giuliano Ciannella is Cassio. James Levine conducts. Francis Robinson hosts the performance. (September 24, 1979; 240 min.)

Production and set design by: Franco Zeffirelli
Television director: Kirk Browning
Producer: Christopher Sarson

The Rise and Fall of the City of Mahagonny

Written between 1927 and 1931 during Hitler's rise to power, *The Rise and Fall of the City of Mahagonny* is set in a fictional American boom-town and caricatures the hypocrisy of a society ruled by greed. It was banned in Nazi Germany in 1933. This production of Kurt Weill and Bertolt Brecht's opera stars Teresa Stratas as Jenny Smith; Richard Cassilly as Jimmy Mahoney; Astrid Varnay as Begbick; Cornell MacNeil as Moses. The announcer's role is played by Nico Castel. James Levine conducts. (November 27, 1979; 210 min.)

Production by: John Dexter
Television director: Brian Large
Producer: Christopher Sarson

Un Ballo in Maschera (The Masked Ball)

Giuseppe Verdi's *Un Ballo in Maschera (The Masked Ball)* (1859) tells a story originally written about the king of Sweden, sung in Italian and

Placido Domingo and Ileana Cotrubas in Verdi's La Traviata. *Photo by James Heffernan.*

set in Boston of the 1770s. The incongruous story and setting were arrived at to satisfy the political censors of Naples, who objected to the libretto's tale of revolutionary ferment and regicide. In this production, Katia Ricciarelli sings the role of Amelia;

Luciano Pavarotti is Riccardo; Louis Quilico is Renato; Bianca Berini is Ulrica and Judith Blegen is Oscar. Giuseppe Patane conducts. (February 16, 1980; 210 min.)

Production by: Elijah Moshinsky
Television director: Brian Large
Producer: Christopher Sarson
Source: Paramount Home Video;
Pioneer (laser disc)

Don Carlo

First performed in Paris in 1867, *Don Carlo* is a product of Giuseppe Verdi's middle period. Yet the tragic, brooding opera has come to be recognized as the equal of the masterpieces of Verdi's final years, *Aida*, *Otello* and *Falstaff*. The performance stars Vasile Moldoveanu in the title role; Renata Scotto as Elisabetta; Sherrill Milnes as Rodrigo; Tatiana Troyanos as Eboli and Paul Plishka as Filippo II. James Levine conducts. Taped February 21, 1980. (April 12, 1980; 270 min.)

Production by: John Dexter
Television director: Kirk Browning
Producer: Christopher Sarson

Don Pasquale

Gaetano Donizetti's *Don Pasquale* (1843) is the story of a rich, aging bachelor who arranges to marry in order to produce an heir and deprive his rebellious young nephew, Ernesto, of his inheritance. In this performance Gabriel Bacquier sings the title role; Beverly Sills is Norina; Alfredo Kraus is Ernesto; Hakan Hagegard is Doctor Malatesta and Nico Castel is the Notary. Nicola Rescigno conducts. Taped January 11, 1979. (May 17, 1980; 150 min.)

Production by: John Dexter
Television director: Kirk Browning
Producer: Christopher Sarson

SEASON FIVE, 1980 - 1981

Manon Lescaut

Giacomo Puccini's opera *Manon Lescaut*, which premiered in Turin in 1893, was the composer's first critical and popular success. This performance stars Renata Scotto as the amoral Manon; Placido Domingo as her ardent young lover, Des Grieux; Pablo Elvira as Manon's scheming brother, Lescaut; Renato Capecchi as

Dear LIVE FROM THE MET:

What a thoroughly unforgettable and magnificent performance, LIVE FROM THE MET *with Luciano Pavarotti, this very Sunday evening!*

The equally fine camera work brought out every superb facet of the vocal music, as well as telling true to Mr. Pavarotti's radiant personality.

More like this please!

M.V., Elmira, N.Y.

---

the corrupt sensualist, Geronte, and Philip Creech as Des Grieux's carefree friend, Edmondo. James Levine conducts. Taped March 29, 1980. (September 27, 1980; 180 min.)

Production by: Gian Carlo Menotti
Television director: Kirk Browning
Producer: Christopher Sarson

Lulu

Alban Berg had completed all but the orchestration for the final act of his tragic opera *Lulu* at the time of his death in 1935, but not until 1978 did the opera receive its premiere. Based on Wedekind's plays *Earth Spirit* and *Pandora's Box*, Berg's *Lulu* is a story of psychological turmoil, decadence and murder composed entirely within the twelve-tone system. Julia Migenes-Johnson sings the title role; Franz Mazura is Doctor Schoen and Jack the Ripper; Kenneth Riegel is Alwa; Evelyn Lear is the Countess Geschwitz and Andrew Foldi is Schigolch. James Levine conducts. (December 20, 1980; 240 min.)

Production by: John Dexter
Television director: Brian Large
Producer: Clemente D'Alessio

Elektra

Richard Strauss's *Elektra* (1909), the first work to issue from the composer's historic collaboration with Hugo von Hofmannsthal, follows closely the Sophoclean tragedy based on the curse on the house of Atreus. Birgit Nilsson sings the title role of Elektra, a role she first performed at the Met in 1966. The role of Chrysothemis, Elektra's sister is sung by Leonie Rysanek; Klytemnestra by Mignon Dunn; Orestes by Donald McIntyre and Aegisthus by Robert Nagy. James Levine conducts. Taped February 16, 1980. (January 28, 1981; 210 min.)

Production by: Herbert Graf
Television director: Brian Large
Producer: Clemente D'Alessio
Source: Paramount Home Video;
Pioneer (laser disc)

L'Elisir d'Amore (The Elixir of Love)

In Gaetano Donizetti's *L'Elisir d'Amore (The Elixir of Love)* (1832), a sincere but shy peasant lad pursues an independent-minded woman, his confidence enhanced by an alleged love potion. This comic opera was revived at the Met in 1904 to showcase Enrico Caruso's rendition of the second act aria, *Una furtiva lagrima*. In this production, the role of Adina is sung by Judith Blegen; Nemorino by Luciano Pavarotti; Sergeant Belcore by Brent Ellis; Doctor Dulcamara by Sesto Bruscantini and Giannetta by Louise Wohlafka. Nicola Rescigno conducts. (March 2, 1981; 210 min.)

Production by: Nathaniel Merrill
Television director: Kirk Browning
Producer: Clemente D'Alessio
Source: Paramount Home Video;
Pioneer (laser disc)

SEASON SIX, 1981 - 1982

La Traviata

Since it was first performed in 1853, the lead role of *La Traviata*, Giuseppe Verdi's opera based on the story of the doomed courtesan Violetta, who leaves her wealthy benefactor for true love, has been one of opera's most coveted. This performance features Ileana Cotrubas as Violetta; Placido Domingo as Alfredo; Cornell MacNeil as Germont; Ariel Bybee as Flora and Dana Talley as Gastone. James Levine conducts. Broadcast live to Europe March 28, 1981. (September 30, 1981; 180 min.)

Production by: Colin Graham
Television director: Brian Large
Producer: Clemente D'Alessio

Il Trittico (The Tryptich)

Giacomo Puccini's tryptich of three short operas is the composer's last completed work. *Il Tabarro* stars Renata Scotto in the role of Giorgetta; Cornell MacNeil as Michele and Vasile Moldoveanu as Luigi. In *Suor Angelica*, Renata Scotto performs the role of Sister Angelica; Jocelyn Taillon, the Princess and Jean Kraft, the Abbess. *Gianni Schicchi* features Gabriel Bacquier in the title role; Renata Scotto as Lauretta and Philip Creech as Rinuccio. James Levine conducts. *Il Trittico* had its world premiere at the Metropolitan Opera in 1918. (November 14, 1981; 210 min.)

Production by: Fabrizio Melano
Television director: Kirk Browning
Producer: Clemente D'Alessio

Rigoletto

Louis Quilico sings the title role in the Metropolitan Opera's production of *Rigoletto* (1851), Giuseppe Verdi's tragic opera that traces the ramifications of cruelty and deception. The role of Gilda is sung by Christiane

Eda-Pierre, the Duke of Mantua by Luciano Pavarotti and Maddalena by Isola Jones. James Levine conducts the Metropolitan Opera Orchestra and Chorus. (December 16, 1981; 210 min.)

Production by: John Dexter
Television director: Brian Large
Producer: Clemente D'Alessio

La Bohème

This version of *La Bohème* (1896), Giacomo Puccini's romantic tale of young love, struggling artists and their dreams and despair, is staged by the noted Italian director and designer Franco Zeffirelli. This performance stars Teresa Stratas as Mimi and Jose Carreras as Rodolfo. Musetta is sung by Renata Scotto, Marcello by Richard Stilwell and Colline by James Morris. James Levine conducts. Taped January 16, 1982. (January 20, 1982; 180 min.)

Production and set design by: Franco Zeffirelli
Television director: Kirk Browning
Producer: Clemente D'Alessio
Awards: Emmy Award: Outstanding Classical Program in the Performing Arts

SEASON SEVEN, 1982 - 1983

Der Rosenkavalier

Richard Strauss's sophisticated romantic comedy *Der Rosenkavalier* (1911) is set in Vienna of the 1740s, as Strauss and the librettist Hugo von Hofmannsthal evoke a long-ago time through magical waltzes. Starring in this production are Tatiana Troyanos as Octavian, Kiri Te Kanawa as the Marschallin, Judith Blegen as Sophie and Luciano Pavarotti as the Singer. James Levine conducts. (October 7, 1982; 180 min.)

Production by: Nathaniel Merrill
Television director: Kirk Browning
Producer: Clemente D'Alessio

Hansel and Gretel

Engelbert Humperdinck's *Hansel and Gretel* (1893) is traditionally performed during the Christmas season. The opera, sung here in English, enhances the story based on the Grimm fairy tale with a powerful musical score in the Wagnerian style. Starring in the performance are Judith

Blegen as Gretel, Frederica von Stade as Hansel and Rosalind Elias as the Witch. Jean Kraft sings the role of Gertrude and Michael Devlin, Peter. Thomas Fulton conducts. (December 25, 1982; 120 min.)

Production by: Nathaniel Merrill
Television director: Kirk Browning
Producer: Clemente D'Alessio
Source: Paramount Home Video; Pioneer (laser disc)

Idomeneo

This is the first time Wolfgang Amadeus Mozart's opera *Idomeneo* (1781) has been performed by the Metropolitan Opera. The story is set in Crete at the end of the Trojan War. Idomeneo, king of Crete, finds that he must sacrifice his son to fulfill a promise to the gods. The performance features Ileana Cotrubas as Ilia, Hildegard Behrens as Elettra, Frederica von Stade as Idamante and Luciano Pavarotti as Idomeneo. James Levine conducts. Broadcast live to Europe November 6, 1982. (January 26, 1983; 240 min.)

Production, set and costume design by: Jean-Pierre Ponnelle
Television director: Brian Large
Producer: Clemente D'Alessio
Source: Paramount Home Video; Pioneer (laser disc)

Tannhaeuser

Set in 13th-century Germany, *Tannhaeuser* (1845) is Richard Wagner's parable of a singer's harrowing struggle to defy Venus and attain salvation, aided by the devotion of a woman. The production stars Eva Marton as Elisabeth, Tatiana Troyanos as Venus, Richard Cassilly as Tannhaeuser, Bernd Weikl as Wolfram and John Macurdy as

Luciano Pavarotti plays the title role in Mozart's Idomeneo. *Photo by James Heffernan.*

Hermann, Landgrave of Thuringia.
James Levine conducts. Taped December 20, 1982. (March 23, 1983; 210
min.)

Production by: Otto Schenk
Television director: Brian Large
Producer: Clemente D'Alessio
Source: Paramount Home Video;
Pioneer (laser disc)

SEASON EIGHT, 1983 - 1984

Lucia di Lammermoor

Gaetano Donizetti's *Lucia di
Lammermoor* (1835), set in 17th-
century Scotland, is based on Sir
Walter Scott's novel, *The Bride of
Lammermoor*, in which a young
woman is forced into an arranged
marriage to bolster her family's fortune. Lucia, whose "mad scene" aria is
one of the most famous in opera, is
played by Joan Sutherland; the cast
features Alfredo Kraus as Edgardo,
Pablo Elvira as Lord Ashton, Paul
Plishka as Raimondo and John

Gilmore as Normanno. Richard
Bonynge conducts. Taped November
13, 1982. (September 28, 1983; 180
min.)

Production by: Bruce Donnell
Television director: Kirk Browning
Producer: Clemente D'Alessio
Source: Paramount Home Video;
Pioneer (laser disc)

Metropolitan Opera Centennial Gala, Part One

In celebration of the 100th anniversary—and nearly 20,000 performances—of the Metropolitan Opera,
the Met staged two galas featuring
nearly 100 singers and the entire
Metropolitan Opera company: orchestra, chorus and ballet. Part one took
place Saturday afternoon, October 22,
1983. Arias, overtures and choruses
from 22 operas are performed, including works by Bizet, Donizetti,
Gershwin, Gounod, Leigh, Mascagni,
Mozart, Puccini, Rossini, Smetana, R.
Strauss, Verdi, Wagner and Weill.
James Levine, Richard Bonynge,
David Stivender and Jeffrey Tate

conduct. Act one scenery by David
Hockney; act two, by Guenther
Schneider-Siemssen. (October 22,
1983; 210 min.)

Television director: Kirk Browning
Producer: Clemente D'Alessio
Source: Paramount Home Video;
Pioneer (laser disc)

Metropolitan Opera Centennial Gala, Part Two

Part two of the Centennial Gala, Sat-
urday evening, October 22, 1983,
presents excerpts from 30 operas from
the history of the Met, representing
works by Barber, Beethoven,
Debussy, Delibes, Donizetti,
Giordano, Gounod, Mozart,
Offenbach, Ponchielli, Puccini,
Romberg, Saint-Saens, Tchaikovsky,
Verdi and Wagner. Leonard
Bernstein, James Levine, Sir John
Pritchard and Thomas Fulton con-
duct. The gala is staged amid scenery

from three of the Met's most famous productions: Franco Zeffirelli's Cafe Momus scene from *La Bohème*; Robert O'Hearn's temple scene from *Samson and Delilah*; and Marc Chagall's setting for *The Magic Flute* from the Met's 1966 - 1967 season. (October 22, 1983; 300 min.)

Television director: Kirk Browning
Producer: Clemente D'Alessio
Source: Paramount Home Video;
Pioneer (laser disc)

Ernani

Giuseppe Verdi's *Ernani* (1844) was the first work for which the youthful composer earned international acclaim. The story, based on a romance by Victor Hugo, is set in 16th-century Spain where three suitors fight for the hand of the heroine, Elvira, who loves the bandit Ernani. Starring as Ernani is Luciano Pavarotti; Leona Mitchell sings the role of Elvira. The principals include Sherrill Milnes as Don Carlo; Jean Kraft as Giovanna and Ruggero Raimondi as Don Gomez de Silva. James Levine conducts. Taped December 17, 1983. (December 21, 1983; 210 min.)

Production and set design by: Pier Luigi Samaritani
Television director: Kirk Browning
Producer: Clemente D'Alessio
Source: Paramount Home Video

Don Carlo

Giuseppe Verdi's tragic opera *Don Carlo* (1867) probes the conflicts between husband and wife, father and son and church and state. The libretto, by Mery and du Locle, is drawn from a play by the German playwright Friedrich Schiller. The story takes place in 16th-century Spain during the reign of King Philip II. This production features Mirella Freni in the role of Elizabetta, Grace Bumbry as Eboli, Placido Domingo as Don Carlo and Nicolai Ghiaurov as King Philip. James Levine conducts. Telecast live to Europe March 26, 1983. (February 1, 1984; 270 min.)

Production by: John Dexter
Television director: Brian Large
Producer: Clemente D'Alessio
Source: Paramount Home Video;
Pioneer (laser disc)

Les Troyens (The Trojans)

Hector Berlioz's epic opera *Les Troyens* (1890) is based on Virgil's *Aeneid*—the adventures of Aeneas, the hero of the Trojan War and mythical founder of Rome. The first act features John Macurdy as Priam, king of Troy, and Jessye Norman as Cassandra (the role in which Norman made her Met debut in September, 1983). Placido Domingo performs the role of Aeneas and Morley Meredith, the ghost of Hector. In the second act, Tatiana Troyanos stars as Dido, queen of Carthage; Paul Plishka is Narbal and Jean Kraft is the ghost of Cassandra. James Levine conducts. Taped October 8, 1983. (March 28, 1984; 210 min.)

Production by: Fabrizio Melano
Television director: Brian Large
Producer: Clemente D'Alessio
Source: Paramount Home Video;
Pioneer (laser disc)

SEASON NINE, 1984 - 1985

La Forza del Destino

Based on a play by the Spanish dramatist, the Duke of Pivas, Giuseppe Verdi's *La Forza del Destino* (1862) is the story of two doomed lovers. In it, a half-Incan nobleman of Peru, Don Alvaro, elopes with his beloved, Leonora di Vargas, and accidentally kills her father. Leontyne Price performs as Leonora and Giuseppe Giacomini as Don Alvaro. The cast includes Isola Jones, Leo Nucci, Enrico Fisore and Bonaldo Giaiotti. James Levine conducts. Taped March 24, 1984. (October 31, 1984; 210 min.)

Production by: John Dexter
Television director: Kirk Browning
Producer: Samuel J. Paul, III
Source: Paramount Home Video;
Pioneer (laser disc)

Aida

This live telecast of Giuseppe Verdi's *Aida* (1871) marks Leontyne Price's farewell appearance in operatic performance. Commissioned in the 1860s by the Khedive (Viceroy) of Egypt, *Aida* is the larger-than-life realization of the story by Auguste Edouard Mariette—the fatal love triangle between Aida, Amneris and Radames, and the filial ties binding Aida and her father Amonasro. The cast features Fiorenza Cossotto, James McCracken, Simon Estes, John Macurdy and Dimitri Kavrakos. Metropolitan Opera artistic director James Levine conducts. (January 3, 1985; 240 min.)

Production by: John Dexter
Television director: Brian Large
Producer: Samuel J. Paul, III

Francesca da Rimini

Blazing battle scenes and passionate love scenes dominate *Francesca da Rimini* (1914) by Riccardo Zandonai. The Metropolitan Opera's production features Renata Scotto and Placido Domingo as the guilty lovers. Cornell MacNeil and William Lewis star as the vengeful brothers. James Levine conducts. Taped April 7, 1984. (January 30, 1985; 180 min.)

Production by: Piero Faggioni
Television director: Brian Large
Producer: Samuel J. Paul, III
Source: Paramount Home Video;
Pioneer (laser disc)

Tosca

The Metropolitan Opera's spectacular 1984 - 1985 production of Giacomo Puccini's *Tosca* (1900) features Hildegard Behrens, Placido Domingo, Cornell MacNeil and Italo Tajo in the principal roles. Giuseppe Sinopoli conducts. Joanne Woodward hosts the performance, and the intermission features a documentary in which the production designer Franco Zeffirelli visits the historic sites in Rome he has recreated for this staging of the opera—the church of Sant'Andrea della Valle, the Farnese Palace and the fortress of Sant'Angelo. (March 27, 1985; 180 min.)

Production and set design by: Franco Zeffirelli
Television director: Kirk Browning
Producer: Samuel J. Paul, III
Awards: Emmy Award: Outstanding Classical Program in the Performing Arts
Source: Paramount Home Video; Pioneer (laser disc)

Simon Boccanegra

This Metropolitan Opera's production of Giuseppe Verdi's *Simon Boccanegra* (1857) features Sherrill Milnes as the great-hearted ruler and father, Simon Boccanegra; Anna Tomowa-Sintow as his long-lost daughter; Vasile Moldoveanu as her fiery lover and Paul Plishka as the unrelenting enemy. James Levine conducts. Broadcast live to Europe December 29, 1984. (April 17, 1985; 180 min.)

Production by: Tito Capobianco
Television director: Brian Large
Producer: Samuel J. Paul, III
Source: Paramount Home Video; Pioneer (laser disc)

SEASON TEN, 1986

L'Italiana in Algeri

Gioacchino Rossini's *L'Italiana in Algeri* (1813) tells the story of Isabella, a courageous Italian beauty shipwrecked off the coast of Africa while searching for her sweetheart, Lindoro. Fate brings her together again with the long-lost Lindoro, after she has been inducted into the Mustafa's harem. The performance, which was telecast live, features Marilyn Horne, Gail Robinson, Douglas Ahlstedt, Allan Monk, Spiro Malas and Paolo Montarsolo. James Levine conducts. (January 11, 1986; 180 min.)

Production by: Jean-Pierre Ponnelle
Television director: Brian Large
Producer: Samuel J. Paul, III

Lohengrin

Richard Wagner's most popular opera, *Lohengrin* (1850) is based on the legend of a knight who miraculously appears to save an innocent maiden accused of a heinous crime. In taking her for his bride, he forbids her from ever asking his name or whence he came. The cast features Peter Hofmann as the Swan Night; Eva Marton as the maiden Elsa; Leonie Rysanek as Ortrud; Leif Roar as Telramund and John Macurdy as the King. James Levine conducts. Taped January 10, 1986. (March 26, 1986; 240 min.)

Production by: August Everding
Television director: Brian Large
Source: Paramount Home Video; Pioneer (laser disc)

Le Nozze di Figaro (The Marriage of Figaro)

The first of three collaborations between Wolfgang Amadeus Mozart and the librettist Lorenzo da Ponte, *Le Nozze di Figaro (The Marriage of Figaro)* (1786) is based on a controversial comedy by the French writer Beaumarchais set in Seville. On the day before the wedding of Figaro and Susanna, the young couple attempt to keep the Count Almaviva from exercising his aristocratic privilege—*le droit de seigneur*—of sleeping with the maiden on the eve of her wedding. In this new production, the principals are Carol Vaness, Kathleen Battle, Frederica von Stade, Ruggero Raimondi, Thomas Allen, Jocelyn Taillon, Michel Senechal and Arthur Korn. James Levine conducts. Taped December 14, 1985. (April 23, 1986; 210 min.)

Production by: Jean-Pierre Ponnelle
Television director: Brian Large
Producer: Samuel J. Paul, III

SEASON ELEVEN, 1986 - 1987

Die Fledermaus

Die Fledermaus (1874), Johann Strauss's operatic masterpiece, is set in Vienna. Eisenstein, a dapper financier, must go to jail because of a minor civil offense, making it possible for Rosalinde, his beautiful young wife, to rendezvous with an old flame. Husband and wife are invited, unknown to each other, to a costume ball, where this comedy of errors begins. The principals are Kiri Te Kanawa, Judith Blegen, Tatiana Troyanos, David Rendall, Hakan Hagegard and Michael Devlin. Jeffrey Tate conducts. Joanne Woodward hosts this live New Year's Eve telecast. (December 31, 1986; 210 min.)

Production by: Otto Schenk
Television director: Kirk Browning
Producer: Samuel J. Paul, III

An Evening with Joan Sutherland and Luciano Pavarotti

In this gala concert (a benefit for the Metropolitan Opera Pension Fund) Dame Joan Sutherland and Luciano Pavarotti perform scenes from three operas: Donizetti's *Lucia di Lammermoor* and Verdi's *Rigoletto* and *La Traviata*. (Both singers made their Metropolitan Opera debuts in *La Traviata* in 1970.) Also performing are the tenor Leo Nucci and a cast that includes Ariel Bybee, James Courtney, Ferruccio Furlanetto, Hillary Johnsson, Isola Jones and Julien Robbins. Richard Bonynge conducts. Taped January 11, 1987. (March 4, 1987; 120 min.)

Television director: Kirk Browning
Producer: Samuel J. Paul, III
Source: Deutsche Grammophon (laser disc)

Carmen

Georges Bizet's *Carmen* (1875), with its passionate music and powerful drama, is the story of a toreador, a young officer and the tempestuous gypsy Carmen who bewitches them both. Leading the cast are Agnes Baltsa, Gabriela Benackova, Jose Carreras and Samuel Ramey. James Levine conducts. Taped February 18, 1987. (April 1, 1987; 180 min.)

Production by: Sir Peter Hall
Television director: Brian Large
Source: Deutsche Grammophon (home video, laser disc)

Les Dialogues des Carmélites (Dialogues of the Carmelites)

Set in a convent of Carmelite nuns during the French Revolution, Francis Poulenc's *Les Dialogues des Carmélites (Dialogues of the Carmelites)* (1947) deals with faith and spiritual courage in a world in chaos. The cast includes Maria Ewing, Jessye Norman, Regine Crespin, Florence Quivar and David Kuebler. Manuel Rosenthal, a close friend of Poulenc, conducts. Taped April 4, 1987. (May 6, 1987; 180 min.)

Production by: John Dexter
Television director: Brian Large
Producer: Samuel J. Paul, III

SEASON TWELVE, 1987 - 1988

Turandot

The Metropolitan Opera opens its 12th season of telecasts with Giacomo Puccini's *Turandot* (1924), a fantastic tale of love, pride and death set in legendary China. Unfinished at the time of Puccini's death, the opera was completed by Franco Alfano. Heading the cast are Eva Marton as the princess Turandot and Placido Domingo as the prince Calaf. Nello Santi conducts. (January 27, 1988; 150 min.)

Production and set design by: Franco Zeffirelli
Television director: Kirk Browning
Producer: Samuel J. Paul, III

Les Contes d'Hoffmann (The Tales of Hoffmann)

Jacques Offenbach's *Les Contes d'Hoffmann (The Tales of Hoffmann)* (1881) is a story of love and magic, of seduction and betrayal. The production features Neil Shicoff as the tormented poet Hoffmann; Roberta Alexander, Gwendolyn Bradley and Tatiana Troyanos as the poet's three great loves and James Morris as the demons who torment the poet. Charles Dutoit conducts. (March 2, 1988; 180 min.)

Production by: Otto Schenk
Television director: Brian Large
Producer: Samuel J. Paul, III
Source: Deutsche Grammophon (home video, laser disc)

Ariadne auf Naxos

Ariadne auf Naxos (1916) by Richard Strauss combines Greek tragedy and Italian comedy. The performance stars Jessye Norman as Ariadne; Kathleen Battle as Zerbinetta; Tatiana Troyanos as the composer and James King as Bacchus. James Levine conducts. This is the first cultural program to be broadcast live to the Soviet Union, March 12, 1988. (April 27, 1988; 180 min.)

Production by: Bodo Igesz
Television director: Brian Large
Producer: Samuel J. Paul, III
Source: Deutsche Grammophon (home video, laser disc)

SEASON THIRTEEN, 1988 - 1989

Pavarotti and Levine in Recital

Luciano Pavarotti, tenor, and James Levine, on piano, perform for the first time together in a full recital in this live telecast. The musical selections include the arias *Un'aura amorosa* from Mozart's *Cosi fan tutte*, *Odi il voto* from Verdi's *Ernani* and *M'appari* from Flotow's *Martha*; Rossini's spirited tarantella *La Danza*; bel canto songs by Bellini and vocal tone poems by Respighi. The recital concludes with songs by Mascagni, Sibella and Denza. (September 18, 1988; 120 min.)

Produced and directed by: Brian Large
Source: Decca International (home video, laser disc)

Il Trovatore

Giuseppe Verdi's opera *Il Trovatore* (1853) takes place in medieval Spain. It is the story of four characters: the Troubadour Manrico and the Count di Luna, bitter rivals in love and war; Leonora, the object of their desires, and Azucena, the gyspy woman who raised Manrico and who yearns to avenge her mother's death. The performance stars Eva Marton and Luciano Pavarotti. James Levine conducts. The host is F. Murray Abraham. Telecast to eight countries in Europe and to the Soviet Union, New Zealand, Japan and Korea. (October 2, 1988; 180 min.)

Production by: Fabrizio Melano
Television director: Brian Large
Source: Deutsche Grammophon (home video, laser disc)

Dear LIVE FROM THE MET:

On Wednesday, December 27th, I sat in my living room and watched in awe as glorious voices surrounded me. Never in my life have I enjoyed television as I did that night. Your production of Aida had to be [one of] the grandeurs of telecasting.

If I were rich, I'd send a dozen orchids to each of the great voices that enriched my night. But I am not rich, but am one of the millions of elderly who probably would never get to see such a superb offering of great music, great voices, great ballet, and even greater conducting of an opera. For this I am truly grateful.

I wish I could send something, but my social security limits me to what I can spend.

Maybe my gracious and sincere thanks for allowing me to watch such a spectacle in my living room can be sufficient.

Thank you, THE MET, from a grateful listener and viewer.

W.R., Arlington, Texas

Il Barbiere di Siviglia (The Barber of Seville)

Gioacchino Rossini's *Il Barbiere di Siviglia (The Barber of Seville)* (1816) is a story of courtship and deception: the Count Almaviva contrives to win Rosina from her jealous guardian Dr. Bartolo. At the center of the tangle of schemes is the barber, Figaro. The production stars Kathleen Battle as Rosina and Leo Nucci as Figaro. Ralf Weikert, music director of the Zurich Opera, conducts. (February 17, 1989; 180 min.)

Production by: John Cox
Television director: Brian Large
Source: Deutsche Grammophon (home video, laser disc)

Bluebeard's Castle/Erwartung (Expectation)

Two landmark one-act operas of the early 20th century, *Bluebeard's Castle* (1918) by Bela Bartok and *Erwartung (Expectation)* (1924) by Arnold Schoenberg, plumb the depths of psychological conflict. Jessye Norman performs opposite Samuel Ramey in *Bluebeard's Castle*, a story of terrifying discovery following the marriage of the adoring Judith and the insidious Bluebeard. Norman performs the solo role in *Erwartung*, an ecstatic yet fearful monologue of a woman searching for her lost lover in a moonlit forest. James Levine conducts. (March 31, 1989; 120 min.)

Production by: Goran Jarvefelt
Television director: Brian Large

SEASON FOURTEEN 1989 - 1990

Aida

Giuseppe Verdi's *Aida* (1871), the story of a slave torn between her passion for her country and her lover, is one of opera's grandest spectacles. Performing in this new production are Aprile Millo, Dolora Zajick, Placido Domingo, Sherrill Milnes, Paata Burchuladze, Dimitri Kavrakos and Juan Pons. James Levine conducts. Telecast to Austria, Great Britain, West Germany, Spain and Japan. (December 27, 1989; 180 min.)

Production by: Sonja Frisell
Television director: Brian Large
Awards: Emmy Award: Outstanding Classical Program in the Performing Arts
Source: Deutsche Grammophon (home video, laser disc)

Der Ring des Nibelungen (The Ring of the Nibelung)

Over four evenings in June, 1990, the Metropolitan Opera broadcast one of opera's crowning achievements, Richard Wagner's epic cycle of the Ring (1876): *Das Rheingold, Die Walkuere, Siegfried* and *Goetterdaemmerung*. Fifteen months in the making, the telecast fulfilled the composer's original intention of presenting the cycle on four consecutive evenings—a feat that has always proved physically and vocally impossible for singers performing live. Singing in the principal roles are Hildegard Behrens, Gary Lakes, Jessye Norman, Siegfried Jerusalem, James Morris, Christa Ludwig, Mari-Anne Haeggander, Mark Baker, Alan Held and Birgitta Svenden. James Levine conducts. F. Murray Abraham hosts. The 17-hour production, the longest opera telecast in the history of American television, reached an estimated 12 million viewers over four nights. (June 18 - 21, 1990; 17 hours in full)

Production by: Otto Schenk
Television director: Brian Large
A production of the Metropolitan Opera in association with La Sept (France), Channel Four/Great Britain, ORF and Deutsche Grammophon
Source: Deutsche Grammophon (home video, laser disc)

AMERICA'S MUSICAL THEATER

The development of a rich regional opera and musical theater culture in the 1970s and 1980s offered the possibility of a major series drawing on outstanding companies. A request for proposals resulted in an award to WGBH/Boston. Three classic works were broadcast from Washington, D.C.'s Arena Stage, New York City's American Place Theater, and the Houston Grand Opera. Despite the expenditure of considerable energies, matching funds were not forthcoming and the series did not survive its initial season. Productions from regional opera and musical theater companies now appear intermittently on GREAT PERFORMANCES.

Executive Producer: Greg Harney
Producers: Bernice Olenick, Glenn Litton
Additional funders include: M&M/Mars Foundation, Massachusetts Council for the Arts and Humanities
A production of WGBH/Boston

Happy End

Chicago's underworld in 1919 is the setting for *Happy End* (1929), a musical melodrama by Bertolt Brecht and Kurt Weill which includes some of Weill's most famous songs. Directed by Garland Wright at Arena Stage in Washington, D.C., *Happy End* tells of the romance between a small-time gangster and a Salvation Army soul-saver. The cast includes Richard Bauer, Casey Biggs, Marilyn Caskey, Kevin McClarnon, Joe Palmieri, Lizabeth Pritchett, Judith Anna Roberts and Henry Strozier. The program host is the singer and actress, Martha Schlamme. (January 19, 1986; 120 min.)

Director, executive producer: Greg Harney
Producer: Bernice Olenick
A production of WGBH/Boston

The Cradle Will Rock

Marc Blitzstein's musical *The Cradle Will Rock* (1936) probes the corruption of American institutions and personal values during the Depression. Performed by the Acting Company at the American Place Theatre in New York City, it stars Patti LuPone, with Casey Biggs, James Harper, Tom Robbins, Mary Lou Rosato, David Schramm and Charles Shaw-Robinson. Introducing the play is John Houseman, the coproducer, with Orson Welles, of the musical's 1937 premiere. (January 26, 1986; 90 min.)

Director: Bruce Minnix
Producers: Glenn Litton, John Lollos
Executive producer: Greg Harney
A production of WGBH/Boston

Treemonisha

Scott Joplin composed the folk opera *Treemonisha* in 1908, but it was not performed during his lifetime. The work is a parable in which a young woman leads her community away from superstition and fear toward education and enlightenment. The score entwines operatic melodies with Joplin's popular rags. Performed by the Houston Grand Opera and directed by Frank Corsaro, the cast includes Obba Babatunde, Carmen Balthrop, Raymond Bazemore, Dorceal Duckens, Michael Grey, Kenn Hicks, Delores Ivory, Ray Jacobs, Cora Johnson, Curtis Rayam and Cleveland Williams. Ossie Davis and Ruby Dee host the program. (February 2, 1986; 90 min.)

Director: Sid Smith
Producer: Bernice Olenick
Executive producers: Greg Harney, David Gockley
A production of the Houston Grand Opera

MUSICAL COMEDY TONIGHT

Sylvia Fine Kaye, a composer and historian of the American musical comedy, created this three-part series chronicling the accomplishments of the genre from the 1920s to the 1970s. The first two programs were broadcast in 1979 and 1981; the third appeared as a special on GREAT PERFORMANCES in season 13, 1985.

Producer: Sylvia Fine Kaye
Additional funders include: Prudential Insurance Company
A production of Dena Pictures and KCET/Los Angeles

Musical Comedy I

Traces the history of American musical comedy decade by decade, from the 1920s to the 1970s, combining newsreel footage, graphic animation, monologues and interviews, with musical numbers in their original Broadway stagings. The musicals excerpted include *Good News, Anything Goes, Oklahoma* and *Company*. Choreographed by Walter Painter. Sylvia Fine Kaye hosts the program. (October 1, 1979; 90 min.)

Director: Stan Harris
Producer: Eric Lieber
Executive producer, writer: Sylvia Fine Kaye
Awards: 1980 Peabody Award

Musical Comedy II

Recreates the sets, costumes, stagings and orchestrations of four classic American musicals: *Finian's Rainbow, South Pacific, Lady in the Dark* and *Sweet Charity*. The musical selections are choreographed by Tony Charmoli. In the cast are Annette Charles, Cathleen Cordell, Richard Crenna, Nancy Dussault, Lorraine Fields, Sergio Franchi, Bonnie Franklin, Danny Kaye, Jack Lemmon, William Mallory, Juliet Prowse, Lynn Redgrave and Larry Storch. The program host, Sylvia Fine Kaye, interviews Joshua Logan, the original

director of *South Pacific*, and Burton Lane, the composer of *Finian's Rainbow*. (February 11, 1981; 90 min.)

Director: Tony Charmoli
Producer, writer: Sylvia Fine Kaye
Executive producer: Herbert Bonis

Musical Comedy III

Includes selections from *The Boys from Syracuse, The Mikado, Lady Be Good, Show Boat, A Connecticut Yankee* and *As Thousands Cheer*. In the cast are Eddie Albert, Kaye Ballard, Dick Van Dyke, Florence Henderson, Patti LaBelle, Donna McKechnie and Elaine Stritch. (November 22, 1985; 120 min.)

Director: Stan Harris
Producer: Sylvia Fine Kaye
Executive producer: Jac Venza

OPERA SPECIALS

In the Shadow of the Stars: The Lives of Singers

A documentary that goes behind the scenes of the San Francisco Opera to meet the choristers, singers who aspire to become soloists and dream of being stars. We meet such diverse individuals as a tenor who grew up in the Bronx slums and preserved his sanity through music; a soprano whose life resembles a tragicomic opera plot; a

baritone from rural North Carolina who has come to love opera; a truck driver who practices arias in the cab of his tractor-trailer. Interviews with 12 singers take place in various settings—backstage in full makeup and costume, at rehearsals, auditions and at home with their families. (Date of release: 1990; 95 min.)

Directed and produced by: Irving Saraf, Allie Light
A production of Light-Saraf Films
Source: Light-Saraf Films

Vanessa

Samuel Barber's *Vanessa* (1958) was recorded live at the 1978 Spoleto Festival USA in Charleston, South Carolina. The Pulitzer Prize-winning opera, libretto by Gian Carlo Menotti, presents an aging beauty who panics as her youth fades. Johanna Meier sings the title role. The cast includes Katherine Ciesinski, Henry Price, Alice Garrott and Irwin Densen. Christopher Keene conducts the Spoleto Festival Orchestra and Chorus. Broadcast as a special during season 6 of GREAT PERFORMANCES. (January 31, 1979; 120 min.)

Production by: Gian Carlo Menotti
Television director: Kirk Browning
Producers: Sidney Palmer, David Griffiths
A production of South Carolina ETV and WNET/Thirteen

Chapter 3:

PERFORMING ARTS

The first LIVE FROM LINCOLN CENTER *telecast: The New York Philharmonic with Van Cliburn, Andre Previn, conducting. Photo by Susanne Faulkner Stevens/ Lincoln Center.*

LIVE FROM LINCOLN CENTER

GREAT PERFORMANCES

KENNEDY CENTER TONIGHT

LIVE FROM LINCOLN CENTER

Soon after the first of the great multiplexes of the performing arts, Lincoln Center, came into existence, discussions began on how its programs might be brought to a national audience. The inaugural telecast of Van Cliburn and the New York Philharmonic, Andre Previn conducting, in 1976 was the result of a pioneering funding partnership between the Arts Endowment and the Corporation for Public Broadcasting, and exemplified the Jacksonian vision of Nancy Hanks, the Endowment's second chairman.

Between 1976 and 1990, Lincoln Center's major performing arts organizations contributed 89 programs, divided thus: New York Philharmonic—29; New York City Opera—15; the Great Performers' recital series—15; American Ballet Theater—7; Chamber Music Society of Lincoln Center—6; Lincoln Center's own Mostly Mozart Festival—5; New York City Ballet—5; Film Society of Lincoln Center—2; Lincoln Center Theater—1; the Juilliard School—1, and Classical Jazz at Lincoln Center—1. Also seen were two gala specials: Beverly Sills's farewell appearance in concert performance in 1981 and the gala celebration of Lincoln Center's 25th anniversary in 1984. The series is the longest-running magazine of the live performing arts on television.

The notion of "live" broadcasts, enabling the home audience to co-exist simultaneously with the audience in the theater, would, it was felt, return to television some of the suspense and risk of its pre-videotape days. But it was necessary that the cameras not interfere with the live audience's pleasures, and that the stage not be over-lighted to facilitate the transmission of an adequate picture. With the assistance of an Endowment grant, John Goberman, the series producer, developed cameras sensitive to low levels of light. The cameras' ubiquitous presence became as unnoticed as that of the ushers seeing 2,700 ticket holders to their seats in Avery Fisher Hall. Over 5 million people "attend" each broadcast.

Producer: John Goberman*
Director: Kirk Browning*
Awards: First TV Critics' Circle Award for Achievements in Music, 1976; Peabody Award for Ten Years of Quality Programming, 1985
Additional funders include: Corporation for Public Broadcasting, Exxon Corporation, General Motors Corporation, Robert Wood Johnson Charitable Trust, Andrew W. Mellon Foundation, Charles A. Dana Foundation
A production of Lincoln Center for the Performing Arts. Presented in collaboration with WNET/Thirteen and GREAT PERFORMANCES
*And others as noted.

The American Ballet Theatre telecast of Swan Lake, June 30, 1976; Natalia Makarova as Odette/Odile, Ivan Nagy as the Prince Siegried. Photo by Susanne Faulkner Stevens.

SEASON ONE, 1976

New York Philharmonic with Van Cliburn, Andre Previn, conductor

The premiere telecast presents the New York Philharmonic, conducted by Andre Previn, with the pianist Van Cliburn as guest soloist. On the program are Berlioz's *Overture to Beatrice and Benedict*, Grieg's *Piano Concerto in A minor, opus 16*, and Richard Strauss's *Ein Heldenleben*. Carlos Moseley, president of the New York Philharmonic, hosts the program and interviews Previn backstage at intermission. The telecast received three Emmy nominations. (January 30, 1976; 120 min.)

New York City Opera: The Ballad of Baby Doe

The Ballad of Baby Doe (1956), an American opera with music by Douglas Moore and libretto by John LaTouche, is based on the story of three real-life characters from Colorado's fabled silver mining days. Judith Somogi conducts; Patrick Bakman directed the production. The cast includes Frances Bible, Richard Fredricks, Jane Shaulis and Ruth Welting. Julius Rudel, the program host, interviews the director Harold Prince at intermission. (April 21, 1976; 180 min.)

American Ballet Theatre: Swan Lake

American Ballet Theatre's *Swan Lake* (1895) is the first live telecast of a full-length ballet on American television. Akira Endo conducts Tchaikovsky's classic ballet, choreographed by Marius Petipa and Lev Ivanov. The principal dancers are Natalia Makarova and Ivan Nagy. At intermission the program host, Dick Cavett, interviews American Ballet Theatre artistic director Lucia Chase, Makarova, Erik Bruhn and the dance critic Clive Barnes. (June 30, 1976; 180 min.)

Awards: Emmy Award: Outstanding Classical Program in the Performing Arts
Source: Paramount—Bel Canto (home video)

Dear LIVE FROM LINCOLN CENTER:

I want to thank you and all the talented and dedicated people of commerce and art who made possible the live concert from Lincoln Center at 8:30 pm, Saturday, September 24th, conducted by Zubin Mehta with singer Shirley Verrett. I can truly say that I will remember this concert as long as I live.

. . . The camera work was superb zeroing in on the players and instruments. At the high point of the Liebestod the camera on Mehta caught a thrilling moment. He looked like a Master Magician of Music.

I believe this program is a first. Perhaps it sets a new high standard, artistically and technically. . . . Finally, I must say that this tremendous effort so that one lone TV viewer in a small town in Florida could share instantly and simultaneously what others are doing musically and artistically a thousand miles away in their quest for beauty, excellence and perfection makes me feel happy to be an American living in America and hopeful that the great and good qualities of the human species will ultimately prevail in this unsettled world.

Sincerely,

H.P., Avon Park, Fla.

SEASON TWO, 1976 - 1977

New York City Opera: Il Barbiere di Siviglia (The Barber of Seville)

Beverly Sills stars in the New York City Opera's production of Rossini's *Il Barbiere di Siviglia (The Barber of Seville)* (1816). The cast includes Donald Gramm, Henry Price, Samuel Ramey and Alan Titus. Sarah Caldwell conducts. At intermission, the program host, Dick Cavett, interviews

Sills, Gramm and Julius Rudel. (November 3, 1976; 180 min.)

Source: Paramount—Bel Canto (home video)

New York Philharmonic with Claudio Arrau, Rafael Kubelik, conductor

The pianist Claudio Arrau is the soloist on this program of works by Beethoven: *Egmont Overture, opus 84,* and *Piano Concerto no. 3 in C minor, opus 37);* and by Dvorak: *Symphony no. 9 "From the New World."* Rafael Kubelik conducts the New York Philharmonic. At intermission the program host, Dick Cavett, interviews Amyas Ames, chairman of Lincoln Center, and Cyril Harris, a renowned acoustician. (November 20, 1976; 120 min.)

Great Performers: Andre Watts

In this recital at Avery Fisher Hall, the pianist Andre Watts performs Liszt's *Les Jeux d'Eau a la Villa d'Este* and *Sonata in B minor;* Rachmaninoff's *Variations on a Theme of Corelli;* four selections from Schubert's *Moments Musicaux, opus 94,* and Gershwin's *Rhapsody in Blue.* At intermission the program host, Dick Cavett, interviews Watts. (November 28, 1976; 120 min.)

American Ballet Theatre: Giselle

Mikhail Baryshnikov, Martine van Hamel and Natalia Makarova perform in the great romantic classic *Giselle,* choreographed by Jean Coralli and Jules Perrot. John Lanchbery conducts the American Ballet Theatre's production, which was staged by David Blair of the Royal Ballet. At intermission the program host, Dick Cavett, interviews Erik Bruhn. (June 2, 1977; 120 min.)

Director: Robert Schwarz
Awards: Emmy Award: Outstanding Classical Program in the Performing Arts
Source: Paramount—Bel Canto (home video)

SEASON THREE, 1977 - 1978

New York Philharmonic with Shirley Verrett, Zubin Mehta, conductor

Shirley Verrett, soprano, performs with the New York Philharmonic, Zubin Mehta conducting. The selections are Mozart's Overture to *The Marriage of Figaro* and *Exultate Jubilate,* the Prelude and Liebestod from Wagner's *Tristan und Isolde* and Stravinsky's *Le Sacre du Printemps (The Rite of Spring).* The program host, Robert MacNeil, interviews Mehta and Verrett at intermission. (September 24, 1977; 120 min.)

New York City Opera: Manon

Julius Rudel conducts the New York City Opera's production of Massenet's *Manon* (1884), with Beverly Sills, Nico Castel, Henry Price, Richard Fredricks, Samuel Ramey and Robert Hale. At intermission, the program host, Robert MacNeil, interviews Kitty Carlisle Hart, head of the New York State Council of the Arts, and the New York governor Hugh Carey. (October 18, 1977; 210 min.)

Source: Paramount—Bel Canto (home video)

New York Philharmonic with Andre Watts, Erich Leinsdorf, conductor

The pianist Andre Watts is the soloist in this program of works by Brahms: *Piano Concerto no. 2 in B flat, opus*

83; and Richard Strauss: *Also Sprach Zarathustra*. Erich Leinsdorf conducts the New York Philharmonic. At intermission the program host, Robert MacNeil, interviews Watts and Leinsdorf. (October 29, 1977; 120 min.)

New York City Ballet: Coppelia

The New York City Ballet's production of Delibes's *Coppelia*, choreographed by George Balanchine and Alexandra Danilova after Marius Petipa, features the principal dancers Patricia McBride, Shaun O'Brien and Helgi Tomasson. Robert Irving conducts. At intermission, the program host, Edward Villella, interviews Danilova, the principal dancers and Irving. (January 31, 1978; 150 min.)

Directors: Kirk Browning, Emile Ardolino

Great Performers: Luciano Pavarotti

The tenor Luciano Pavarotti performs selections from Beethoven, Donizetti, Gluck, Leoncavallo, Liszt, Puccini, Tosti and Verdi in this recital from the stage of the Metropolitan Opera House. John Wustman accompanies on piano. At intermission Terry McEwen interviews Pavarotti (pretaped). (February 12, 1978; 120 min.)

Awards: Emmy Award: Outstanding Program Achievement

New York City Opera: The Saint of Bleecker Street

Cal Stewart Kellogg conducts the New York City Opera's production of Gian Carlo Menotti's *The Saint of Bleecker Street* (1954) with Catherine Malfitano and Enrico di Giuseppe. At intermission the program host, Beverly Sills,

interviews Menotti, Malfitano, di Giuseppe and the production director Francis Rizzo. (April 19, 1978; 164 min.)

Executive producer: John Goberman Producer: Emile Ardolino

American Ballet Theatre: Repertory Evening

American Ballet Theatre performs *Les Sylphides* (1909), choreographed by Michel Fokine; the *Don Quixote* pas de deux, choreography after Marius Petipa; *Theme and Variations* (1947), choreographed by George Balanchine, and *The Firebird* (1910), choreographed by Michel Fokine. The principal dancers are Mikhail Baryshnikov, Leslie Browne, Fernando Bujones, Cynthia Gregory, Gelsey Kirkland, Natalia Makarova, John Meehan, Ivan Nagy, Marcos Paredes, Marianna Tcherkassky and Rebecca Wright. At intermission the program host, Robert MacNeil, interviews Makarova, Bujones, Kirkland and Erik Bruhn. (May 17, 1978; 165 min.)

Executive producer: John Goberman Producer: Emile Ardolino

SEASON FOUR, 1978 - 1979

New York Philharmonic with Rudolf Serkin, Zubin Mehta, conductor

The pianist Rudolf Serkin performs with the New York Philharmonic in Wagner's *"Rienzi" Overture*, Prokofiev's *Romeo and Juliet* and Beethoven's *Piano Concerto no. 5, "The Emperor."* Zubin Mehta conducts. At intermission the program host, Robert, MacNeil interviews Mehta and Carlos Moseley, vice-chairman of the New York Philharmonic's board of directors. (September 20, 1978; 120 min.)

New York City Opera: The Turk in Italy

Julius Rudel conducts and Beverly Sills stars in the New York City Opera's production of Rossini's *The Turk in Italy* (1814), English version by Andrew Porter. Also featured are James Billings, Donald Gramm, Jonathan Green, Susanne Marsee, Henry Price and Alan Titus. Harold Prince, the program host, interviews Sills, Gramm and Rudel at intermission. (October 4, 1978; 180 min.)

Chamber Music Society of Lincoln Center with Itzhak Perlman

The Chamber Music Society of Lincoln Center with Itzhak Perlman performs Beethoven's *Serenade no. 6 in D, opus 25*, Brahms's *Clarinet Quintet in B minor, opus 115*, and Mendelssohn's *Octet for Strings in E flat, opus 20*. At intermission Perlman, Paula Robinson and Charles Wadsworth, artistic director of the Chamber Music Society, are interviewed by Gene Shalit, the program host. (December 10, 1978; 120 min.)

New York Philharmonic with Itzhak Perlman, Zubin Mehta, conductor

The New York Philharmonic with Itzhak Perlman, conducted by Zubin Mehta, performs *Scherzo Fantastique*, *Fireworks* and *Scherzo a la Russe* by Stravinsky; *Concerto for Violin, opus 35*, by Tchaikovsky and *Pictures at an Exhibition* by Mussorgsky-Ravel. Joan Mondale hosts the program and interviews Perlman and Mehta at intermission. (January 17, 1979; 120 min.)

Great Performers: Joan Sutherland and Luciano Pavarotti

Luciano Pavarotti, tenor, and Joan Sutherland, soprano, perform works by Balfe, Bellini, Donizetti, Giordano, Massenet, Meyerbeer, Mozart,

Ponchielli, Thomas and Verdi. Richard Bonynge conducts. At intermission pretaped scenes from rehearsals and interviews with the performers are shown. (January 22, 1979; 150 min.)

American Ballet Theatre: The Sleeping Beauty

American Ballet Theatre's production of Tchaikovsky's *The Sleeping Beauty* features Cynthia Gregory and Fernando Bujones in the principal roles. Staged by Mary Skeaping after Marius Petipa and Nicholas Sergeyev. John Lanchbery conducts. At intermission the program host, Robert MacNeil, interviews Gregory, Bujones, Lanchbery, Marcos Paredes and Jolinda Menendez. (May 2, 1979; 180 min.)

SEASON FIVE, 1979 - 1980

Great Performers: Joan Sutherland and Marilyn Horne

Joan Sutherland, soprano, and Marilyn Horne, mezzo-soprano, perform arias, duets and songs by Bellini, Delibes, Donizetti, Foster, Handel, Lehar, Offenbach, Rossini, Saint-Saens and Verdi. Richard Bonynge conducts the New York Philharmonic. At intermission pretaped scenes from rehearsals and interviews with Bonynge, Sutherland and Horne are shown. (October 15, 1979; 150 min.)

New York City Opera: Street Scene

The New York City Opera performs Kurt Weill's *Street Scene* (1946), an opera based on the book by Elmer Rice with lyrics by Langston Hughes. Leading the cast are William Chapman, Harlan Foss, Alan Kays,

Catherine Malfitano and Eileen Schauler. John Mauceri conducts. At intermission a pretaped interview between the program host, Beverly Sills, and Lotte Lenya is shown. (October 27, 1979; 180 min.)

New York Philharmonic with Emil Gilels, Zubin Mehta, conductor

The New York Philharmonic, conducted by Zubin Mehta, and guest pianist Emil Gilels perform Beethoven's *Leonora Overture no. 3 in C, opus 72a*; Bartok's *Concerto for Orchestra* and Tchaikovsky's *Piano Concerto no. 1 in B flat minor, opus 23*. At intermission Mehta is interviewed by the program host, Pia Lindstrom. (November 14, 1979; 120 min.)

New York Philharmonic with Luciano Pavarotti, Zubin Mehta, conductor

Luciano Pavarotti performs with the New York Philharmonic in works by Verdi, Donizetti, Respighi, Puccini, Leoncavallo and De Curtis. Surprise guest Itzhak Perlman joins Pavarotti. Perlman sings the role of the jailor in the opening scene from *Tosca* and performs Paganini's *Caprice no. 24*. The intermission features are a backstage conversation between Mehta and Pavarotti and a pretaped visit with Pavarotti at his home in Modena, Italy. (January 14, 1980; 150 min.)

Film Society of Lincoln Center: Tribute to John Huston

The Film Society of Lincoln Center's program honoring the director John Huston consists of tributes by Lauren

Bacall, Richard Burton, Brendan Gill, Bill Mauldin, Paul Newman and Eli Wallach, interspersed with scenes from Huston's films. Alfred Stern, president of the Film Society, introduces Huston. (May 5, 1980; 90 min.)

American Ballet Theatre: La Bayadere

American Ballet Theatre's presentation of A.L. Minkus's *La Bayadere*, choreographed by Natalia Makarova after Petipa, is performed by principal dancers Victor Barbee, Anthony Dowell, Cynthia Harvey, Natalia Makarova, Alexander Minz, Danilo Radojevic and Marianna Tcherkassky. John Lanchbery conducts. At intermission Lanchbery, Israel Chorberg, Dowell and Makarova are interviewed by Pia Lindstrom, the program host. (May 28, 1980; 180 min.)

SEASON SIX, 1980 - 1981

New York Philharmonic with Isaac Stern, Itzhak Perlman, Pinchas Zukerman

The New York Philharmonic and guest soloists Isaac Stern, violin, Itzhak Perlman, violin, Pinchas Zukerman, violin and viola, celebrate Isaac Stern's 60th birthday in works by Bach, Mozart and Brahms and Vivaldi's *Concerto in F for Three Violins*. Zubin Mehta conducts. Schuyler Chapin is the program host. (September 24, 1980; 150 min.)

Source: Paramount—Bel Canto (home video)

New York Philharmonic: Verdi Requiem

Zubin Mehta conducts the New York Philharmonic and the Westminster Choir in Verdi's *Requiem*. The soloists are Montserrat Caballe, soprano;

Bianca Berini, mezzo-soprano; Placido Domingo, tenor, and Paul Plishka, bass-baritone. The program host, Schuyler Chapin, interviews Caballe, Domingo and Mehta after the performance. (October 22, 1980; 120 min.)

New York City Opera: La Cenerentola (Cinderella)

Rossini's *La Cenerentola (Cinderella)* (1817) is performed by the New York City Opera conducted by Brian Salesky. Leading the cast are Ralph Bassett, James Billings, Rockwell Blake, Rosemarie Freni, Susanne Marsee, Gianna Rolandi and Alan Titus. The English libretto is by Gimi Beni. Beverly Sills hosts the program. (November 6, 1980; 180 min.)

Beverly! Her Farewell Performance

A special program honoring Beverly Sills in her farewell performance. Sills performs in act two of Strauss's *Die Fledermaus* with members of the New York City Opera; Julius Rudel conducts. Special guests are John Alexander, Carol Burnett, Placido Domingo, Eileen Farrell, James Galway, Donald Gramm, Cynthia Gregory, Mary Martin, Peter Martins, Ethel Merman, Sherrill Milnes, Leontyne Price, Renata Scotto, Dinah Shore, Bobby Short and Heather Watts. The performance was taped October 27, 1980. (January 5, 1981; 120 min.)

Chamber Music Society of Lincoln Center with Itzhak Perlman

The Chamber Music Society of Lincoln Center performs Bach's *Trio Sonata in C, BWV 1037*; Beethoven's

"Kreutzer" Sonata in A, opus 47, and Tchaikovsky's *"Souvenir de Florence" in D minor, opus 70*. Charles Wadsworth, artistic director of the Chamber Music Society, hosts the program. (February 2, 1981; 120 min.)

New York Philharmonic with Vladimir Ashkenazy, Zubin Mehta, conductor

Zubin Mehta conducts the New York Philharmonic with the pianist Vladimir Ashkenazy. Featured on the program is the world premiere of *In Praise of Folly* by George Walker. Also performed are Beethoven's *Piano Concerto no. 4 in G, opus 58*, and Richard Strauss's *Ein Heldenleben, opus 40*. At intermission Carlos Moseley interviews Ashkenazy, Mehta, Walker, the concertmaster Glenn Dicterow and the principal horn player Philip Myers. (February 18, 1981; 120 min.)

Great Performers: Joan Sutherland, Marilyn Horne, Luciano Pavarotti

Joan Sutherland, soprano, Marilyn Horne, mezzo-soprano, and Luciano Pavarotti, tenor, perform classic trios by Verdi, Bellini, Ponchielli and Rossini and other works in their first joint recital. Richard Bonynge conducts the New York City Opera Orchestra and discusses the art of *bel canto* with the performers at intermission (pretaped). (March 23, 1981; 150 min.)

American Ballet Theatre: Repertory Evening

American Ballet Theatre performs *Jardin Anime* from *Le Corsaire* (1899), *Raymonda* (1898), act three from Tchaikovsky's *Sleeping Beauty* (1890), choreographed by Marius Petipa, and *La Fille Mal Gardee*

(1882), choreographed by Jean Dauberval and Petipa. Alan Barker conducts. The principal dancers are Mikhail Baryshnikov, Fernando Bujones, Alexander Godunov, Martine van Hamel, Cynthia Harvey, Susan Jaffe, Elaine Kudo, Natalia Makarova, Ruth Mayer, Kevin McKenzie, George de la Pena, Danilo Radojevic, Lisa de Ribere, Marianna Tcherkassky and Cheryl Yeager. Dick Cavett hosts the program. (May 20, 1981; 150 min.)

SEASON SEVEN, 1981 - 1982

An Evening with Danny Kaye and the New York Philharmonic

Zubin Mehta is host and music director for this New York Philharmonic performance conducted by Danny Kaye of works by Strauss, Ravel, Tchaikovsky, Verdi, Merrick, Beethoven, Rimsky-Korsakov, Schubert, Anderson, H. Clark and Sousa. A conversation between Mehta, Kaye, Isaac Stern, Gregory Peck, Henry Kissinger and Placido Domingo takes place at intermission. (September 23, 1981; 150 min.)

Executive producer: Herbert Bonis
Director: Robert Scheerer
Awards: Peabody Award
Source: Paramount—Bel Canto (home video)

An Evening with Itzhak Perlman and the New York Philharmonic

Itzhak Perlman and the New York Philharmonic perform *Winter* from Vivaldi's *Four Seasons*, Mendelssohn's *Violin Concerto in E minor, opus 64*, and Brahms's *Violin Concerto in D, opus 77*. David Zinman conducts. At intermission a pretaped feature on Perlman with high school students at New York City's Collegiate School is presented. (February 10, 1982; 120 min.)

New York City Opera: Lucia di Lammermoor

Judith Somogi conducts the New York City Opera's production of Donizetti's *Lucia di Lammermoor* (1835). The cast stars Brent Ellis, Robert Hale, Barry McCauley and Gianna Rolandi. Beverly Sills hosts the program. (April 10, 1982; 180 min.)

Film Society of Lincoln Center: Tribute to Billy Wilder

The director Billy Wilder is honored for his body of work spanning four decades. With tributes by Film Society president Alfred Stern, John Huston, I.A.L. Diamond, Ginger Rogers, Austin Pendleton, Shirley MacLaine and others; filmed tributes by Jack Lemmon and Walter Matthau and highlights from many of Wilder's films. (May 3, 1982; 120 min.)

Two Philharmonics: Israel and New York

Zubin Mehta conducts an historic joint concert of the New York Philharmonic and the Israel Philharmonic. The New York Philharmonic performs Tchaikovsky's *Romeo and Juliet Overture Fantasy*; the Israel Philharmonic performs Bartok's *Miraculous Mandarin Suite*. Both orchestras perform Berlioz's *Symphonie Fantastique*. At intermission pretaped conversations with Mehta and members of the orchestras are shown. (June 3, 1982; 120 min.)

James Galway Plays Mostly Mozart

The flutist James Galway performs with the Mostly Mozart Festival Orchestra at Avery Fisher Hall in Handel's *Entrance of the Queen of Sheba*; Mozart's *Andante in C, K. 315*, and *Flute Concerto no. 2 in D, K. 314*, and Vivaldi's *Four Seasons*. At intermission the program host, Joanna Simon, interviews Galway and Gerard Schwarz, music advisor of the Mostly Mozart Festival. (July 14, 1982; 120 min.)

Source: Paramount—Bel Canto (home video)

SEASON EIGHT, 1982 - 1983

New York Philharmonic with Leontyne Price, Zubin Mehta, conductor

Zubin Mehta conducts the New York Philharmonic with Leontyne Price, soprano, as soloist. On the program are Mozart's *Symphony no. 41 (Jupiter)* and *Come scoglio* from *Così fan tutte*; Verdi's *Ave Maria*, the *Act Four Prelude* from *Otello* and *Willow Song*; and Richard Strauss's *Don Juan* and the final scene from *Salome*. The program host, Schuyler Chapin, interviews Leontyne Price at intermission (pretaped). (September 15, 1982; 124 min.)

Awards: Emmy Award: Outstanding Individual Performance in a Variety or Musical Program—Leontyne Price Source: Paramount—Bel Canto (home video)

New York City Ballet: Balanchine and Stravinsky—Genius Has a Birthday!

The New York City Ballet performs *Apollo* (1928) and *Orpheus* (1948), two ballets choreographed by George Balanchine to music by Igor

Stravinsky. Maria Calegari, Suzanne Farrell, Peter Martins and Kyra Nichols perform in *Apollo*. Victoria Hall, Adam Luders, Peter Martins and Karin von Aroldingen perform in *Orpheus*. Balanchine and Lincoln Kirstein introduce the works. Taped June 18 and 19, 1982. (October 4, 1982; 70 min.)

Director: Emile Ardolino

New York City Opera: Madama Butterfly

Christopher Keene conducts the New York City Opera's production of Puccini's *Madama Butterfly* (1904). The principals include James Billings, Judith Christin, Judith Haddon, Jerry Hadley and Alan Titus. At intermission the program host, Beverly Sills, interviews the director Frank Corsaro, the costume and set designer Lloyd Evans, and Keene, Haddon and Hadley. (October 20, 1982; 180 min.)

Chamber Music Society of Lincoln Center with Chick Corea

The composer and pianist Chick Corea and the Chamber Music Society of Lincoln Center perform classical works and compositions by Corea: Kuhlau's *Grand Quartet for Four Flutes in E minor, opus 103*; Bach's *Brandenburg Concerto no. 4 in G major, BWV 1049*; Brahms's *Sonata for Viola and Piano in F minor, opus 120, no. 1*; the New York premiere of Corea's *Septet for Winds, Strings and Piano* and Corea's *Day Danse* for piano and string quartet. Charles Wadsworth hosts the program. (January 9, 1983; 120 min.)

New York Philharmonic: Beethoven's Ninth Symphony, Zubin Mehta, conductor

Zubin Mehta conducts the New York Philharmonic in Beethoven's *Ninth Symphony in D minor, opus 125*.

Guest artists include Margaret Price, soprano; Marilyn Horne, mezzo-soprano; Jon Vickers, tenor; Matti Salminen, bass, and the New York Choral Artists under the direction of Joseph Flummerfelt. Patrick Watson hosts the program, which includes a special tribute to Nancy Hanks, chairman of the National Endowment for the Arts from 1969 to 1977, who died in January of 1983. (February 2, 1983; 90 min.)

Great Performers: Luciano Pavarotti

Luciano Pavarotti and the New York Philharmonic, Zubin Mehta, conductor, perform several works by Verdi as well as selections from operas by Bizet, Massenet, Gounod and Donizetti. Also performing are James Morris, bass, and the New York Choral Artists' men's chorus directed by Joseph Flummerfelt. The program host, Patrick Watson, interviews Pavarotti, Mehta and Herbert Breslin, Pavarotti's manager, at intermission. (April 4, 1983; 150 min.)

SEASON NINE, 1983 - 1984

New York City Ballet: Tribute to George Balanchine

The New York City Ballet presents three Balanchine ballets: *Vienna Waltzes* (1977), music by Johann Strauss II, Franz Lehar, Richard Strauss; *Mozartiana* (1933), music by Tchaikovsky, and *Who Cares?* (1970), music by Gershwin. The principal dancers are Ib Andersen, Elyse Borne, Victor Castelli, Bart Cook, Suzanne Farrell, Sean Lavery, Lourdes Lopez, Adam Luders, Peter Martins, Patricia McBride, Kyra Nichols, Helgi Tomasson, Karin von Aroldingen and Heather Watts. Taped May 27 and 28, 1983. (October 10, 1983; 120 min.)

Director: Emile Ardolino

New York City Opera: The Cunning Little Vixen

Scott Bergeson conducts the New York City Opera's production of Janecek's opera, *The Cunning Little Vixen* (1924), with scenery and costumes by Maurice Sendak. Gianna Rolandi sings the title role of Vixen Sharp-Ears; also appearing are Richard Cross, John Lankston and Nadia Pelle. Beverly Sills and Patrick Watson host the program and interview the production director Frank Corsaro and Sendak at intermission. (November 9, 1983; 150 min.)

Great Performers: Marilyn Horne

Marilyn Horne's Great American Songbook features patriotic songs, folk songs, hymns, spirituals and works by Stephen Foster and Aaron Copland. Horne performs with the American Symphony Orchestra, Leonard Slatkin, conductor, and the New York Choral Artists, Joseph Flummerfelt, director. Original orchestrations were created under the supervision of Jonathan Tunick. (December 28, 1983; 120 min.)

New York Philharmonic with James Galway and Marisa Robles, Zubin Mehta, conductor

The New York Philharmonic conducted by Zubin Mehta with soloists James Galway, flute, and Marisa Robles, harp, perform *Till Eulenspiegel's Merry Pranks, opus 28*, by Richard Strauss; *Concerto for Flute, Harp and Orchestra in C major, K. 299*, by Mozart; *Fantasia para un Gentilhombre* by Rodrigo, arranged for flute by Galway, and *Capriccio Espagnol, opus 34*, by Rimsky-Korsakov. (February 29, 1984; 120 min.)

SEASON TEN, 1984 - 1985

Chamber Music Society of Lincoln Center: Bach to Bach

The Chamber Music Society of Lincoln Center and the Academy of Ancient Music Ensemble perform alternately on modern and original instruments in an all-Bach program conducted by Christopher Hogwood. Charles Wadsworth hosts the program. (September 12, 1984; 120 min.)

New York City Opera: Carmen

Christopher Keene conducts this new production of Bizet's *Carmen* (1875) by the New York City Opera, staged by Frank Corsaro and set during the Spanish Civil War. It stars Victoria Vergara, Jacques Trussel, Marianna Christos and Robert Hale. Beverly Sills and Patrick Watson host the program. (September 26, 1984; 210 min.)

New York Philharmonic with Pinchas Zukerman, Zubin Mehta, conductor

Zubin Mehta conducts the New York Philharmonic and Pinchas Zukerman performs on violin and viola in works by Susato, Telemann, Hindemith, Vivaldi, Bruch and Wagner. Patrick Watson, the program host, interviews Zukerman and Mehta at intermission. (October 3, 1984; 150 min.)

Lincoln Center's 25th Anniversary Fanfare

This gala event celebrates Lincoln Center's 25th anniversary with highlights of performances originally broadcast on LIVE FROM LINCOLN CEN-

TER and LIVE FROM THE MET; historical film footage of the construction of Lincoln Center and opening nights; appearances by the artistic heads of Lincoln Center's major resident performing arts organizations: Zubin Mehta, Peter Martins, Beverly Sills, Charles Wadsworth and James Levine. (October 26, 1984; 120 min.)

Director: Gary Halvorson

New York Philharmonic with Kathleen Battle and Shlomo Mintz, Zubin Mehta, conductor

In a special New Year's Eve gala concert, the soprano Kathleen Battle and the violinist Shlomo Mintz perform in works by Johann Strauss, Sr., Johann Strauss II, Lehar, Saint-Saens, Wieniawski, Mozart, Kreisler, Paganini and Sieczynski. Patrick Watson is the program host. (December 31, 1984; 150 min.)

Great Performers: Andre Watts

Andre Watts performs Scarlatti's *Sonata in D minor, L.422,* and *Sonata in A, L.345;* Beethoven's *Sonata, opus 27, no. 2 ("Moonlight");* Chopin's *Sonata no. 2 in B flat minor, opus 35;* Gershwin's *Three Preludes;* Debussy's *La Plus que Lente, Danse* and *L'Isle Joyeuse;* Liszt's *Etude d'Execution Transcendante no. 10* and encores by Chopin and MacDowell. Andre Previn hosts the program. (February 20, 1985; 120 min.)

Source: Paramount—Bel Canto (home video)

New York Philharmonic: Great Russian Theater Music

The New York Philharmonic, Zubin Mehta, conductor, Galina Vishnevskaya, soprano, and Matti Salminen, bass, perform the *Alexander Nevsky Cantata* by Prokofiev, scenes from *Boris Godunov* by Mussorgsky and other works.

Scenes from the Eisenstein film *Alexander Nevsky,* for which the cantata was originally written, are shown. Also included is a tribute to the great bass-baritone George London, to whom Mehta dedicates the performance of *Boris Godunov.* Gene Shalit hosts the program. (May 11, 1985; 120 min.)

Mostly Mozart Meets Salieri

Mostly Mozart Meets Salieri, a Mostly Mozart Festival program, affords viewers an opportunity to compare the musical composition styles of Wolfgang Amadeus Mozart and his rival, Antonio Salieri—whose relationship was dramatized in the film *Amadeus.* Each is represented by a concerto, an aria and an overture. Gerard Schwarz conducts the Mostly Mozart Festival

Orchestra, with soprano Elly Ameling and pianist Horacio Gutierrez. At intermission the program host, Patrick Watson, interviews Schwarz and Gutierrez. (July 10, 1985; 120 min.)

SEASON ELEVEN, 1985 - 1986

Juilliard at 80

Talented students and distinguished graduates of The Juilliard School celebrate the school's 80th anniversary in musical works by Glinka and Brahms, Barber and Britten; a dance by Paul Taylor; and scenes from dramatic works by Brecht, O'Morrison, Chekhov, Friel, Fugard and Tennessee Williams. Featured are the Juilliard Orchestra conducted by Jorge Mester with guest soloist Leontyne Price; the Juilliard String Quartet (with student performers); the Juilliard Dance Ensemble and the Juilliard Theater Center. Patrick Watson, Kelly McGillis and John Rubinstein host the program. (October 5, 1985; 120 min.)

New York City Opera: La Rondine

Alessandro Siciliani conducts the New York City Opera's production of Puccini's *La Rondine* (1917) directed by Lotfi Mansouri. The cast features Elizabeth Knighton, soprano; Jon Garrison, tenor; Claudette Peterson, soprano; David Eisler, tenor, and Richard McKee, baritone. Beverly Sills is the program host. (October 30, 1985; 165 min.)

New York Philharmonic: Aaron Copland's 85th Birthday

The New York Philharmonic and the guest soloist Bennett Lerner, piano, perform in this birthday concert. On this all-Copland program, conductor-laureate Leonard Bernstein conducts *Fanfare for the Common Man* and Zubin Mehta conducts *Letter from Home, John Henry, Concerto for Piano and Orchestra, Proclamation, Prairie Journal* and *Symphony no. 1.* (November 14, 1985; 120 min.)

Great Performers: Dame Joan Sutherland Sings Anna Bolena

Dame Joan Sutherland in a concert performance of Donizetti's opera *Anna Bolena* (1830) at Avery Fisher Hall. Also performing are Judith Forst, mezzo-soprano; Jerry Hadley, tenor; Cynthia Clarey, mezzo-soprano; Gregory Yurisich, bass-baritone; Jan Opalach, bass-baritone, and Gran Wilson, tenor. Richard Bonynge conducts the New York City Opera Orchestra and New York Choral Artists. Robert Jacobson hosts. (November 25, 1985; 180 min.)

Great Performers: Pavarotti Plus!

The tenor Luciano Pavarotti, accompanied by Susan Dunn, Jerry Hadley, Mary Jane Johnson, James Morris, Cheryl Parrish, Alan Titus, Carol Vaness and Delores Ziegler, performs arias from Verdi, Donizetti, Bellini, Mozart, Cilea, Puccini, Gounod and others. Emerson Buckley conducts the New York City Opera Orchestra. (January 6, 1986; 180 min.)

Chamber Music Society of Lincoln Center

The Chamber Music Society of Lincoln Center performs with the actress Irene Worth and the pianist Horacio Gutierrez in Vivaldi's *Sonata in G minor for Flute, Oboe, Bassoon and Harpsichord*; Saint-Saens's *Carnival of the Animals*, with verse by Ogden Nash; Satie's *Sports and Divertissements* and Brahms's *Trio no. 1 in B major, opus 8.* Charles Wadsworth hosts the program. (January 12, 1986; 120 min.)

Awards: Emmy Award: Outstanding Special Class Program

New York Philharmonic Celebration with Zubin Mehta

The New York Philharmonic, Zubin Mehta, conductor, the violinists Isaac Stern and Itzhak Perlman and the soprano Montserrat Caballe perform works by Vivaldi, Dvorak, Saint-Saens, Donizetti, Rossini and Richard Strauss. At intermission Patrick Watson interviews Stern, Perlman and Mehta. (April 29, 1986; 120 min.)

New York City Ballet: A Midsummer Night's Dream

The New York City Ballet's production of Balanchine's *A Midsummer Night's Dream* (1962), music by Mendelssohn, features the principal dancers Maria Calegari, Ib Anderson, Jean-Pierre Frohlich, Merrill Ashley and Adam Luders. Robert Irving conducts. Patrick Watson, the program host, interviews Irving and Peter Martins at intermission. (May 24, 1986; 120 min.)

Aaron Copland with Zubin Mehta and members of the New York Philharmonic celebrating Copland's 85th birthday at Avery Fisher Hall. Photo by Susanne Faulkner Stevens.

SEASON TWELVE, 1986 - 1987

New York Philharmonic: Opening Night with Zubin Mehta and Itzhak Perlman

The New York Philharmonic, with Zubin Mehta and Itzhak Perlman, performs Ravel's *Tzigane*; Chausson's *Poeme, opus 25*; Sarasate's *Concert Fantasy on Motifs from Bizet's Carmen* and Tchaikovsky's *Symphony no. 5 in E minor, opus 64*. At intermission the program host, Patrick Watson, interviews Mehta and Perlman. Perlman discusses music and the violin with high school students at New York City's Collegiate School (pretaped). (September 16, 1986; 120 min.)

New York City Opera: Candide

Scott Bergeson conducts the New York City Opera's production of Leonard Bernstein's *Candide*. The two-act opera house version features James Billings, Muriel Costa-Greenspon, Deborah Darr, David Eisler, Jack Harrold, John Lankston, Erie Mills and Scott Reeve. At intermission the program host, Beverly Sills, interviews Harold Prince, the production director. (November 12, 1986; 150 min.)

Great Performers: An Evening with Placido Domingo

Placido Domingo performs in recital from Avery Fisher Hall. Also performing are the guitarist Christopher Parkening, the mezzo-soprano Victoria Vergara and the cellist Jascha Silberstein. John De Main conducts the New York City Opera Orchestra. Parkening is interviewed at intermission by the program host, Kitty Carlisle Hart. (February 18, 1987; 120 min.)

Lincoln Center Theater: The Comedy of Errors

Robert Woodruff directs this new vaudeville-style production of Shakespeare's *Comedy of Errors*. Performing are the Flying Karamazov Brothers, Avner "the Eccentric" Eisenberg, Karla Burns, Ethyl Eichelberger, Sophie Hayden, Gina Leishman, Alec Willows, Vaudeville Nouveau and the Kamikaze Ground Crew. Robert Krulwich hosts the program. (June 24, 1987; 150 min.)

Mostly Mozart Festival Gala

Gerard Schwarz conducts the Mostly Mozart Festival Orchestra in a program of works by Mozart, Bach and Handel, including Mozart's *Symphony no. 39 in E flat, K. 543*. Featured guest performers are the pianist Alicia de Larrocha, the mezzo-soprano Marilyn Horne and the violinist Nadja Salerno-Sonnenberg. (July 8, 1987; 120 min.)

SEASON THIRTEEN, 1987 - 1988

New York Philharmonic Opening Night

Sir Colin Davis conducts the New York Philharmonic's opening night performance of Brahms's *Symphony no. 2 in D, opus 73*, and Beethoven's *Piano Concerto no. 4 in G, opus 58*, with Murray Perahia, soloist. At intermission the program host, Patrick Watson, interviews Perahia, the concertmaster Glenn Dicterow and the principal oboist Joseph Robinson. (September 15, 1987; 110 min.)

New York City Opera: Die Zauberfloete (The Magic Flute)

Sergiu Comissiona conducts the New York City Opera's production of Mozart's *Die Zauberfloete (The Magic Flute)* (1791), featuring Stephen Dickson, Faith Esham, Jon Garrison, Rachel Rosales and Gregory Stapp. The program host, Beverly Sills, interviews Comissiona and the production director Lotfi Mansouri at intermission. (October 14, 1987; 195 min.)

New York Philharmonic New Year's Eve Celebration

Zubin Mehta conducts the New York Philharmonic in this New Year's Eve concert with Kathleen Battle, soprano, and the Boys Choir of Harlem. On the program are *An American in Paris*, by Gershwin; several spirituals arranged by Robert Sadin; selections from *Die Fledermaus* and *Tales from the Vienna Woods* by Strauss; and selections from *The Merry Widow* by Lehar. (December 31, 1987; 120 min.)

Great Performers: Andre Watts's 25th Anniversary Gala

Zubin Mehta and the New York Philharmonic celebrate the pianist Andre Watts's 25-year career in performances of three works: Liszt's *Piano Concerto no. 1 in B flat*; Beethoven's *Piano Concerto no. 2 in B flat, opus 19*, and Rachmaninoff's *Piano Concerto no. 2 in C minor, opus 18*. (January 13, 1988; 120 min.)

American Ballet Theatre: Romeo and Juliet

American Ballet Theatre performs *Romeo and Juliet* (1965), choreographed by Kenneth MacMillan, music by Prokofiev. The principal dancers are Natalia Makarova, Kevin McKenzie and Johan Renvall; Jack Everly conducts. At intermission Patrick Watson interviews McKenzie and the dance mistress, Georgina Parkinson. (May 7, 1988; 180 min.)

An Evening at the Mostly Mozart Festival

Gerard Schwarz conducts the Mostly Mozart Festival Orchestra in selections from three Mozart operas, Mozart's *Piano Concerto in B flat, K. 595,* and Haydn's *Symphony no. 100 in G ("Military").* The soloists are Frederica von Stade, mezzo-soprano, and Vladimir Feltsman, pianist. Patrick Watson hosts the telecast. (July 13, 1988; 120 min.)

SEASON FOURTEEN 1988 - 1989

New York City Opera: Rigoletto

Opening the 14th season is the New York City Opera's production of Verdi's *Rigoletto* (1851). Elio Boncompagni conducts. In the cast are Mark S. Doss, Brent Ellis, Faith Esham, Richard Leech and Susanne Marsee. Beverly Sills is the program host; at intermission the camera goes backstage to witness the scene change between acts one and two. (September 21, 1988; 180 min.)

New York Philharmonic with Yo-Yo Ma, Zubin Mehta conductor

Zubin Mehta conducts the New York Philharmonic and guest soloist, the cellist Yo-Yo Ma, in *Concerto for Cello and Orchestra in B minor, opus 104,* by Dvorak and *Symphony no. 1 in D* by Mahler. Hugh Downs hosts the program. (October 5, 1988; 130 min.)

New York Philharmonic New Year's Eve Gala

Soloists Adriana Morelli, soprano, and Placido Domingo, tenor, perform selections by Giordano, Lehar, Reznicek, Mascagni, Rimsky-Korsakov, Lara, Johann Strauss, Verdi, Tosti, Puccini and Gastaldon. Zubin Mehta conducts the New York Philharmonic, except for the overture to *Die Fledermaus,* which Domingo conducts. (December 31, 1988; 120 min.)

Great Performers: Pavarotti Plus!

Appearing with the tenor Luciano Pavarotti in recital at Avery Fisher Hall are Mariella Devia, Kallen Esperian, Cynthia Lawrence and Shirley Verrett, sopranos; Pietro

Paula Robison, Leonard Arner, Charles Wadsworth, Robert Routch, Loren Glickman and Gervase De Peyer, members of the Chamber Music Society of Lincoln Center. Photo by Susanne Faulkner Stevens.

Ballo, tenor; Thomas Hampson and Sherrill Milnes, baritones, and Paul Plishka, bass. On the program are works by De Curtis, Di Capua, Donizetti, Flotow, Gounod, Meyerbeer, Mozart, Ponchielli, Puccini, Rossini and Verdi. Anton Guadagno conducts the New York City Opera Orchestra. (January 9, 1989; 180 min.)

Chamber Music Society of Lincoln Center: 20th Anniversary Concert

The Chamber Music Society of Lincoln Center honors Charles Wadsworth, pianist and artistic director, in a farewell concert: Ravel's *Introduction and Allegro for Harp, Winds and Strings;* Poulenc's *Sextet for Piano and Winds* and Schubert's *String Quintet in C, opus 163.* New York City mayor Edward Koch presents Wadsworth with the Handel Medallion, and Wadsworth delivers a farewell talk to the audience. (May 5, 1989; 120 min.)

Ray Charles in Concert with the New York City Ballet

Ray Charles, his band and the Raeletts provide the music for *A Fool for You,* a dance piece choreographed by Peter Martins. Principal dancers are Judith Fugate, Stephanie Saland, Heather Watts, Lindsay Fischer, Robert LaFosse and Jock Soto. The music includes *Georgia, Ol' Man River, America the Beautiful* and other classics from Hoagy Carmichael, Jerome Kern, Oscar Hammerstein II and Percy Mayfield. (May 12, 1989; 60 min.)

Mostly Mozart with Itzhak Perlman

Gerard Schwarz conducts the Mostly Mozart Festival Orchestra and guest soloist Itzhak Perlman in Mozart's *Allegro con spirito* from *Serenade in D, K. 320* ("Posthorn"); *Violin Concerto no. 3 in G, K. 216; Symphony no. 36 in C, K. 425* ("Linz"); and Bach's *Violin Concerto no. 2 in E, BWV 1042.* Patrick Watson hosts the program. (July 12, 1989; 120 min.)

SEASON FIFTEEN, 1989 - 1990

New York Philharmonic Opening Night with Soprano Jessye Norman, Zubin Mehta Conducts

In this opening night concert the soprano Jessye Norman performs five songs by Mahler and *Liebestod* from Wagner's *Tristan und Isolde.* The New York Philharmonic performs the overture to *Tannhaeuser* and Mozart's *Symphony no. 40 in G minor, K. 550.* Zubin Mehta conducts. At intermission Patrick Watson interviews Mehta, and a pretaped interview with Norman is presented. (September 20, 1989; 130 min.)

A Classical Jazz Christmas with Wynton Marsalis

The Wynton Marsalis Band with Jon Hendricks, vocalist, and the Lincoln Center Classical Jazz Orchestra perform traditional and modern seasonal selections: Marsalis's composition *Carol of the Bell Blues* and his arrangements of *Let it Snow, Let it Snow, Let it Snow, O Tannenbaum* and *Deck the Halls.* The Ellington/Strayhorn arrangement of Tchaikovsky's *Nutcracker Suite* is performed by the Lincoln Center Classical Jazz Orchestra, conducted by David Berger. (December 22, 1989; 120 min.)

A New York Philharmonic Five-Star Evening

Zubin Mehta conducts the New York Philharmonic in works by Beethoven, Haydn, Weber, Faure, Bizet/Waxman and Ravel. The performance features four of the orchestra's first chair players: Philip Smith, trumpeter; Stanley Drucker, clarinetist; Lorne Munroe, cellist, and Glenn Dicterow, violinist. (January 17, 1990; 120 min.)

Great Performers: Pavarotti Plus!

Luciano Pavarotti performs in selections from the Puccini operas *Tosca* and *Manon Lescaut* and Verdi's *Un Ballo in Maschera.* Also performing are seven soloists: Harolyn Blackwell, Leona Mitchell and Carol Vaness, sopranos; Ted Huffman, boy soprano; Leo Nucci, baritone, and Robert Briggs and Alan Held, basses. Anton Guadagno conducts the New York City Opera Orchestra and the Collegiate Chorale. (February 28, 1990; 120 min.)

Great Performers: Flicka and Friends: From Rossini to Show Boat

The mezzo-soprano Frederica von Stade (Flicka), the bass Samuel Ramey and the tenor Jerry Hadley perform works by Meyerbeer, Massenet, Gounod, Thomas, Mozart, Donizetti and Rossini and selections from *Show Boat* by Jerome Kern and Oscar Hammerstein II. Henry Lewis conducts the Orchestra of St. Luke's and the New York Concert Singers. (April 18, 1990; 150 min.)

GREAT PERFORMANCES

Since 1973, GREAT PERFORMANCES has been public television's cultural cornucopia, presenting opera, music, theater and dance from national and international sources; engaging in coproduction, research and development; working tirelessly to bring historic performances to the national audience and adjusting alertly to the changing ecology of media. Produced by an alliance of six public television stations (in Chicago, Dallas, Maryland, New York, San Francisco and South Carolina), the series built, through its regularity and impeccable standards, an audience of 3.4 million per program that could tolerate, even welcome, risk-taking.

Such programs as *Einstein on the Beach* and *The Orchestra* are unorthodox certificates of the series' vitality; presentations such as Houston Grand Opera's *Nixon in China* resulted from carefully harvesting material from regional theaters and opera companies. Since 1983, the Endowment has supported the series' American productions. Two other Endowment-supported series, DANCE IN AMERICA and LIVE FROM LINCOLN CENTER, appear on GREAT PERFORMANCES, thereby maximizing their audiences.

Executive producer: Jac Venza
Additional funders include: Corporation for Public Broadcasting, Exxon Corporation, Martin Marietta, Texaco, public television stations
A production of the Great Performances Alliance: KERA/Dallas, KQED/San Francisco, MPT/Maryland, South Carolina ETV Network, WNET/Thirteen, WTTW/Chicago

SEASON TEN, 1982 - 1983

The Regard of Flight

A comic commentary by Bill Irwin—comedian, clown, mime, vaudevillian, performance artist and avant-garde exponent of the "new" new theater. Irwin banters verbally and in slapstick, discoursing on theater and on postmodern performance art—dissecting theatrical conventions and the theory behind them. Taped live at the American Place Theatre in New York City. Originally presented for the stage by Matthew Cohen. (February 7, 1983; 60 min.)

Created by: Bill Irwin, Doug Skinner, Michael O'Connor
Director: Gary Halvorson
Producer: Samuel J. Paul, III

Ellington—The Music Lives On

A celebration of Duke Ellington's rich legacy. New interpretations of legendary Ellington tunes are presented by Sister Sledge, Carly Simon, Karen Akers, Patti LaBelle and others. Ellington's son, Mercer Ellington, conducts the late Ellington's orchestra. Other notable performers are Kathleen Battle, Cynthia Gregory, Tammy Grimes, Ben Harney, Esther Marrow, Treat Williams and the Harlem Boys' Choir. Alvin Ailey, Cab Calloway, Aaron Copland, Al Hibbler, Kitty Carlisle Hart, Yves Montand and Bobby Short pay tribute to the Duke. Cicely Tyson hosts the program. (March 7, 1983; 90 min.)

Director: Jerome Schnur
Producers: Bob Bach, Bill W. Chastain

Festival! Spoleto, USA

Events from the Seventh Annual Spoleto Festival USA, held in Charleston, South Carolina, May - June, 1983, are highlighted: scenes from Gian Carlo Menotti's production of Samuel Barber's *Antony and Cleopatra*; the work of several visual artists including the sculptor Louise Nevelson; chamber music selections presented by Charles Wadsworth, directed by Scott Nickrenz and Paula Robison, and jazz by the Dave Brubeck Quartet and Mongo Santamaria. Also presented is Piccolo Spoleto, a gathering of some of the finest musicians in the southeastern United States performing for children. (June 27, 1983)

Director: Kirk Browning
Producers: Sidney Palmer, Samuel J. Paul, III, Peter Weinberg
Writer: John Ardoin
A production of South Carolina ETV and WNET/Thirteen

SEASON ELEVEN, 1983 - 1984

Princess Grace Remembered

A musical tribute to the late first lady of Monaco who died in September, 1982. The National Symphony Orchestra, conducted by Mstislav Rostropovich, performs Samuel Barber's *Adagio for Strings, opus 11*, Tchaikovsky's *Symphony No. 5 in E minor, opus 64* and Saint-Saens's *The Carnival of Animals*, with First Lady Nancy Reagan reciting the text by Ogden Nash. The Russian-born Rostropovich had originally invited Princess Grace, one of the first people to befriend him after his defection to the West, to participate in the program. The host is the journalist Pierre Salinger. Taped live at the John F. Kennedy Center for the Performing Arts. (September 26, 1983)

Director: Gary Halvorson
Producer: Robert Dalrymple
A production of Johnston Films and WNET/Thirteen

Alice in Wonderland

A new musical production of the classic fantasy, adapted from the Broadway revival of the 1932 Eva La Gallienne/Florida Friebus production. Starring Kate Burton as Alice and her father Richard Burton as the White Knight, it retains many elements from the Broadway production: costumes by Patricia Zippordt, setting by John Lee Beatty and Jonathan Tunick's adaptation of Richard Addinsell's score. *Principal cast:* Eve Arden, Kaye Ballard, James Coco, Andre de Shields, Colleen Dewhurst, Andre Gregory, Geoffrey Holder, Maureen Stapleton. (October 3, 1983; 90 min.)

Director: Kirk Browning
Producer: Ann Blumenthal
A production of WNET/Thirteen

An American Christmas

Personal impressions of Christmas in song, drama and poetry: Burt Lancaster narrates a dramatization of Robert Frost's poem, *The Christmas Tree*; Linda Lavin appears in an adaptation of Grace Paley's short story *The Loudest Voice*; James Earl Jones reads the Frederick Douglass essay, *New Duties and Relations*. Music by the Harlem Children's Choir, the Columbus Boychoir of Princeton, New Jersey, and the Ella Mitchell Gospel Singers. (December 19, 1983; 60 min.)

Director: Edward Sherin
Producer, writer: Bo Goldman

The Soldier's Tale

Stravinsky's celebrated work from the 1920s is based on a popular Russian folk tale involving a soldier, the devil and a princess. In this animated version created by the artist Robert Blechman the voice of the soldier is Dusan Makavejev; the devil, Max von Sydow and the princess, Galina Panova. The Los Angeles Chamber Orchestra (Gerard Schwarz, music director) performs Stravinsky's score. Andre Gregory narrates. (March 19, 1984; 60 min.)

Director: Robert Blechman
Producer: Chloe Aaron
A production of WGBH/Boston
Source: MGM/United Artists (home video)

SEASON TWELVE, 1984 - 1985

The Dining Room

The play by A.R. Gurney, Jr., examines the upper middle class. A cast of six, mostly drawn from the original off-Broadway production at Playwrights' Horizons, performs more than 50 parts, ranging from a senile grandmother to a riotous cluster of five-year-olds. The characters enact a multitude of dramas, all set in dining rooms. *Principal cast:* W.H. Macy, Pippa Pearthree, Remak Ramsay, Jeanne Ruskin, John Shea, Frances Sternhagen. (October 19, 1984; 90 min.)

Stage director: David Trainer
Video director: Allan Goldstein
Producers: John H. Williams, Howard K. Grossman
A production of the Program Development Company
Source: PBS Video

You Can't Take It With You

Moss Hart and George S. Kaufman's classic 1936 comedy is the story of the Sycamore family and the chaos that ensues when the only "sane" daughter falls in love with her wealthy boss's son and introduces her stodgy in-laws-to-be to her eccentric family. This is the 1983 Broadway revival of the play

R.O. Blechman's animated version of Stravinsky's The Soldier's Tale *features the voices of Andre Gregory, Max Von Sydow and Galina Panova. Gerard Schwartz conducts the Los Angeles Chamber Orchestra.*

adapted for television. *Principal cast:* Maureen Anderman, Colleen Dewhurst, Jason Robards, George Rose, Elizabeth Wilson. (November 21, 1984)

Stage director: Ellis Rabb
Television director: Kirk Browning
Producers: Dan Bohr, Ellen M. Krass
A production of Ellen M. Krass Associates for GREAT PERFORMANCES *and Showtime Entertainment*

Dance Black America

A review of the black contribution to dance—historical and contemporary, classical and popular, African and American. A diversity of talent appears in the 1983 festival at the Brooklyn Academy of Music and the State University of New York, including the Alvin Ailey Dance Theater with Donna Wood and Gregory DeLoatch; Mama Lu Parks's Jazz Dancers; Garth Fagan's Bucket Dance Theatre; the Charles Moore Dance Theatre; the Chuck Davis Dance Company; Eleo Pomare; Chuck Green of "Chuck and Chuckles"; the Magnificent Force; the Jazzy Jumpers. Black-and-white

footage from earlier eras is interspersed among the performance sequences. Geoffrey Holder narrates. (January 25, 1985; 90 min.)

Directed and produced by: D.A. Pennebaker, Chris Hegedus
A production of Pennebaker and Associates and Unitel
Source: Princeton Book Company (home video)

Judy Garland: The Concert Years

Judy Garland's electric combination of showmanship and vulnerability is captured in highlights of her career after leaving MGM—her television concerts and nightclub appearances in the 1950s and 1960s. Interviews with Tony Bennett, Melissa Manchester, Nelson Riddle, Garland's ex-husband and manager, Sidney Luft, and their son Joe Luft. Judy Garland's daughter, Lorna Luft, hosts the program. (March 22, 1985; 90 min.)

Directed and produced by: David Heeley, Joan Kramer

Sweeney Todd

In Stephen Sondheim's *Sweeney Todd*, the inventive, highly expressive score is indivisible from the brilliant and abrasive lyrics. A barber is wrongly convicted and transported to Australia by a wicked judge who covets his wife. Upon his return, the barber takes the name Sweeney Todd and wreaks general and particular revenge by slitting the throats of his clients, who are then turned into meat pies by his industrious associate, Mrs. Lovett. *Principal cast:* George Hearn, Angela Lansbury. (May 3, 1985; 150 min.)

Stage director: Harold Prince
Television director: Terry Hughes
A production of RKO-Nederlander and the RCA Entertainment Channel
Source: RKO Home Video, Image Entertainment (home video)

Taking My Turn

The off-Broadway musical comedy deals with aspects of growing old. The story, its original score by Gary Friedman and lyrics by Will Holt, are based on interviews with elderly people around the country. Their observations are the source of the musical's dialogue and lyrics. *Principal cast:* Tiger Haynes, Cissy Houston, Marni Nixon, Margaret Whiting. (May 10, 1985; 90 min.)

Stage director: Robert H. Livingston
Television director: Terry Hughes
A production of Sonny Fox Productions and WNET/Thirteen
Source: Pacific Arts Home Video

SEASON THIRTEEN, 1985 - 1986

The Gospel at Colonus

A collaboration between the director Lee Breuer, the composer Bob Telson and Clarence Fountain (a key performer and the main inspiration for the work). The Sophoclean trilogy is adapted into parable-like sermons on the vicissitudes of fate that project the emotional power of the black gospel experience. Recorded at the American Music Theater Festival in Philadelphia. *Principal cast:* Morgan Freeman, Robert Earl Jones, Carl Lumbley, Isabell Monk, Clarence Fountain and the Five Blind Boys of Alabama, J.J. Farley and the Original Soul Stirrers, the J.D. Steele Singers with Jevetta Steele, Kevin Davis, Soul Stirrer Willie Rogers. (November 8, 1985; 90 min.)

Stage director: Lee Breuer
Television director: Kirk Browning
Producers: David Horn, Yvonne Smith
A production of Bioscope, Inc.
Source: Films for the Humanities

Master Harold . . . and the Boys

A play by the South African playwright Athol Fugard that dramatizes the human tragedy of apartheid. Set in South Africa in 1950, the play explores the relationship between a white teenage boy and two black waiters. Their close friendship ends when the boy's natural instincts are co-opted by the mores of a racist society—summed up in his request that these black men, whom he comes to term "boys," refer to him only as "Master Harold." Originally staged by the author at the Yale Repertory Theatre. On Broadway it received the 1982 Drama Desk and

Outer Critics' Circle awards. *Principal cast:* Matthew Broderick, John Kani, Zakes Mokae. (November 15, 1985; 90 min.)

Director: Michael Lindsay-Hogg
Producer: Iris Merlis
Executive producers: Michael Brandman, Emannuel Azenberg
A production of Lorimar and WNET/ Thirteen
Source: Lorimar Home Video

Heartbreak House

George Bernard Shaw's classic play about love, money and power, is set in an English country house on the eve of World War I as an empire hovers on the brink of disaster. The play offers some of Shaw's most profound insights into the nature of human relationships, youth and age, power and servitude, art and commerce. Adapted from the Circle in the Square production of 1984. *Principal cast:* Tom Aldredge, Rosemary Harris, Rex Harrison, Amy Irving, Dana Ivey, Remak Ramsey. (January 24, 1986; 120 min.)

Director: Anthony Page
Producers: John Williams, Howard Grossman
A production of the Program Development Company and WNET/Thirteen
Source: PBS Video

Einstein on the Beach: The Changing Image of Opera

A documentary examining Robert Wilson's and Philip Glass's 1976 opera, *Einstein on the Beach*, from the perspectives of its creators, contributing artists and performers. Interviews with Wilson and Glass reveal how the work and its creators' unusual backgrounds—Wilson's in architecture and Glass's in Eastern and Western music—complement each other. Filmed in

conjunction with the 1984 production of the opera for the Brooklyn Academy of Music's "Next Wave" Festival. (January 31, 1986; 60 min.)

Director: Mark Obenhaus
Producer: Chrisann Verges
A production of WNET/Thirteen, the Brooklyn Academy of Music and Obenhaus Films
Source: Direct Cinema

Grown Ups

Jules Feiffer's insightful play about the disintegration of the American family had its premiere at the American Repertory Theater in Cambridge, Massachusetts, and played on Broadway in 1981. With biting humor, the play captures the rhythms of everyday speech, the simple irritations and the minor arguments that mask destructive forces in the contemporary family. *Principal cast:* Martin Balsam, Charles Grodin, Marilu Henner, Jean Stapleton. (May 9, 1986; 120 min.)

Director: John Madden
Producer: Patrick Whitley
Executive producers: Emmanuel Azenberg, Michael Brandman
A production of the Interchange Group and Playboy Productions
Source: Lorimar Home Video

SEASON FOURTEEN 1986 - 1987

Miles Ahead: The Music of Miles Davis

Among the highlights of the trumpeter and composer Miles Davis's 40-year career are his pioneering work with Charlie Parker, his precedent-setting collaborations with Gil Evans resulting in such classic albums as *Sketches of*

Spain and *Kind of Blue*, and his electronic albums inaugurating the fusion sound. Also, interviews with Davis, Evans, George Benson, Bill Cosby, Dizzy Gillespie and Herbie Hancock and rare footage of concerts from 1959 to the recent past. (October 17, 1986; 60 min.)

Director: Mark Obenhaus
Producers: Yvonne Smith, David Horn
A production of WNET/Thirteen and Obenhaus Films

Gian Carlo Menotti: The Musical Magician

Created to coincide with his 75th birthday on July 7, 1986, this documentary on the composer, director and impresario Gian Carlo Menotti shows him at work on his operas and managing his three festivals: Spoleto's Festival of Two Worlds in Spoleto, Italy; Spoleto USA in Charleston, South Carolina; and Spoleto Melbourne, in Melbourne, Australia. It includes excerpts from nine operas and interviews with friends and artists that Menotti has influenced: John Butler, Colleen Dewhurst, Alwin Nikolais, Luciano Pavarotti and many others. (November 21, 1986; 90 min.)

Director, producer: Tom Bywaters
A production of WNET/Thirteen and South Carolina ETV

Goya

Gian Carlo Menotti's opera *Goya* is based on the legendary love affair between the great Spanish painter Francisco de Goya and the Duchess of Alba. The opera contrasts the sweep and spectacle of history with the protagonists' private tragedies. The November, 1986, premiere at the John F. Kennedy Center for the Performing Arts stars the tenor Placido Domingo in the title role and the mezzo-soprano Victoria Vergara as the Duchess.

Rafael Fruebeck de Burgos conducts. (November 28, 1986; 150 min.)

Production director: Gian Carlo Menotti
Television director: Kirk Browning
Producer: David Horn
A production of the Washington Opera and WNET/Thirteen

James Stewart: A Wonderful Life

A profile of Jimmy Stewart, the actor known for his image as the idealistic, honest and proud American off the screen as well as on. It includes excerpts from many of Stewart's films; interviews with family, costars, directors and friends; photos from Stewart's private collection and home movie footage. (March 13, 1987; 120 min.)

Producers: David Heeley, Joan Kramer
A production of WNET/Thirteen and MGM/United Artists Television

Broadway Sings: The Music of Jule Styne

A major figure in America's musical theater, Jule Styne is the composer of over 20 musicals, among them *High Button Shoes, Gentlemen Prefer Blondes, Peter Pan, Bells Are Ringing, Gypsy* and *Funny Girl*. Many of the songs he composed for musicals, such as *Just in Time* and *Time After Time*, have become classics, recorded by dozens of artists. The program includes interviews with Styne and artists with whom he has collaborated: Sammy Cahn, Betty Comden and Adolphe Green, E.Y. Harbourg and Stephen Sondheim; and performances by Tony Bennett, Carol Burnett, Carol Channing, Sandy Duncan, Hal Linden, Barry Manilow, Leslie Uggams and others. (March 20, 1987; 120 min.)

Producer: David Horn
A production of WNET/Thirteen

Ozawa

Seiji Ozawa, the internationally celebrated conductor and music director of one of America's oldest and most prestigious orchestras, the Boston Symphony, is shown as he rehearses, performs, oversees his musical projects in Japan and relaxes at his Tanglewood home with his family. We see the cellist Yo-Yo Ma, the pianist Rudolf Serkin and the soprano Jessye Norman in rehearsal and performance under Ozawa's direction. (March 27, 1987; 60 min.)

Directed and produced by: Albert and David Maysles
A production of Cami Video with AT2, NHK/Japan, ZDF/Germany and CBS/Sony
Source: Kultur, Sony Video Software (home video)

Steve Reich: A New Musical Language

Steve Reich, one of the originators of minimalist music, has significantly influenced contemporary music. Through interviews and performance, this documentary introduces Reich and his music, tracing the origins and development of his musical ideas and their current impact on the international music scene. (April 10, 1987; 60 min.)

Director: Margaret Williams
Producer: Mary Jane Walsh
An MJW production for the Arts Council of Great Britain and WNET/Thirteen

Seize the Day

In this adaptation of Saul Bellow's novella, Tommy Wilhelm, a failed actor-turned-salesman suffers a midlife crisis. Having lost his job, his father repudiates him, his ex-wife hounds him and finally a con-man fleeces him of the money he has left. Filmed on location on New York City's Upper West Side, this is the first work by Bellow to be adapted for television. *Principal cast:* Catherine Borowitz, Jerry Stiller, Robin Williams, Joseph Wiseman. (May 1, 1987; 90 min.)

Director: Fielder Cook
Writer: Ronald Ribman
Executive producer: Robert Geller
Additional funding: National Endowment for the Humanities
A production of Learning in Focus and WNET/Thirteen
Source: HBO Video, Image Entertainment (home video)

Vladimir Horowitz: The Last Romantic

Since his American debut in 1928, no pianist has received wider acclaim than Vladimir Horowitz. This documentary by the Maysles brothers includes a recital by the 81-year-old Horowitz in his New York home with complete performances of works by Bach-Busoni, Chopin, Liszt, Moszkowski, Mozart, Rachmaninoff, Schubert, Schumann and Scriabin. It illuminates Horowitz's career and includes personal accounts by Horowitz and his wife Wanda of their personal relationships with leading figures in 20th century music, including Rachmaninoff, Scriabin and Mrs. Horowitz's father, Arturo Toscanini. (May 22, 1987; 90 min.)

Directed and produced by: Albert and David Maysles
Executive producer: Peter Gelb
A production of CAMI Video Film
Source: MGM/United Artists, Pioneer Artists/Pioneer Signature (home video)

SEASON FIFTEEN, 1987 - 1988

The Music Makers: An ASCAP Celebration of American Music at Wolf Trap

This live special, presenting the variety and scope of American music, stars a host of performers: Ashford and Simpson, Patti Austin, Tony Bennett, Gregg Burge, Sammy Cahn, Gary Chryst, Glenn Close, Judy Collins, Cy Coleman, Clamma Dale, Sammy Fain, Jean Pierre Frohlich, Johnny Green, Robert Guillaume, Marvin Hamlisch, Richie Havens, Burton Lane, Carmen de Lavallade, Lieber and Stoller, Henry Mancini, Bobby McFerrin, the Oak Ridge Boys, Jeffrey Osborne, Bernadette Peters, Melinda Roy, Charles Strouse, Sweet Honey in the Rock, Randy Travis, Andy Williams, Peter Yarrow and the United States Marine Band. Glenn Close is the program host. (October 16, 1987; 90 min.)

Stage director: Joe Layton
Television director: Phillip Byrd
Producers: Ellen M. Krass, David Griffiths, John T. Potthast, Karen Sherry
Executive producers: Alan and Marilyn Bergman
A production of MPT/Maryland, ASCAP, WNET/Thirteen and the Wolf Trap Foundation for the Performing Arts

Aida

This broadcast of Giuseppe Verdi's *Aida* (1871) is the first of two programs celebrating Houston Grand Opera's inauguration of its new home at the Wortham Center. An international cast led by Placido Domingo, Mirella Freni and Ingvar Wixell performs in this new production. Emil Tchakarov conducts. (October 30, 1987; 180 min.)

Stage director: Pierluigi Pizzi
Television director: Brian Large
Producer: Michael Bronson
A production of WNET/Thirteen, Houston Grand Opera and KUHT/ Houston

Tales from the Hollywood Hills: Natica Jackson

In these three short stories the Hollywood of the 1930s is depicted as a vulgar, sometimes brutal place inhabited by people with no particular devotion to any artistic concept. The first of the three programs, *Natica Jackson*, based on a story by John O'Hara, is a portrait of an ambitious young actress tired of her boring, loveless life. *Principal cast:* Hector Elizondo, Brian Kerwin, Michelle Pfeiffer, Holland Taylor. (November 6, 1987; 60 min.)

Director: Paul Bogart
Writer: Andy Wolk
Series producer: Kimberly Myers
Series executive producer: David Loxton
A production of WNET/Thirteen, Zenith and KCET/Los Angeles

Tales from the Hollywood Hills: A Table at Ciro's

Budd Schulberg builds his tale, *A Table at Ciro's*, around a studio head not unlike his father, B.P. Schulberg, the head of Paramount Studios in the 1930s. The executive in the story throws a dinner party at Ciro's, the legendary Hollywood nightclub, and discovers that everyone wants a favor from him. A phone call from the studio's New York money man brings the story to a dramatic conclusion. *Principal cast:* Steven Bauer, Lois Chiles, Ann Magnuson, Darren McGavin, Kenneth McMillan, Stella Stevens. (November 13, 1987; 60 min.)

Director: Leon Ichaso
Writers: Budd Schulberg, Stan Silverman

Tales from the Hollywood Hills: Pat Hobby Teamed with Genius

The program is adapted from three of F. Scott Fitzgerald's Pat Hobby stories: *Teamed with Genius, Boil Some Water—Lots of It* and *Homes of the Stars.* The escapades of Fitzgerald's hack screenwriter-hero, Pat Hobby, are as daffy as any comedy of the 1930s—whether taking a Missouri couple on a screwball tour of movie stars' homes, cribbing another writer's

work or just getting though the studio gate. In Fitzgerald's hands, this eternal hustler is strangely endearing. *Principal cast:* Joseph Campanella, Dennis Franz, Christopher Lloyd. (November 20, 1987; 60 min.)

Director, writer: Rob Thompson

Celebrating Gershwin: The Jazz Age and 'S Wonderful

An event honoring the 50th anniversary of George Gershwin's untimely death in 1937. *The Jazz Age* explores Gershwin's theater work, his collaborations with his brother Ira Gershwin and the jazz-orchestral compositions *Rhapsody in Blue, Piano Concerto in F,* and *An American in Paris.* 'S *Wonderful* chronicles Gershwin's Broadway productions. It includes arias from *Porgy and Bess,* sung by Ruby Hinds and Cynthia Haymon. Performing are Mikhail Baryshnikov, Leonard

Bernstein, Gregg Burge, the Copacetics, Peter Donohoe, Bob Dylan, Michael Feinstein, Madeline Kahn, Nigel Kennedy, Larry Kert, Cleo Laine, the Manhattan Rhythm Kings, Maureen McGovern, Julia Migenes, Erie Mills, Liza Minelli, Bobby Short, the Orchestra of St. Luke's and the London Symphony Orchestra. Michael Tilson Thomas is music director and host. (November 27 and December 4, 1987; 180 min.—2 x 90 min.)

Directors: Humphrey Burton, Patricia Birch
Producer: Arthur Whitelaw
Television producer: David Horn
A production of WNET/Thirteen, the British Broadcasting Corporation and the Brooklyn Academy of Music

Christmas with Flicka (Frederica von Stade)

The American mezzo-soprano Frederica von Stade (Flicka) leads a celebration of Christmas music over the centuries set in the mountain village of St. Wolfgang, Austria. Melba Moore, and Rex Smith join von Stade in well-known and little-known songs from many countries. Von Stade sings classical works by Handel, Mozart and others, accompanied by Julius Rudel, and eleven holiday songs from eleven countries, arranged by Joseph Cantaloube. (December 18, 1987; 60 min.)

Director: Pat Birch
Producer: Yanna Kroyt Brandt
A production of WNET/Thirteen, Anthar Productions, RVR Productions and ORF/Austria
Source: Image Entertainment (home video)

John Duykers as Mao Tse-Tung and James Maddalena as Richard M. Nixon in the Emmy Award-winning telecast of Houston Grand Opera's Nixon in China. *Photo by Jim Caldwell.*

Toscanini: The Maestro

Arturo Toscanini (1867 - 1957), the 20th century's most celebrated conductor, was also known as an ambassador against injustice of all kinds. Over his 70-year career Toscanini served as music director of Milan's La Scala, the Metropolitan Opera, the New York Philharmonic and the NBC Symphony Orchestra. His accomplishments are seen here in the context of major historical events—World War I, the rise of fascism and World War II. Excerpts from *La Forza del Destino*, *Nabucco*, *La Traviata* and *Hymn of Nations* are shown. (January 8, 1988; 90 min.)

Writer: Harvey Sachs
A production of Peter Rosen Productions and the Center for Non-Broadcast Television
Source: Video Artists International

Wolf Trap Salutes Dizzy Gillespie: A Tribute to the Jazz Master

This special concert is a musical retrospective of Dizzy Gillespie's 50-year career, held to honor the trumpeter and composer's 70th birthday. Joining Gillespie in performance are Airto, Jon Faddis, Freddie Hubbard, Carmen MacRae, Wynton Marsalis, Flora Purim, Sonny Rollins, Lalo Schifrin and many others. Film clips of Gillespie with Louis Armstrong, Charlie Parker and other jazz masters of the past are also shown. (February 26, 1988; 90 min.)

Director: Philip Byrd
Producers: John Potthast, Charles Fishman
A production of MPT/Maryland and WNET/Thirteen

Bacall on Bogart

Lauren Bacall hosts and narrates this examination of Humphrey Bogart's life and career—his early stage work, his screen debut in the short subject

Boston Symphony Orchestra music director Seiji Ozawa leads the symphony in a celebration from Tanglewood, Bernstein at 70.

Broadway's Like That and his 75 films. Included are interviews with friends, acquaintances and colleagues and rarely seen footage from film and television archives: newsreel footage of Bacall and Bogart's wedding and their 1954 appearance on Edward R. Murrow's *Person to Person*. (March 11, 1988; 90 min.)

Director: David Heeley
Producers: David Heeley, Joan Kramer
A production of WNET/Thirteen

Nixon in China

This world premiere production of *Nixon in China* by Houston Grand Opera was part of the festivities inaugurating the Wortham Center. Conceived by Peter Sellars with a libretto by Alice Goodman, it was composed by John Adams and choreographed by

Mark Morris. Based on Richard Nixon's historic trip to China in 1972, the opera examines the exhilaration of anticipated triumph and the nervous apprehension of failure. The principals are Trudy Ellen Craney, John Duykers, Thomas Hammons, James Maddalena, Carol Ann Page and Sanford Sylvan. John DeMain conducts. Commissioned jointly by Houston Grand Opera, the Brooklyn Academy of Music, the John F. Kennedy Center and the Netherlands Opera. (April 15, 1988; 180 min.)

Stage director: Peter Sellars
Television director: Brian Large
Producer: Michael Bronson
Awards:Emmy Award: Outstanding Classical Program in the Performing Arts
A production of WNET/Thirteen, the Houston Grand Opera and KUHT/Houston

SEASON SIXTEEN, 1988 - 1989

Tales from the Hollywood Hills: The Old Reliable

Three dramas probe the often vulgar reality behind the glamorous facade of Hollywood's fabled studio system. The first, *The Old Reliable* is based on a story by P.G. Wodehouse and set in 1937. Two aging sisters—one a former silent-screen star—scheme to ensure themselves a financially secure retirement. Sometimes farcical, sometimes outrageous, at the end all involved receive their just desserts. *Principal cast:* Rosemary Harris, Joseph Maher, Lynn Redgrave, Paxton Whitehead. (November 4, 1988; 60 min.)

Director: Michael Blakemore
Writer: Robert Mundy

Tales from the Hollywood Hills: Golden Land

Based on a story by William Faulkner, *Golden Land* concerns Ira Sternholt, a self-made, wealthy realtor, whose success has matched his ambition in a land of golden opportunity. The price of his success is the collapse of his family. Disdainful of his wife, son, daughter and mistress, he relies on his mother to reinforce his sense of confidence and achievement. He discovers that his mother, long uprooted from Nebraska, never wanted to be in Hollywood at all and pines for her long-lost home. *Principal cast:* Audra Lindley, Christina Pickles, James B. Sikking. (November 11, 1988; 60 min.)

Director: Gene Reynolds
Writer: William Hanley

Tales from the Hollywood Hills: The Closed Set

In *The Closed Set,* based on a story by Gavin Lambert, a successful film star whose popularity has declined hires a young director to help launch her comeback. The partnership appears promising, but actress and director clash repeatedly over the nature of the film they are making, and the seasoned actress puts her experience and ruthlessness to work to get her own way. *Principal cast:* D.W. Moffett, Rita Moreno. (November 18, 1988; 60 min.)

Director: Mollie Miller
Writer: Ellen Violett

Wynton Marsalis: Blues and Swing

The trumpet player Wynton Marsalis, the only musician to win Grammy Awards in both the jazz and classical fields in the same year, performs with his acclaimed quartet. The concert includes *Caravan,* by Duke Ellington; *Cherokee,* by Ray Noble; *Crepuscule with Nellie,* by Thelonious Monk; *J Mood,* by Marsalis and *Delfeayo's Dilemma,* by Marsalis. Bob Hurst is on bass, Marcus Roberts on piano, Jeff

"Tain" Watts on drums and Todd Williams on saxophone. Recorded at the Westwood Playhouse in Los Angeles in December, 1987. Marsalis is also seen as a teacher, coaching young musicians at Harvard University and at Duke Ellington School of the Arts in Washington, D.C. (February 24, 1989; 60 min.)

Director, producer: Stanley Dorfman
A production of CBS Music Video Enterprises and Pioneer Artists
Source: Pioneer Artists/Pioneer Signature, CBS Music Video Enterprises (home video)

Canciones de mi Padre

Subtitled "A Romantic Evening in Old Mexico," Linda Ronstadt's *Canciones de mi Padre (Songs of My Father)* celebrates mariachi, the folk music of Mexico, which she learned as a child from her father and her relatives in Sonora, Mexico. Appearing with Ronstadt in this program of song and dance are Danny Valdez, Sal Lopez, Urbanie Lucero, the Ballet Folklorico de la Fonda and the Mariachi Vargas de Tecalitlan. Ruben Fuentes conducts his arrangements; choreography by Michael Smuin. (March 3, 1989; 60 min.)

Directors: Michael Smuin, Bruce Franchini
Producer: David Horn

Bernstein at 70

This tribute to maestro Leonard Bernstein was filmed on the occasion of his 70th birthday at Tanglewood, the summer home of the Boston Symphony Orchestra. Bernstein's career as a composer is chronicled in performances from *Candide, West Side Story, On the Town, Songfest, Chichester Psalms* and *Kaddish (Symphony no. 3).* John Mauceri, Seiji Ozawa, Michael Tilson Thomas and John Williams conduct. The soloists include Patty Austin, Betty Comden, Barbara Hendricks, Yo-Yo Ma and Frederica von Stade. Also included are filmed tributes by artists and orchestras around the world and special performances from Victor Borge, Lauren Bacall and Bernstein's children. (March 19, 1989; 90 min.)

Producers: Michael Bronson, Tom Skinner
A production of the Boston Symphony Orchestra, Unitel, Video Music, Inc., and WNET/Thirteen

The New Moon

An operetta by Sigmund Romberg with book and lyrics by Oscar Hammerstein II, *The New Moon* (1928) is a dashing tale of romance, comedy and adventure. The action begins in New Orleans just prior to the French Revolution and on the ship, *The New Moon*. The score includes well-known songs such as *Lover Come Back to Me; One Kiss; Wanting You; Softly, as in a Morning Sunrise* and *Stouthearted Men*. The New York City Opera's performance was taped in June, 1988, at Wolf Trap National Park for the Performing Arts. The company's general director, Beverly Sills, hosts the program. (April 7, 1989; 150 min.)

Stage director: Robert Johanson
Producer: David Horn
A production of WNET/Thirteen and MPT/Maryland

The Philadelphia Orchestra at Wolf Trap

This concert by the Philadelphia Orchestra with guest conductor Yuri Temirkanov opens with Britten's *Variations on a Theme of Purcell*. The pianist Andre Watts joins the orchestra for Shostakovich's *Piano Concerto no. 1*; the concert concludes with Rachmaninoff's *Symphonic Dances*. All three compositions were premiered in this country by the Philadelphia Orchestra. Taped in June, 1988, at Wolf Trap. (May 26, 1989; 90 min.)

Producer: David Horn
A production of WNET/Thirteen and MPT/Maryland

The Aspern Papers

A musical mystery tale by the Pulitzer Prize-winning composer Dominick Argento. Based on Henry James's story, the work had its premiere in November, 1988, at the Dallas Opera with the sopranos Frederica von Stade and Elisabeth Soederstroem. A renowned prima donna and a stranger arrive one day to unearth the story of the life and death of the great composer who had been in love with the diva and then died mysteriously. As the stranger courts the diva's niece in order to learn the truth, struggle and intrigue follow. (June 9, 1989; 120 min.)

Stage director: Mark Lamos
Television director: Kirk Browning
Producer: David Horn
A production of WNET/Thirteen, KERA/Dallas and the Dallas Opera

SEASON SEVENTEEN 1989 - 1990

Show Boat

Based on Edna Ferber's novel, *Show Boat* (1927), by Jerome Kern and Oscar Hammerstein II, is a landmark in the history of musical theater. Songs introduced in *Show Boat*, such as *Old Man River, Can't Help Lovin' that Man* and *Make Believe*, remain popular. This production was taped in summer, 1989, at New Jersey's Paper Mill Playhouse, a leading regional theater. *Principal cast:* Rebecca Baxter, Eddie Bracken, P.L. Brown, Shelly Burch, Ella English, Richard White. (October 27, 1989; 120 min.)

Stage director: Robert Johansen
Television director: Kirk Browning
Producer: John Walker
Executive producer: David Horn
A production of WNET/Thirteen

Our Town

Lincoln Center's production of Thornton Wilder's *Our Town* won five Tony nominations and the award for best revival during the 1989 theater season. This production is reconceived for television in the empty Lyceum Theater, one of Broadway's oldest and most beautiful. The work is played on the bare stage, with the Stage Manager introducing the audience to the citizens of Grover's Corner and the ordinary events that make up their lives. *Principal cast:* Spalding Gray, Frances Conroy, William Duell, Peter Maloney, Roberta Maxwell, Ann Miller, James Rebhorn, Eric Stoltz, Jeff Weiss. (November 3, 1989; 120 min.)

Stage director: Gregory Mosher
Television director: Kirk Browning
A production of Lincoln Center Theater, Michael Brandman Productions and WNET/Thirteen

An Evening with Alan J. Lerner

A tribute to the lyricist Alan J. Lerner, held at Lincoln Center's New York State Theater on October 23, 1989. Author of some of the most elegant lyrics for Broadway and Hollywood musicals, Lerner's librettos include *My Fair Lady, Camelot, Brigadoon, Paint Your Wagon*, and the original film musical, *Gigi*. Julie Andrews, Georgia Brown, Meg Bussert, Len Cariou, John Cullum, Robert Goulet, Judy Kaye, Richard Kiley, Hal Linden, Rudolf Nureyev and Jane Powell perform. Leonard Bernstein, Walter

Cronkite, Douglas Fairbanks, Jr., Van Johnson and other friends and collaborators introduce the songs and read from Lerner's autobiography. (November 24, 1989; 90 min.)

Stage director: Hugh Wooldridge
Television director: Kirk Browning
Producer: David Horn
Executive producer: Ellen Krass

L'Africaine

The San Francisco Opera revives its remarkable production of Giacomo Meyerbeer's *L'Africaine* (1865), in which Placido Domingo and Shirley Verrett recreate their original roles. Maurizio Arena conducts. The opera, which premiered in Paris in 1865, tells the story of the explorer Vasco da Gama. His dangerous sea journey takes him to the African coast where he falls in love with the beautiful and exotic Selika. (December 15, 1989; 240 min.)

Production by: Lotfi Mansouri
Television director: Brian Large
Producer: David Horn
A production of WNET/Thirteen, KQED/San Francisco and RM Arts/ London
Source: Home Vision (home video)

Michael Tilson Thomas Conducts Miami's New World Symphony

Michael Tilson Thomas and nearly 100 young musicians appear in this performance documentary about the New World Symphony of Miami, Florida, an orchestra designed to launch the careers of musicians aged 21 to 30. Thomas, the symphony's artistic director, leads the players in Tchaikovsky's *Romeo and Juliet Fantasy Overture*, the second movement of Mendelssohn's *Violin Concerto in E minor* and the fifth movement of Janaceks's *Sinfonietta*. (December 29, 1989; 60 min.)

Director, producer: Ken Howard
A production of Landseer Film and Television Productions and WNET/ Thirteen

Shirley Verrett stars as the regal Selika in the San Francisco Opera's revival of Giacomo Meyerbeer's L'Africaine. Photo by Marty Sohl.

Music by Richard Rodgers

This tribute honors Richard Rodgers and the music he has contributed to Broadway and Hollywood over six decades—some 1,000 songs, 45 musical plays, 12 films and television shows and a ballet. The host, Shirley Jones, was discovered by Rodgers and became a star through her performances in Rodgers and Hammerstein's *Oklahoma* and *Carousel*. (March 9, 1990; 90 min.)

Director: John Musilli
Producer: JoAnn G. Young
Executive producer: Stephan Chodorov
A production of Camera Three, WNET/Thirteen and the Rodgers and Hammerstein Organization

Largo Desolato: A Play by Vaclav Havel

Largo Desolato, by the Czech playwright Vaclav Havel, presents intellectual life in a totalitarian state. The action occurs over two days in the life of professor Leopold Nettles, whose writings on philosophy and politics have displeased the authorities; its dark tone is relieved by comic irony and paradox. The English-language adaptation by Tom Stoppard. *Principal cast:* F. Murray Abraham, Phoebe Cates, Sally Kirkland, Amy Wright. (April 20, 1990; 90 min.)

Director: Jiri Zizka
Producer: Kimberly Myers
A production of WNET/Thirteen and the Wilma Theater, Philadelphia

Solti's Beethoven: The Fifth Symphony Revisited

Sir George Solti, music director of the Chicago Symphony Orchestra, presents a revised interpretation of Beethoven's *Fifth Symphony in C minor*, justly celebrated for its structural sophistication and expressive power. Maestro Solti conducts the work at the fast tempo originally intended by Beethoven, resulting in an electrifying performance. (March 23, 1990; 90 min.)

Director: Humphrey Burton
Producer: Fawn Ring
Executive producer: Glenn Dubose
A production of WTTW/Chicago and WNET/Thirteen

The Orchestra

In *The Orchestra*, the filmmaker Zbigniew Rybczynski marries the technological capabilities of high-definition video to a fantastical visual sensibility, resulting in "music videos" of six classical compositions: Ravel's *Bolero*, Schubert's *Ave Maria*, Chopin's *Piano Sonata no. 2 in B flat minor*, Mozart's *Piano Concerto no. 21*, Rossini's overture from *The Thieving Magpie* and Albinoni's *Adagio in G minor for Strings and Organ*. The director integrates background footage of historic settings in France with live action. Choreography by Pat Birch and Christopher Gillis. (April 27, 1990; 60 min.)

Director: Zbigniew Rybczynski
Producer: Stuart Samuels
Awards: Emmy Award: Outstanding Visual Effects
A production of Zbig Vision, Ex Nihilo/Paris, WNET/Thirteen, Canal Plus/France and NHK/Japan

KENNEDY CENTER TONIGHT

The five stages of the Kennedy Center for the Performing Arts in Washington, D.C., present an array of national and international productions in dance, theater, opera, music and performance art. Through the initiative of the Pittsburgh public television station, QED Communications, several of these productions were first presented in 1980. The Arts Endowment contributed to the funding of the third season in 1982 - 83, which included the acclaimed revival of Robinson Jeffers's *Medea*.

Executive producer: Dale Bell
A production of WQED/Pittsburgh in association with the John F. Kennedy Center for the Performing Arts
Additional funders include: Shell Companies Foundation, CPB Program Fund

Zoe Caldwell and Dame Judith Anderson in Robinson Jeffers's adaptation of the Greek tragedy, Medea. *Caldwell won a Tony Award for her performance. Photo by Kenneth Love.*

Dear KENNEDY CENTER TONIGHT:

I am writing to request permission to use the film Medea *in my Humanities 12 senior English [high school] classes. The film would be used once a year in conjunction with the teaching of the play by Euripides. . . .*

Thank you for an excellent presentation of the play. My students had read the play several weeks before it was presented, and they were enthralled with the visual presentation. I hope that we may continue to receive the superior productions offered by the Center. . . .

Sincerely,

M.T., Cheney, Wash.

Christmas at the Kennedy Center Starring Leontyne Price

Leontyne Price, soprano, performs in a Christmas concert from the Kennedy Center with Paula Robison, flutist; Eliot Fisk, guitarist; the Washington Choral Arts Society and the Holiday Festival Orchestra conducted by Norman Scribner. Richard Thomas hosts the program. (December 22, 1982; 60 min.)

Director: Rodney Greenberg
Producer: Linda Blythe
Writer: John O'Toole

My Father Stravinsky

A commemoration of the 100th anniversary of the composer's birth. Igor Stravinsky's son, Soulima Stravinsky, himself a pianist and composer, recalls memories of his father; the St. Paul Chamber Orchestra under the direction of Pinchas Zuckerman performs works by Stravinsky. Included are excerpts from *L'Histoire du Soldat* with Timothy Paradise, clarinet, and Mark Neikrug, piano; *Suite no. 1 for Small Orchestra;* the suite from the ballet *Pulcinella* and an excerpt from Soulima Stravinsky's *Prelude and Fugue.* (January 19, 1983; 60 min.)

Director: David E. Gerber
Producer: Linda Blythe
Writer: Jim Sweene

Medea

Recreated especially for public television, Robinson Jeffers's adaptation of the classic Greek tragedy *Medea* by Euripides captures the turmoil and anger of a woman rejected and betrayed. Zoe Caldwell's extraordinary performance in the title role won her a Tony Award on Broadway in 1982. Dame Judith Anderson (for whom Jeffers originally wrote the part of Medea in 1947) portrays the Nurse, a role for which she received a Tony nomination. (April 20, 1983; 90 min.)

Stage director: Robert Whitehead
Television director: Mark Cullingham
Producer: Mary Rawson
Executive producers: Dale Bell, Barry Weissler

Eubie Blake: A Century of Music

A musical salute to the "King of Ragtime" for his 100th birthday. Twenty-six songs from the more than 1,000 that Blake composed are performed. These include *Love Will Find a Way, It's All your Fault, See America First, Shuffle Along, Daddy, Low Down Blues, Memories of You* and *I'm Just Wild about Harry.* Performing are Gregg Burge, Terry Burrell, Cab Calloway, Rosemary Clooney, Lola Falana, Phyllis Hyman, Patti LaBelle, Eddie Mekka, Anita Morris, Lee Roy Reams, Joe Williams and Stevie Wonder. Billy Dee Williams hosts the program. (May 7, 1983; 90 min.)

Director: Dick Feldman
Producer: Ron Abbott
Writers: Mark Flanagan, Craig Heller

Chapter 4:
MUSIC

The Boston Symphony Orchestra, Seiji Ozawa, music director.

EVENING AT SYMPHONY SPECIALS

THE GIULINI CONCERTS

JAZZ IN AMERICA

SOUNDINGS

MUSIC WITH ROOTS IN THE AETHER

MUSIC SPECIALS

EVENING AT SYMPHONY SPECIALS

The Boston Symphony Orchestra's concerts have been presented to local audiences by the public television station, WGBH/Boston, since the 1950s, and the symphony has appeared on PBS since 1973. In 1981, the Endowment funded EVENING AT SYMPHONY SPECIALS, three programs in honor of the orchestra's centennial.

Executive producer: Glenn Litton
Additional funders include: ABC Video Enterprises, ZDF/Germany, Polaroid Corporation, Unitel
A production of WGBH Educational Foundation

Boston Symphony Orchestra Centennial Gala

The Boston Symphony Orchestra conducted by Seiji Ozawa celebrates its 100th birthday with performances by Itzhak Perlman, Leontyne Price, Mstislav Rostropovich, Rudolf Serkin, Isaac Stern and the Tanglewood Festival Chorus. The works performed are: *Consecration of the House Overture* by Beethoven; *Concerto in D for Two Violins and Orchestra* by Vivaldi; *Concerto in C for Cello and Orchestra* by Haydn; *D'Amor sull'ali rosee* from Verdi's *Il Trovatore*; *Zweite Brautnacht* from Strauss's *Die Aegyptische Helena*; *Tu che di gel sei cinta* from Puccini's *Turandot*; *Fantasia for Piano, Chorus and Orchestra* by Beethoven and *Finale from the Concerto for Orchestra* by Bartok. Broadcast live in Boston, October 18, 1981. (November 4, 1981; 120 min.)

Director: Kirk Browning

Guerrelieder

Seiji Ozawa and the Boston Symphony Orchestra performing Arnold Shoenberg's *Guerrelieder*, sometimes regarded as a monument to the romantic era, with soloists James McCracken, Jessye Norman, Tatiana Troyanos, David Arnold and Kim Scown. The narrator is Werner Klemperer, son of the conductor Otto Klemperer. John Oliver conducts the Tanglewood Chorus. (August 11, 1982; 120 min.)

The Boston Symphony Orchestra in Japan

Japan is the first stop on the orchestra's world tour in honor of its centennial. Taped at Tokyo's Bunka Kaikan Hall, the concert features Schubert's *Symphony no. 7, the Unfinished Symphony in B minor*, Webern's *Five Pieces for Orchestra, opus 10*, and Bartok's *Concerto for Orchestra*. Seiji Ozawa conducts. (September 4, 1982; 90 min.)

THE GIULINI CONCERTS

When Carlo Maria Giulini arrived in Los Angeles in 1978 as music director of the Los Angeles Philharmonic, Ernest Fleischmann, the Philharmonic's manager, capitalized on the maestro's brilliant teaching gifts. Classical music, always in search of a successor to the Bernstein of CBS's *Young People's Concerts*, found him as Giulini, in eight programs, explicated the interpretive role of the conductor through rehearsals, interviews, commentary and complete performances of symphonic works. The concerts were cut short by Giulini's return to Milan, where he had been music director of La Scala.

Executive producer: Jeanne Mulcahy
Producer: John Goberman
Directors: Kirk Browning, Alan Skog
Additional funders include: Getty Oil Company
A production of KCET/Los Angeles, the Los Angeles Philharmonic Association and Polytel Music Productions

SEASON ONE, 1981 - 1982

Rossini Overtures

The works performed are Rossini's overtures to *L'Italiana in Algeri*, *Semiramide* and *William Tell* and Rossini's *Theme and Variation for Clarinet*, Michael Zukovsky, soloist. (November 25, 1981; 60 min.)

Brahms Piano Concerto no. 1

The pianist Vladimir Ashkenazy is the soloist in Brahms's *Piano Concerto no. 1*. (December 23, 1981; 60 min.)

Works by Beethoven and Schumann

Performed in this concert are Beethoven's *Symphony no. 2* and Schumann's *Manfred Overture*. (December 30, 1981; 60 min.)

Verdi's Overtures and Preludes

A performance of overtures and preludes from four operas by Verdi: *La Forza del Destino*, *Un Ballo in Maschera*, *I Vespri Siciliani* and *La Traviata*. (January 6, 1982; 60 min.)

SEASON TWO, 1983

Giulini in Japan I

The first of two concerts by the Los Angeles Philharmonic on tour in Japan. Beethoven's *Symphony no. 5* is performed. (April 6, 1983; 60 min.)

Giulini in Japan II

The second of two concerts in Japan features Tchaikovsky's *Symphony no. 6*. (April 13, 1983; 60 min.)

Brahms Program

The concert features Brahms's *Symphony no. 1*. Taped at the Dorothy Chandler Pavilion at the Los Angeles Music Center. (June 1, 1983; 60 min.)

Hindemith and Beethoven

Two works are performed: Hindemith's *Concert Music for Strings and Brass* and Beethoven's *Piano Concerto no. 2*, Murray Perahia, soloist. (June 8, 1983; 60 min.)

JAZZ IN AMERICA

Jazz, a powerful presence on radio, rarely appears on the small screen. Twentyfour organizations responded to an invitation for proposals for a series on jazz which, it was hoped, would join other long-running Endowment series. The series was eventually limited to four programs: one big-band concert at Lincoln Center and three night-club appearances, exploring styles evolved from Charlie Parker and Dizzy Gillespie's bebop of the 1940s. The performances, augmented with interviews and commentary, show how the bebop legacy has been developed in the work of the trumpet master Gillespie, the drummer Max Roach and the saxophonist, Gerry Mulligan.

Executive producers: Paul Rosen, Dick Reed, Jeanne Mulcahy, John Goberman
Producers: Gary Keys, Timothy Owens
Director: Stanley Dorfman
Additional funding: Atlantic Richfield Corporation
A production of KCET/Los Angeles and JazzAmerica
Source: Embassy Entertainment

Dizzy's Dream Band

The trumpeter Dizzy Gillespie, the drummer Max Roach and the baritone sax player Gerry Mulligan perform with a line-up of jazz all-stars at New York City's Lincoln Center. The band features Frank Foster, Jimmy Heath, Paquito d'Rivera and Frank Wess on saxophone; Pepper Adams on baritone sax; Curtis Fuller, Melba Liston, Benny Powell and Janice Robinson, trombone. On trumpet are John Faddis, Victor Paz, Marvin Stamm and Joe Wilder. Also performing are George Davis on guitar; George Duvivier and Paul West, bass; Roland Hanna and John Lewis, piano; John Hendricks, vocals; Milt Jackson, vibraharp; Grady Tate, drums; and Candido, percussion. Arrangements by Chico O'Farrill. Interview and rehearsal segments are shown. Taped in February, 1981. (September 8, 1983; 90 min.)

Max Roach

The legendary drummer Max Roach is seen in a nightclub appearance at Blues Alley in Washington, D.C. Roach leads the four-piece ensemble, with Cecil Bridgewater on trumpet, Odean Pope on tenor saxophone,

Calvin Hill on bass. Among the eight compositions performed are *Six-Bit Blues* and *Effie*. Taped in March, 1981. (September 15, 1983; 60 min.)

Gerry Mulligan

Gerry Mulligan, one of jazz's most creative saxophonists, leads a quartet in an appearance at Eric's Night Club in New York City. On piano is Harold Danko, Frank Luther is on bass and Billy Hart on drums. The set consists of Mulligan compositions including *17-Mile Drive, For an Unfinished Woman, Walk on the Water, K-4 Pacific* and *Song for Strayhorn*. Taped in February, 1981. (September 22, 1983; 60 min.)

Dizzy Gillespie

Dizzy Gillespie leads an octet at Concert by the Sea in Redondo Beach, California. The band includes alto saxophonist Paquito d'Rivera, Ed Sherry on guitar, pianist Valerie Capers, drummer Tom Campbell, Tom MacIntosh on trombone, Michael Howell on electric bass and Ray Brown on stand-up bass. The compositions include *Bebop, Kush* and *Hard of Hearing Mama*. (September 29, 1983; 60 min.)

SOUNDINGS

The passion of a single producer for contemporary music resulted in nine documentaries on composers not usually available to the television audience. Bernice Olenick presented each composer at work, in rehearsal and in performance, discussing their influences, musical philosophies and artistic aims. During the first season, WGBH/Boston repeated each program for five successive nights to familiarize viewers with these new musical forms and styles.

Producer: Bernice Olenick
Director: Fred Barzyk
Additional funders include: Meet the Composer, New England Foundation
for the Arts
A production of WGBH/Boston

SEASON ONE, 1983

The Music of Michael Colgrass

The Pulitzer Prize-winning composer Michael Colgrass, who insists that "serious" music can be accessible and enjoyable for anyone, conducts an unconventional workshop in composition and rehearses and performs his new music, including the song *Skyscrapers are Trees of the City (and People are Fallen Leaves)* and a composition for violin, guitar, percussion and flute entitled *Light Spirit*. (October 30, 1983; 30 min.)

A production of WGBH/Boston and the Canadian Broadcasting Corporation in association with WMHT/ Schenectady

The Music of Joan Tower

Joan Tower's works have been performed by leading orchestras and chamber ensembles throughout the United States and abroad, and she is founder of and pianist for the Da Capo Chamber Players. Compositions *performed on the program include Snow Dreams* and *Wings* (a solo for clarinet). In 1990, Tower received the prestigious Grawemeyer Award for a work composed during a residency in St. Louis, funded in part by an Arts Endowment grant to Meet the Composer. (November 6, 1983; 30 min.)

The Music of Lukas Foss

The works of Lukas Foss, one of the more gifted composer/conductors of our time, are surveyed. Though grounded in the 20th-century western classical tradition, Foss was among the first to champion the avant-garde and experimental music and introduce them to audiences and scholars alike. Three works are performed: *Curriculum Vitae with Time Bomb, Paradigm* and *Three Airs for Frank O'Hara's Angel*. (November 13, 1983; 30 min.)

A production of WGBH/Boston and WNED/Buffalo

The Music of Ivana Themmen

A portrait of the contemporary composer whose romantic symphonic music has wide appeal. *Mystic Trumpeter* and works in progress are performed. (November 20, 1983; 30 min.)

The Music of Ralph Shapey

Dubbed a "radical-traditionalist" by some, Ralph Shapey admits that his music "combines two contradictory impulses—radical language and romantic sensibility." His music contains dissonant melodies, atonal harmonies and extremes in dynamics and texture; yet the musical structures are grandly formed. Three works are performed:

O Jerusalem, Mutations no. 2 and *Three for Six*, a composition for flute, piano, cello, clarinet, violin and percussion. (November 27, 1983; 30 min.)

A production of WGBH/Boston and WTIU Indiana University Television

SEASON TWO, 1986

The Music of Joseph Schwantner

Interviews with the composer Joseph Schwantner and performances taped in four locations: St. Paul, Minnesota, as Pinchas Zukerman rehearses *Dreamcallers*; St. Louis, Missouri, as Schwantner works with the St. Louis Symphony Orchestra; Rochester, New York, where Willie Stargell narrates *New Morning for the World*; and Hartford, Connecticut, in a performance of *Sparrows*, with Collage. (July 7, 1986; 30 min.)

A production of WGBH/Boston and WEDH/Hartford

The Music of George Rochberg

The award-winning composer George Rochberg is shown in rehearsal with the oboist Joseph Robinson and in a performance of *Between Two Worlds* with the Concord String Quartet and Sue Ann Kahn and Andrew Willis. (July 14, 1986; 30 min.)

A production of WGBH/Boston and WHYY/Philadelphia

The Music of Walter Robinson

The composer Walter Robinson is seen at Harvard University as a fellow at the W.E.B. DuBois Institute and at a church during rehearsals of his gospel opera, *Look What A Wonder...* The program also features the songs, *The Ballad of Harriet Tubman* and *Cross Keys to Jerusalem.* (July 21, 1986; 30 min.)

A production of WGBH/Boston

The Music of Harry Somers

Rehearsal and performance segments from Harry Somers's opera *Luis Riel*, including *Kuyas*, sung in the Cree language. Also performed is *The Shaman Song*, sung in the Inuit language. (July 28, 1986; 30 min.)

A production of WGBH/Boston and the Canadian Broadcasting System

Carlo Maria Giulini, music director of the Los Angeles Philharmonic from 1978 to 1984.

MUSIC WITH ROOTS IN THE AETHER

The subject of one of these videos and the producer of all seven, the composer Robert Ashley is, along with these six other artists, part of a generation of American composers who came of age in the mid-1960s. None uses conventional written musical notation, so that their music has been said to originate in the "aether"—the invisible, weightless medium supposed by the ancients to fill the heavens. Some interviews occur as works by the composers are acted out or performed; all are set against nontraditional backdrops the producers term "landscapes." Each video consists of a landscape and a performance by an ensemble directed by the composer. In 1985, the Endowment awarded Performing Artservices a grant to edit the seven two-hour videos, originally produced in 1976, into one-hour programs for television broadcast.

Director, producer: Robert Ashley
Director of photography: Phil Makanna
Additional funders include: The Rockefeller Foundation, Ford Foundation, Martha Baird Rockefeller Fund for Music, Harry G. Steele Foundation, Broadcast Music, Inc.
A production of Performing Artservices, Inc.
Source: Lovely Music

Robert Ashley

An interview with the composer Robert Ashley and a performance of his work *What She Thinks*. Performing in the ensemble led by the composer are Paul DeMarinis, Mimi Johnson, Robert Sheff and Ashley. (60 min.)

David Behrman

David Behrman discusses his work and is seen in a performance of *Music with Melody-Driven Electronics* with Don Cardoza, E. Jedidiah Denman and Katharine Morton. (60 min.)

Philip Glass

Philip Glass is interviewed and performs *Music in 12 Parts: Part 2*, and act one, scene one, from *Einstein on the Beach*. The Philip Glass Ensemble consists of Glass, Jon Gibson, Dickie Landry, Richard Peck, Kurt Munkacsi, Joan La Barbara and Michael Riesman. (60 min.)

Alvin Lucier

As Alvin Lucier is interviewed, a performance of Lucier's *Outlines of Persons and Things* (1975) takes place. Two other works are also performed: *Bird and Person Dyning* (1975) and *Music for Solo Performer* (1965). The ensemble consists of the composer, Nicolas Collins, Ron Kuivila and two dancers, Anne Koren and Susan Matheke. (60 min.)

Gordon Mumma

Gordon Mumma is interviewed and presents three pieces from *Some Voltage Drop* (1974), a collection of related works: *Simulcast*, *Schoolwork* and *Telepos/Foxbat*. The ensemble consists of Mumma, William Brooks and Tandy Beal. (60 min.)

Pauline Oliveros

While Pauline Oliveros is interviewed, a performance of *Unnatural Acts Between Consenting Adults*, by Oliveros and Carol Vencius, is presented. Performing are Oliveros, Vencius and Linda Montano. Oliveros also performs *Rose Mountain Slow Runner*, a work for voice and accordion. (60 min.)

Terry Riley

Terry Riley is interviewed and performs *Shri Camel: Morning Corona* on the Yamaha electric organ. (60 min.)

MUSIC SPECIALS

America Celebrates Stravinsky

The centennial of the composer's birth is observed in a performance by the National Symphony Orchestra conducted by Leonard Bernstein and Michael Tilson Thomas at Washington's National Cathedral. The works performed span Stravinsky's career: *Symphonies of Wind Instruments*, *Symphony in Three Movements* and *Symphony of Psalms*; and excerpts from *Octet for Wind Instruments*, *The Rite of Spring*, *The Firebird* and *The Owl and the Pussycat*. A short documentary includes footage of Stravinsky conducting his own works. Televised to Europe on June 17, 1982. (June 19, 1982; 90 min.)

Director: Humphrey Burton
Producers: David Griffiths,
Sidney Palmer
A production of South Carolina ETV and the International Television Trading Corporation

Bernstein at 60: An Appreciation

Wolf Trap Farm Park for the Performing Arts in Vienna, Virginia, honors Leonard Bernstein on his 60th birthday. The first part of the program presents Bernstein's symphonic compositions; the second part highlights his musical theater works. The evening concludes with Beethoven's *Triple Concerto,* as Bernstein conducts Mstislav Rostropovich on cello, Andre Previn on piano and Yehudi Menuhin on violin. (August 25, 1978; 180 min.)

A production of WETA/Washington, D.C.

The Bolero

Zubin Mehta conducts the Los Angeles Philharmonic in Maurice Ravel's *The Bolero*, originally composed as a ballet score. Mehta is shown rehearsing the orchestra and discussing the concept and challenge of the work. Members of the orchestra are also interviewed, and they discuss music and musicianship and their parts in the performance. The film demonstrates how a conductor communicates the leadership and discipline necessary to weld highly talented symphony musicians into a whole. (February 19, 1973; 30 min.)

Directors: Allan Miller, William Fertik
Producer: Allan Miller
Academy Award: Live Action Short Subject
Source: Pyramid Films

In Search of Bach

This program documents the first Bach Aria Festival and Institute at Stonybrook, a major festival held at the State University of New York at Stonybrook in summer, 1981. The festival was founded in order to continue the tradition of the Bach Aria Group, founded in 1946 and dissolved in 1980 upon the retirement of its founder, music director and patron, William H. Scheide. The institute's main focus is the study of the ensemble arias from Bach's cantatas, passions and masses.

Director, producer: Allan Miller
A production of the Music Project for Television

Chapter 5:
DRAMA

A hearing before the House Un-American Activities
Committee from AMERICAN PLAYHOUSE's dramatization
of the Whittaker Chambers-Alger Hiss case,
Concealed Enemies. *Photo by Richard Howard.*

AMERICAN PLAYHOUSE

TRYING TIMES

VISIONS

DRAMA SPECIALS

AMERICAN PLAYHOUSE

How to return drama, plays, adaptions, narrative film to public television's regular schedule was the formidable task facing AMERICAN PLAYHOUSE's founder, David Davis, in 1980 and 1981. Since drama, of its nature, proposes issues of conflict for resolution in the matrix of life as it is lived, it is difficult to gain support from funders with a preference for the safer precincts of wordless performing arts. PLAYHOUSE, of which the Endowment was an original supporter, negotiated its entry skillfully, gaining the approval of public television's individual stations, of several foundations and of the writing, directing and acting communities.

Since PLAYHOUSE premiered in 1982, its gifted production staff, under the guidance of Lindsay Law, have supervised the adaption of stage plays, novels and short stories, commissioned original dramas, mini-series and one-person shows, and have contributed significantly to the survival of independent feature films. Some of the latter have been successfully released theatrically, including *Stand and Deliver*, *Longtime Companion* and *The Thin Blue Line*. Aware that the funds available to support drama are increasingly limited, PLAYHOUSE has ingeniously sought co-funders in this country and abroad (*Sunday on the Park with George* was originally seen on Showtime); it has shrewdly invested in Broadway productions later adapted for television (*A Walk in the Woods*); and it has secured Challenge Grant funds from the Endowment for production of independent films.

AMERICAN PLAYHOUSE, which averages 7.5 million viewers per week, has become a standard of reference for television drama and independent feature film. It has given a measure of stability to the latter, a perilous area of individual enterprise. Its programming has been sympathetic to regional works, inclusive in its vision of our society and fearless in its engagement with issues.

Executive director: David M. Davis
Executive producer: Lindsay Law
Awards: 1990 Peabody Award
Major funders include: Atlantic Richfield Company (season 1), Chubb Group of Insurance Companies (seasons 3 - 9), Corporation for Public Broadcasting, the nation's public television stations
A production of Public Television Playhouse: KCET/Los Angeles, South Carolina ETV, WGBH/Boston and WNET/Thirteen

SEASON ONE, 1982

The Shady Hill Kidnapping

The series premiered with an original production written by John Cheever in which the alleged abduction of young Toby Wooster jolts the complacent and well-fed suburb of Shady Hill into surprising action, making transparent the hilarious, often poignant character of life, love and the pursuit of happiness in America's upper middle class suburbs. *Principal cast:* Paul Dooley, David Marshall Grant, George Grizzard, Polly Holliday, Celeste Holm, Judith Ivey, E. Katherine Kerr. (January 12, 1982; 60 min.)

Director: Paul Bogart
Producer: Ann Blumenthal
Writer: John Cheever
Executive producer: Jac Venza
A production of WNET/Thirteen

Susan Sarandon and Christopher Walken in the adaptation of Kurt Vonnegut Jr.'s Who Am I This Time?

King of America

A young Greek sailor jumps ship in New York harbor in 1915, consigning his future to destiny in a strange new land. In search of work, he journeys from New York west to Utah. Fate leads him to confront Harry Mekakis, an ambitious Greek labor agent who exploits his fellow immigrants. *Principal cast:* Larry Atlas, Andreas Katsulas, Barry Miller, Michael Welden. (January 19, 1982; 73 min.)

Director: Dezso Magyar
Producers: Tony Mark, Sue Jett
Writer: B.J. Merholz
Additional funding: National Endowment for the Humanities
A production of the Center for Television in the Humanities

Seguin

Juan Nepomuceno Seguin, who fought under General Sam Houston in Texas's struggle for independence from Mexico, went on to become a respected Texas politician, but was later forced to flee the country because of bigotry and hostility. In 1847, he returned to Texas to write the memoirs on which this film is based. *Principal cast:* Edward James Olmos, Henry Darrow, Danny de la Paz, A. Martinez, Rose Portillo, Pepe Serna, Robert Viharo. (January 26, 1982; 67 min.)

Director, writer, executive producer: Jesus Salvador Trevino
Producer: Severo Perez
Additional funding: National Endowment for the Humanities
A production of KCET/Los Angeles

Who Am I This Time?

The hero of this adaptation of Kurt Vonnegut's short story is a hardware store clerk in a small town whose shyness is so extreme he can barely speak in public. Yet in the local theater's *Streetcar Named Desire* he plays Stanley Kowalski with great passion. A spunky telephone company worker joins the theater group and the two are instantly attracted to one another. Yet his shyness inhibits him from expressing his affection. *Principal cast:* Susan Sarandon, Christopher Walken. (February 2, 1982; 60 min.)

Director: Jonathan Demme
Producer, writer, executive producer: Morton Neal Miller
A Rubicon Film production
Source: Coronet/MTI (educational)

Any Friend of Nicholas Nickleby Is a Friend of Mine

A man who calls himself Charles Dickens arrives in a small midwestern town in order to complete his newest novel, *A Tale of Two Cities*. His presence has a wondrous effect on the lives of the townspeople, including the local librarian—a wistful young woman who fancies herself to be Emily Dickinson. Based on Ray Bradbury's short story. *Principal cast:* Deanna Dunagan, Fred Gwynne, Les Podewell, Brian Svrusis, George Womack. (January 26, 1982; 90 min.)

Director: Ralph Rosenblum
Writer: Mary Trimble
Executive producer: Morton Neal Miller
A Rubicon Film production
Source: Coronet/MTI (educational);
Movies Unlimited (home video)

Come Along With Me

A recently widowed and slightly eccentric woman takes on a new identity and moves to a new town after the death of her husband. She searches for happiness and finds meaning in life by using her natural clairvoyant talents. Adapted from Shirley Jackson's novel. *Principal cast:* Barbara Baxley, Estelle Parsons, Sylvia Sidney. (February 16, 1982; 56 min.)

Director: Joanne Woodward
Writers: June Finfer, Morton Neal Miller, Joanne Woodward
Executive producer: Morton Neal Miller
A Rubicon Film production
Source: Coronet/MTI (educational);
Monterey Home Video

For Colored Girls Who Have Considered Suicide/When the Rainbow is Enuf

Ntozake Shange's vivid choreo-poem takes the black woman in America out of the shadows and into the sunlight, celebrating in song, poetry and dance her strength, beauty and capacity for love. The seven women of the cast share with the audience a magnetic exuberance for life. *Principal cast:* Sarita Allen, Trazana Beverley, Laurie Carlos, Crystal Lilly, Carol L. Maillard, Ntozake Shange, Lynn Whitfield, Alfre Woodard. (February 23, 1982; 78 min.)

Director: Oz Scott
Producer: Lindsay Law
Writer: Ntozake Shange
Executive producer: Jac Venza
A production of WNET/Thirteen and WPBT/Miami

Carl Sandburg—Echoes and Silences

Part drama and part documentary, this program incorporates the writings and early life history of Carl Sandburg, the poet and historian, and recreates a Carl Sandburg lecture and poetry reading filmed live at Bryn Mawr College. *Principal cast:* Frances Conroy, John Cullum, Peter Michael Goetz, James Green, Michael Higgins, Larry Keith, Martin Silbersher. (March 2, 1982; 120 min.)

Director, producer: Perry Miller Adato
Writer: Paul Shyre
Executive producer: Jac Venza
Additional funding: National Endowment for the Humanities
A production of WNET/Thirteen

The Great American Fourth of July and Other Disasters

In Jean Shepherd's midwest, that "great inverted bowl of darkness," lives the quintessential American family. Shepherd sets Dad, Mom, 16-year-old Ralph and his whiney little brother in the middle of Hohman, Indiana, on a hot Fourth of July holiday, mixes them with an excessive supply of fireworks, stirs in the town's eccentrics and creates a recipe for disaster and hilarity. *Principal cast:* Barbara Bolton, James Broderick, Matt Dillon, Jean Shepherd. (March 16, 1982; 55 min.)

Director: Dick Bartlett
Producer: Olivia Tappan
Writer: Jean Shepherd
Executive producer: Fred Barzyk
A production of Creative Television Associates
Source: WGBH/Boston

Pilgrim, Farewell

Kate Deveraux, a fiercely independent and strong-willed woman who is dying of cancer wants to make peace in the brief time she has left with the daughter she abandoned as a child, now an emotionally disturbed teenager. She has also to let go of her long-time lover and learn how to say good-bye to both of them. *Principal cast:* Robert Brown, Elizabeth Franz, Elizabeth Huddle, Christopher Lloyd, Leslie Paxton, Laurie Prange, Shelley Wyant. (March 23, 1982; 104 min.)

Director, writer: Michael Roemer
Producer: Stanley D. Plotnick
A Post Mills production with WGBH/
Boston

Northern Lights

Ray Sorenson, a stoic Norwegian wheat farmer in Crosby, North Dakota, in the early 1900s, loses the family farm to the bank. He reluctantly becomes involved in the Nonpartisan League, whose main objective is to put farmers' finances in their own hands. His decision sets him in conflict with his fatalistic brother, who believes in letting well enough alone. *Principal cast:* Marianne Astrom-de Fina, Robert Behling, Nick Eldridge, Gary Hanisch, Susan Lynch, Helen Ness, Jon Ness, Ray Ness, Melvin Rodvold, Thorbjorn Rue, Joe Spano, Adelaide Thorntveit. (March 30, 1982; 90 min.)

Directed, produced and written by:
John Hanson, Rob Nilsson
A production of Cine Manifest
Source: New Front Films; New World
Entertainment (home video)

Medal of Honor Rag

A young black Vietnam veteran, recently awarded the Congressional Medal of Honor, tries to confront the demons that haunt him from his war days: Why he has survived and why were his buddies killed? How he could be commended for what may well have been the murder of innocents? Adapted from the stage play by Tom Cole. *Principal cast:* Hector Elizondo, Clarence Felder, Damien Leake. (April 6, 1982; 86 min.)

Director: Lloyd Richards
Producer: Joyce Chopra
Writer: Tom Cole
A Kent production with Handelman
Filmworks

Working

A musical adaptation of the book by Studs Terkel examining the "average" American worker. Based on a series of interviews with construction workers, waitresses, firemen, secretaries, cleaning women and others, *Working* emphasizes the dignity of these individuals and their occupations. *Principal cast:* Barbara Barrie, Barry Bostwick, Eileen Brennan, Didi Conn, Scatman Crothers, Charles Durning, Charles Haid, Barbara Hershey, Beth Howland, Patti LaBelle, Rita Moreno, James Taylor, Studs Terkel. (April 13, 1982; 90 min.)

Directors: Stephen Schwartz, Kirk
Browning
Producers: Phylis Geller, Lindsay Law
Writers: Stephen Schwartz, Nina Fasc
Executive producer: Jac Venza
A production of WNET/Thirteen and
KCET/Los Angeles

Weekend

This adaptation of Ann Beattie's short story examines the poles of commitment and infidelity. George is an attractive college professor who has lived with Lenore for many years but never married. When an adoring young coed arrives for the weekend, George is forced to reexamine his relationship with Lenore and to realize that he may need her more than she needs him. *Principal cast:* Barbara Hershey, Helen Hunt, Kaki Hunter, Emily Moultrie, Tony Musante. (April 20,1982; 60 min.)

Director: Paul Bogart
Producers: Ann Blumenthal, Phylis
Geller
Writer: Ann Beattie
Executive producer: Jac Venza
A production of WNET/Thirteen and
KCET/Los Angeles

Private Contentment

In this original teleplay by Reynolds Price, a young soldier bound for the front in World War II makes a last visit home to attend his mother's funeral. He finds that his charming, traveling-salesman father has had a second family for many years. *Principal cast:* Trini Alvarado, Peter Gallagher, John McMartin, Kathryn Walker, Beatrice Winde, Mark Zimmerman. (April 27, 1982; 88 min.)

Director: Vivian Matalon
Producers: Samuel J. Paul, III,
Lindsay Law
Writer: Reynolds Price
Executive producer: Jac Venza
A production of WNET/Thirteen and
South Carolina ETV

My Palikari

Pete Panakos, a successful proprietor of a cafe in Yonkers, New York, has worked, saved and planned for 35 years to revisit Geritsa, the village in Sparta where he was born. He embarks with his American-born son Pete who is embarrassed and bored by his father's constant references to his Greek heritage and "the old country." The trip has a profound effect on father and son. Based on a story by Leon Capetanos. *Principal cast: Michael Constantine, Keith Gordon, Telly Savalas, Dora Volonaki. (May 4, 1982; 88 min.)*

Director: Charles S. Dubin
Producers: Sue Jett, Tony Mark
Writer: George Kirgo
Executive producer: David Horwatt
Additional funding: National Endowment for the Humanities
A production of the Center for Television in the Humanities

Oppenheimer

This mini-series takes us into the life of J. Robert Oppenheimer, the head of the Manhattan Project, the top-secret scientific enclave at Los Alamos, New Mexico, where the atomic bomb was developed. The film reveals Oppenheimer's triumphs and complexities—he worked tirelessly for the bomb's development but later came to question its deployment. The production was nominated for two Emmy Awards. *Principal cast: Sam Waterston, Matthew Guinness, Garrick Hagon, Kate Harper, Manning Redwood, Shane Rimmer, Jana Sheldon, Bob Sherman, David Suchet, Peter Whitman. (May 11 - June 22, 1982; 420 min.—7 x 60 min.)*

Director: Barry Davis
Producer: Pete Goodchild
Writer: Peter Prince
A production of WGBH/Boston and the British Broadcasting Corporation

The Ballad of Gregorio Cortez

In 1901 an itinerant Chicano cowhand, Gregorio Cortez, appeared in Gonzales, Texas, and at the climax of a misunderstanding, shot and killed the town's sheriff. Captured and sentenced to 50 years in prison, he was eventually pardoned for the crime, which he had always claimed was an act of self-defense. Adapted from the novel *With a Pistol in His Hand: A Border Ballad and Its Hero* by Americo Paredes. *Principal cast: Edward James Olmos, Rosana DeSoto, Jaime Gammon, Michael McGuire, Victoria Plata, William Sanderson, Tim Scott, Pepe Serna. (June 29, 1982; 106 min.)*

Director: Robert M. Young
Producers: Moctesuma Esparza, Michael Hausman
Writer: Victor Villasenor
Executive producers: David Ochoa, H. Frank Dominguez
Additional funding: National Endowment for the Humanities
A Moctesuma Esparza production with Filmhaus
Source: Embassy Entertainment (home video)

SEASON TWO, 1983

The Skin of Our Teeth

Broadcast live from the stage of the Old Globe Theatre in San Diego, Thornton Wilder's play chronicles the trials of the Antrobus family. Having survived fire, flood, pestilence, seven-year locusts, the ice age and a dozen wars, the Antrobuses remain durable as radiators and optimistic as a spring day. *Principal cast: Blair Brown, Jeffrey Combs, Monique Fowler,*

Howard Rollins portrays the civil rights worker Medgar Evers in For Us, the Living.

Harold Gould, John Houseman, Rue McClanahan, Sada Thompson. (January 18, 1983; 120 min.)

Director: Jack O'Brien
Producer: Samuel J. Paul, III
Executive producer: Jac Venza
A production of WNET/Thirteen, Old Globe Theatre and Limelight International

Miss Lonelyhearts

During the depths of the Great Depression, a young, idealistic reporter is assigned the task of writing the paper's advice to the lovelorn column. The reporter finally meets one of the unhappy women who has written to him. His reaction to her pitiful attempt at seduction shocks and saddens him. Adapted from the novella by Nathanael West. *Principal cast:* Conchata Ferrell, Arthur Hill, Eric Roberts. (January 25, 1983; 57 min.)

Director: Michael Dinner
Producer: Lydia Woodward
Writers: Michael Dinner, Robert Bailey
Executive producer: H. Jay Holman
An H. Jay Holman production

Family Business

Milton Berle stars as Isaiah Stein, an old man whose imminent death finds his four sons bickering over their inheritances, a conflict that crystallizes the marked differences between them. Adapted from Dick Goldberg's stage play. *Principal cast:* Milton Berle, Brian Ben-Ben, David Garfield, Richard Greene, Jeffrey Marcus, David Rosenbaum. (February 1, 1983; 86 min.)

Director: John Stix
Producers: Hal Weiner, Marilyn Weiner
Writer: Dick Goldberg
Executive producer: Charles Morris
A production of Screenscope and South Carolina ETV
Source: Castle Hill Productions

Keeping On

A black mill worker and minister and a white union organizer face opposition from plant management and from their families as they attempt to unionize a textile mill in a small southern town. The film explores the central role women play in the town and the family's importance as a unit of support. *Principal cast:* Alice Beardsley, Trazana Beverley, James Broderick, Rosalind Cash, Frances Conroy, Jeffrey de Munn, Carol Kane, Marcia Rodd, Sloane Shelton, Dick Anthony Williams. (February 8, 1983; 72 min.)

Director, executive producer: Barbara Kopple
Producer: Coral Hawthorne
Writer: Horton Foote
Additional funding: National Endowment for the Humanities
A production of Many Mansions Institute
Source: Caridi Entertainment

The File on Jill Hatch

This three-part mini-series follows two lovers—a black American G.I. and a white English girl—through their courtship and marriage in England to their troubled life as an interracial couple in the American South in the 1950s and 1960s. The story culminates in their daughter's journey back to England at the time of the Brixton riots. *Principal cast:* John Atkinson, Frances Foster, Gloria Foster, Sheila Gill, Penny Johnson, Joe Morton, Frances Tomelty, Tim Woodward. (February 15, 22, and March 1, 1983; 168 min.—3 x 56 min.)

Director: Alastair Reed
Producers: Ann Blumenthal, Alan Shallcross
Writer: Kenneth Cavander
Executive producer: Jac Venza
A production of WNET/Thirteen and the British Broadcasting Corporation

For Us, the Living

Medgar Evers, an NAACP field director in Jackson, Mississippi, was assassinated June 11, 1963. This is the story of Evers's attempt to secure equal rights for the black people of Jackson and of the irrational hatred that caused his death. The film is adapted from the biography, *For Us, The Living*, by Myrlie Evers with William Peters. *Principal cast:* Margaret Avery, Roscoe Lee Browne, Irene Cara, Larry Fishburne, Howard Rollins, Jr. (March 22, 1983; 90 min.)

Director: Michael Schultz
Producer: J. Kenneth Rotcop
Writers: Ossie Davis, J. Kenneth Rotcop
Executive producer: Charles W. Fries
Additional funding: National Endowment for the Humanities
A Charles Fries production
Source: Movies Unlimited (home video)

Verse Person Singular

Richard Kiley's one-person performance of poetry by the masters. Kiley recites works predominantly written in the first person and assumes the personas of different characters as he appears in stage settings and video landscapes. Poems by Stephen Vincent Benet, Robert Browning, Lewis Carroll, Richard Eberhardt, T.S. Eliot, R.P. Kayes, Rudyard Kipling, Edgar Lee Masters, Edgar Allan Poe, Henry Reed and Edward Arlington Robinson are performed. (March 29, 1983; 60 min.)

Director: Robert Deubel
Producer: Richard Barclay
Writer: Richard Kiley
Executive producer: Frank Lieberman
A production of Concepts Unlimited and NET Enterprises

Until She Talks

Though pressure is brought to bear, a young woman refuses to testify before a grand jury and is jailed. The legal process that put her behind bars is examined, one in which an individual may be held for contempt for refusing to give evidence and jailed indefinitely without trial. *Principal cast:* Penelope Allen, Susan Haskins, Barton Heyman, Kaiulani Lee, Ben Masters, Bruce McClenahan, Pamela Reed, Dale Soules, Madeleine Thornton-Sherwood. (April 5, 1983; 46 min.)

Director, producer: Mary Lampson
Writer: Doris Baizley
An Alaska Street production

Wings

This adaptation of the 1978 Broadway production of Arthur Kopit's drama depicts the frightening experiences of a woman who has recently suffered a stroke and her courage in coping with her disability. Constance Cummings recreates her role from the stage play for which she received a Tony Award. *Principal cast:* Constance Cummings, Mary Joan Negro, James Tolkan. (April 26, 1983; 76 min.)

Director: John Madden
Producer: Phylis Geller
Writer: Arthur Kopit
A production of KCET/Los Angeles

The Rothko Conspiracy

A dramatization of the final years of the artist Mark Rothko. Following his death, the illegal sale of his works resulted in a damages award of $9.2 million to his estate. *Principal cast:* Phil Brown, Norman Chancer, Jerry Harte, Larry Hoodekoff, Ronald Lacey, Douglas Lambert, Andrea Levine, Barry Morse, David Neal, Patt Starr. (May 3, 1983; 90 min.)

Director, producer: Paul Watson
Writer: Michael Baker
Executive producer: John Purdie
A production of the BBC and Lionheart Television
Source: BBC Enterprises

Fifth of July

Richard Thomas and Swoosie Kurtz recreate their original roles from the Broadway production of Lanford Wilson's play. Two old friends who once agitated for a better world now look for a way to revive their idealistic dreams. Kurtz won a Tony for her Broadway performance. Presented in association with Showtime. *Principal cast:* Joyce Reehling Christopher, Jeff Daniels, Jonathan Hogan, Swoosie Kurtz, Cynthia Nixon, Helen Stenborg, Danton Stone, Richard Thomas. (May 10, 1983; 117 min.)

Directors: Marshall W. Mason, Kirk Browning
Producer: Samuel J. Paul, III
Writer: Lanford Wilson
Executive producer: Jac Venza
A production of WNET/Thirteen and Connecticut Public Television

---

SEASON THREE, 1984

The Ghost Writer

Nathan Zuckerman, a 45-year-old writer, recalls the visit he made 22 years earlier to Manny Lonoff, an older, world-famous author. He discovered Lonoff living in seclusion with two women—his spouse of 35 years and a voluptuous young woman, madly in love with the author. Adapted from Philip Roth's novel. *Principal cast:* Rose Arrick, Claire Bloom, Cecile Mann, Patricia Pellows, Paulette Smit, Sam Wanamaker, Joseph Wiseman. (January 17, 1984; 90 min.)

Director, writer: Tristram Powell
Producer: Peter B. Cook
Executive producer: Michael Gill
A production of WGBH/Boston, Malone-Gill and the British Broadcasting Corporation
Source: PBS Video (educational)

Pudd'nhead Wilson

In this film based on Mark Twain's classic novel, the small-town lawyer Pudd'nhead Wilson unravels a fantastic tangle of mistaken identity, deceit and murder. Wilson, whose worldly thinking and wit is considered more eccentric than informed by his neighbors, proves that an unjust "cradle swap" of a light-skinned black and a white infant many years before is at the root of a current case of injustice. *Principal cast:* Lise Hilboldt, Ken Howard, Preston Maybank, Steven Weber. (January 24, 1984; 87 min.)

Director: Alan Bridges
Producer: Jane Iredale
Writer: Philip Reisman, Jr.
Executive producer: William Perry
Additional funding: National Endowment for the Humanities
A production of the Great Amwell Company and Nebraskans for Public Television
Source: Fries Distribution (educational); MCA Home Video

True West

An off-beat look at modern moviemaking and sibling rivalry, this is the first full-length play by Sam Shepard to be presented on television. The story concerns a meeting of two brothers, one a desert rat, the other an up-and-coming screenwriter. In the course of a weekend they exchange roles, steal the neighbors' toasters and destroy their mother's kitchen. *Principal cast:* John Malkovich, Sam

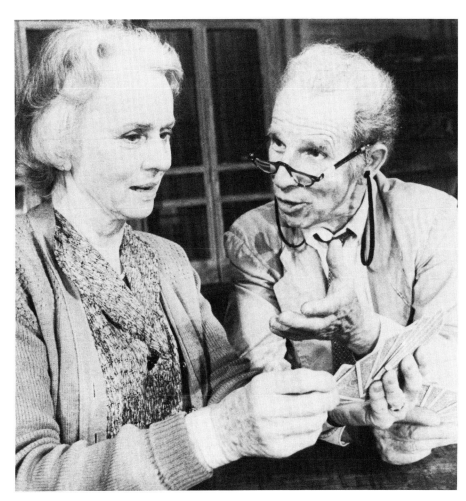

Jessica Tandy and Hume Cronyn in D.L. Coburn's Pulitzer Prize-winning play, The Gin Game. *Photo by Martha Swope.*

Schacht, Gary Sinise, Margaret Thomson. (January 31, 1984; 111 min.)

Director: Allan Goldstein
Stage director: Gary Sinise
Producers: John H. Williams, Howard K. Grossman
Writer: Sam Shepard
Executive producer: Harold A. Thau
A production of the Program Development Company
Source: Academy Entertainment (home video)

Nothing But a Man

In this telecast of a classic independent film made in 1964, Ivan Dixon stars as Duff Anderson, an earnest young black man who sets out to lead a normal life in the deep South following World War II. He must first overcome the white community's animosity and his father's lack of understanding of his needs. *Principal cast:* Ivan Dixon, Gloria Foster, Julius Harris, Yaphet Kotto, Abbey Lincoln, Leonard Parker, Martin Priest. (February 7, 1984; 88 min.)

Director: Michael Roemer
Producers: Robert M. Young, Michael Roemer, Robert Rubin
Writers: Michael Roemer, Robert M. Young
A production of the Nothing But a Man Company

Popular Neurotics

Set in Anywhere, USA, two young urban professionals, both with idiosyncratic neuroses, meet by chance at an automatic bank teller machine and make a date for the movies. Their lives will never be the same again, as each is overwhelmed by the prospect of a "meaningful relationship"—with its undefined expectations, vague yet complex compromises and conflicts of egos and feelings. *Principal cast:* Nathan Cook, Jeff Goldblum, Archie Hahn, Mimi Kennedy, Susan Krebs, Rick Overton, Lynne Stewart. (February 14, 1984; 51 min.)

Director: Sheldon Larry
Producers: Joseph Morgenstern, David Yarnell
Writer: Aubrey Wertheim
A production of the Center Theatre Group of Los Angeles
Source: ABC Video Enterprises

The Cafeteria

In this adaptation of Isaac Bashevis Singer's short story, two refugees in the United States, a successful European-born writer, and a young woman named Esther, a surivor of the Holocaust, meet in a 1960s New York cafeteria. They are but two of the isolated and stray people who fill the cafeteria, a place where they share the fleeting illusion that they belong. Filmed on location at Dubrow's on Manhattan's Seventh Avenue. *Principal cast:* Morris Carnovsky, Howard da Silva, Bob Dishy, Zohra Lampert. (February 21, 1984; 60 min.)

Director, executive producer: Amram Nowak
Producer: Kirk Simon
Writer: Ernest Kinoy
Additional funding: National Endowment for the Humanities
A production of Amram Nowak Associates
Source: Direct Cinema (educational)

Refuge

Four people on vacation on a remote island off the coast of Maine become embroiled in each others' problems. Tensions mount as each is drawn into a tangled web of mutual attractions and jealousies. *Principal cast:* James Congdon, Will Jeffries, Alexandra O'Karma, Anne Twomey. (February 28, 1984; 87 min.)

Director: Huck Fairman
Producers: Charlotte McKim, Huck Fairman
Writers: Huck Fairman, Luther Sperberg
A production of Separate Dreams Company
Source: Caridi Entertainment

The Gin Game

The television adaptation of the Pulitzer Prize-winning Broadway play by D.L. Coburn. Hume Cronyn and Jessica Tandy star as two nursing home residents who challenge each other at gin rummy. Over the course of many rounds of gin, they develop a close, yet contentious relationship, as they reach for companionship and air the frustrations, regrets and resentments of a lifetime. (March 6, 1984; 90 min.)

Alfre Woodard and Damien Leake in the feature film, The Killing Floor. *Photo by Jim Taylor.*

Director, producer: Terry Hughes
Stage director: Mike Nichols
Writer: D.L. Coburn
Executive producers: Ellen M. Krass, Archer King, Robert Dale Martin
A production of RKO/Nederlander
Source: Turner Home Entertainment (home video)

Haunted

A young woman reluctantly pays a visit to the estranged adoptive mother who raised her and who is now dying. She forms a close bond with the neighbors' child, whose parents are on the verge of separation and in whom she sees herself as a child—afraid and alone. *Principal cast:* Brooke Adams, Jon DeVries, Ari Myers, Trish van Devere. (March 20, 1984; 117 min.)

Director, writer: Michael Roemer
Producer: Stanley D. Plotnick
A Post Mills production with WGBH/Boston

The Killing Floor

A black worker takes part in the attempt to unionize the Chicago meatpackers at the end of World War I. The effort was thwarted by the postwar recession, which exacerbated racial tensions in the stockyards, culminating in the Chicago race riot of 1919. Based on a story by Elsa Rassbach. *Principal cast:* Moses Gunn, Damien Leake, Alfre Woodard. (April 10, 1984; 115 min.)

Director: William Duke
Producer: George Manasse
Writer: Leslie Lee
Executive producer: Elsa Rassbach
Additional funding: National Endowment for the Humanities
A Public Forum production with KERA/Dallas
Source: Films, Inc. (educational)

Heartland

In 1910 a Denver widow, Elinore Randall, picked up and moved to the Wyoming wilderness. This feature film based on her diaries tells how Elinore worked as a housekeeper to Clyde Stewart, a homesteader, to raise money to start a ranch of her own. Clyde is determined that she remain as his housekeeper, and they strike a bargain. *Principal cast:* Conchata Ferrell, Megan Folsom, Barry Primus, Lilia Skala, Rip Torn, Amy Wright. (April 17, 1984; 96 min.)

Director: Richard Pearce
Producers: Michael Hausman, Beth Ferris
Writers: Beth Ferris with William Kittredge
Executive producer: Annick Smith
Additional funding: National Endowment for the Humanities
A Wilderness Women production with Filmhaus
Source: Wilderness Women Productions; HBO Video (home video)

City News

A comic and ironic film about the struggles of an "underground" newspaper and its publisher and editor, Tom Dominio. After a lifetime of failures, Dominio succeeds in building a media empire only to find it's lonely at the top. Filmed on location in Manhattan's East Village. *Principal cast:* Nancy Cohen, Elliot Crown, Valerie Felitto, Gail Gibney, Tony Mangia, Richard Schlessinger, Thomas Trivier. (April 24, 1984; 60 min.)

Produced, directed and written by: David Fishelson, Zoe Zinman
Atlanta Independent Film Festival: Best Dramatic Film
A Zi-Fi production

Hughie

Jason Robards is Erie Smith in *Hughie*, Eugene O'Neill's portrait of a down-and-out gambler. Smith's survival depends on his talent for telling tales—and on having someone to listen—in this case, the bored front desk clerk at the flea-bag hotel where Smith resides. *Principal cast:* Jack Dodson, Jason Robards. (May 1, 1984; 57 min.)

Director: Terry Hughes
Stage director: Jose Quintero
Producer: Iris Merlis
Executive producers: Theodore Mann, Paul Libin, Ellen M. Krass
A production of RKO/Nederlander
Source: Turner Home Entertainment (home video)

Concealed Enemies

This four-part series is based on the notorious and controversial Whittaker Chambers-Alger Hiss spy case in the late 1940s. Chambers, a senior editor at *Time* magazine and a former member of the communist party, accused Alger Hiss, a U.S. State Department employee and the head of the Carnegie Endowment for International Peace, of having been a communist spy in the 1930s. The case was propelled onto the national stage by the young congressman, Richard M. Nixon. The meaning of the case is disputed to this day: whether it was an example of political opportunism or an attempt to preserve national security from traitors and spies—"concealed enemies"—in the highest ranks of government. *Principal cast:* John Harkins, Edward Herrmann, Marcia Jean Kurtz, Peter Riegert, Maria Tucci. (May 7 - 9, 1984; 240 min.—4 x 60 min.)

Director: Jeff Bleckner
Producer: Peter B. Cook
Writer: Hugh Whitemore
Executive producers: Lindsay Law, David Elstein
Awards: Emmy Awards: Outstanding Limited Series; Outstanding Directing in a Limited Series
A production of WGBH/Boston and Goldcrest Films and Television

Robert Duvall stars in Tomorrow, *the critically acclaimed 1972 film based on the novel by William Faulkner.*

SEASON FOUR, 1984 - 1985

Testament

In the aftermath of a nuclear explosion, a mother tries to cope with the chaos and devastation—her children are dying from radiation poisoning and her husband's whereabouts are unknown. As she confronts the reality that she is dying, as are all whom she holds dear, she questions the human race one final time. Based on the short story, *The Last Testament* by Carol Amen. Jane Alexander was nominated for an Academy Award for her role in the film. *Principal cast:* Jane Alexander, Kevin Costner, Rebecca de Mornay, William Devane, Lukas Haas, Ross Harris, Lurene Tuttle, Roxana Zal. (November 26, 1984; 86 min.)

Director: Lynne Littman
Producers: Jonathan Bernstein, Lynne Littman
Writer: John Sacret Young
A production of LDL Films and
Entertainment Events, Ltd.
Source: Paramount Pictures; Paramount Home Video

A Matter of Principle

A Christmas show about a poor family from Virginia whose domineering father refuses to buy a Christmas tree as a "matter of principle." His wife finally stands up to him, and he learns that principles must sometimes be set aside. Based on the story by John D. Weaver. *Principal cast:* Alan Arkin, Barbara Dana. (December 3, 1984; 56 min.)

Director: Gwen Arner
Producer, executive producer: Morton Neal Miller
Writers: Morton Neal Miller, Nancy Miller
A Rubicon Film production
Source: Academy Entertainment (home video)

Solomon Northup's Odyssey

Solomon Northup, who was kidnapped into slavery in the mid-19th century, spent 12 years enduring the cruelty and subjugation of slavery on several plantations in Louisiana. Adapted from the autobiography, *My Twelve Years as a Slave*, by Solomon Northup. *Principal cast:* Mason Adams, Avery Brooks, John Saxon. (December 10, 1984; 115 min.)

Director: Gordon Parks
Producer: Yanna Kroyt Brandt
Writers: Lou Potter, Samm-Art Williams
Executive producer: Shep Morgan
Additional funding: National Endowment for the Humanities
A production of Past America

Tomorrow

Robert Duvall stars as a destitute southern farmer whose spirit, dignity and capacity for love are awakened when he adopts the infant son of a sickly woman, only to lose the boy to the natural father. Based on the William Faulkner novel, the film captures the barrenness of these characters' lives and the fierceness of their love. *Principal cast:* Olga Bellin, Sudie Bond, Robert Duvall. (January 17, 1985; 120 min.)

Director: Joseph Anthony
Producers: Gilbert Pearlman, Paul Roebling
Writer: Horton Foote
A Filmgroup Production
Source: Castle Hill Productions

Go Tell It on the Mountain

A film adaptation of James Baldwin's semi-autobiographical novel about a 14-year-old boy in Harlem in the 1930s. Young John Grimes searches for dignity and meaning—drawn by the world of power and wealth and fascinated by the mysteries of his church. Ultimately, he comes to understand how deprivation and tragedy have crippled his family, and he learns to strive for wholeness and power. *Principal cast:* James Bond III, Rosalind Cash, Ruby Dee, Linda Hopkins, C.C.H. Pounder, Paul Winfield, Alfre Woodard. (January 14, 1985; 97 min.)

Director: Stan Lathan
Producer: Calvin Skaggs
Writers: Gus Edwards, Leslie Lee
Executive producer: Robert Geller
Additional funding: National Endowment for the Humanities
A production of Learning in Focus
Source: Films, Inc. (educational)

Noon Wine

In this adaptation of Katherine Anne Porter's story, a Swedish immigrant arrives on a small Texas farm at the turn of the century asking for work. He is hired, but later, through no fault of his own, causes the downfall of his employer when a suspicious visitor comes calling. *Principal cast:* Roberts Blossom, Lise Hilboldt, Pat Hingle, Stellan Skarsgard, Fred Ward. (January 21, 1985; 81 min.)

Director, writer: Michael Fields
Producer: Doro Bachrach
Executive producers: James Ivory, Ismail Merchant
A production of Noon Wine Company
Source: Caridi Entertainment; Monterey Home Video

The Joy That Kills

In turn-of-the-century New Orleans, a frail child-bride is confined to the house by her husband. A set of ironic circumstances leads her to believe she has broken free from her domestic prison, but she ends up chained forever to her quiet, closed-up life. Based on the short story *The Story of an Hour* by Kate Chopin. *Principal cast:* Rosalind Cash, Frances Conroy, Jeffrey DeMunn, Elizabeth Franz, Patrick Tovatt. (January 28, 1985; 55 min.)

Director, executive producer: Tina Rathborne
Producers: Sue Jett, Tony Mark
Writers: Tina Rathborne, Nancy Dyer
A production of Cypress Films and Mark-Jett Productions
Source: Films for the Humanities

Overdrawn at the Memory Bank

A science fiction tale based on a short story by John Varley, set in the near future. Aram Fingal becomes lost in the inner workings of a massive computer when he illegally taps its off-limits old-movie storage bank and finds himself "trans-computerized" into Rick's Cafe in the middle of *Casablanca*. *Principal cast:* Linda Griffiths, Raul Julia, Louis Negin. (February 4, 1985; 84 min.)

Director: Douglas Williams
Producers: Geoffrey Haines-Stiles, Robert Lantos
Writer: Corinne Jacker
Executive producers: David Loxton, Stephen Roth
A production of WNET/Thirteen and RSL Films
Source: New World Entertainment (home video)

The Star-Crossed Romance of Josephine Cosnowski

Jean Shepherd's continuing saga of a typical midwestern family and their teenage son Ralph. The comedy centers on Thanksgiving dinner and Ralph's newly discovered infatuation with an exotic Polish girl from East Chicago who has moved in next door. Adapted from *Wanda Hickey's Night of Golden Memories and Other Disasters. Principal cast:* Barbara Bolton, George Coe, Jay Ine, Pete Kowanko, Jean Shepherd. (February 11, 1985; 56 min.)

Director, executive producer: Fred Barzyk
Producer: Olivia Tappan
Writer: Jean Shepherd
A production of Creative Television Associates

Some Men Need Help

A modern morality play with an ironic twist adapted from the stage play by John Ford Noonan. It concerns two suburban men—one, a young advertising executive-turned-alcoholic whose wife has left him and is bent on his own destruction; the other, an ex-mobster turned Good Samaritan who is determined to save his neighbor from despair. *Principal cast:* Philip Bosco, Treat Williams. (February 18, 1985; 90 min.)

Director: Allan Goldstein
Stage director: John Ferraro
Producer: Daniel A. Bohr
Writer: John Ford Noonan
Executive producers: Ellen M. Krass, Perry Rosemond
An EMK production

Charlotte Forten's Mission: Experiment in Freedom

Based on the true story of Charlotte Forten, a young black woman who, despite lifelong ill health, made it her mission to give black children a decent education and a chance at a better life in the years during and after the Civil War. *Principal cast:* Melba Moore, Mary Alice, Ned Beatty, Carla Borelli, Micki Grant, Moses Gunn, Anna Maria Horsford, Bruce McGill, Jay Patterson, Vyto Ruginis, Glynn Turman, Rodrick Wimberly. (February 25, 1985; 120 min.)

Director: Barry Crane
Producer: Yanna Kroyt Brandt
Writer: Samm-Art Williams
Executive producer: Shep Morgan
Additional funding: National Endowment for the Humanities
A production of Past America

Breakfast with Les and Bess

A comedy about a day in the life of a couple who broadcast a radio talk show from their New York apartment in the early 1960s, adapted from the stage play by Lee Kalcheim. The day starts with high hopes that Princess Grace will call in from Monaco and ends on quite a different note. *Principal cast:* Cloris Leachman, Dick Van Dyke, Shaun Cassidy, Mark Humphrey, Ken James, Wendel Meldrum. (March 11, 1985; 90 min.)

Director: Perry Rosemond
Producers: Perry Rosemond, Garry Blye
Writer: Lee Kalcheim
Executive producers: Ellen M. Krass, Lee Kalcheim
An EMK production

Nightsongs

The story of a Vietnamese woman's will to survive as she carves out a living in New York's Chinatown. Her struggle is juxtaposed with that of her host, a Chinese-American who must work at a menial job and whose teenage son is in trouble with the law. *Principal cast:* Roger Chang, Ida F.O. Chung, Mabel Kwong, David Lee, Rose Lee, Victor Wong. (April 15, 1985; 113 min.)

Director, writer: Marva Nabili
Producer: Thomas A. Fucci
A production of FN Films

Under the Biltmore Clock

This amusing and ironic story of a stylish young flapper's search for a husband begins under New York's legendary Biltmore Hotel clock and ends a fews blocks away on a train departing Grand Central Station—the couple bound on a would-be honeymoon. Based on the short story *Myra Meets His Family*, by F. Scott Fitzgerald. *Principal cast:* Barnard Hughes, Lenny von Dohlen, Sean Young. (April 22, 1985; 83 min.)

Director, producer, executive producer: Morton Neal Miller
Writers: Ilene Cooper, Morton Neal Miller
A Rubicon Film production
Source: Coronet/MTI (educational); Nelson Home Entertainment (home video)

Displaced Person

Based on Kurt Vonnegut's short story, *D.P.*, about a six-year-old black orphan in Germany at the close of World War II and the black American sergeant whom he believes—or wishes—to be his father. *Principal cast:* Julius Gordon, Rosemary Leach, Stan Shaw. (May 6, 1985; 55 min.)

Director: Alan Bridges
Producer: Barry Levinson
Writer: Fred Barron
Executive producers: Patrick Lynch, Allison Maher, Barry Solomon, Rick Traum
Awards: Emmy Award: Outstanding Children's Program
A production of Hemisphere and HTV, Ltd.
Source: Monterey Home Video

The Europeans

This adaptation of Henry James's novel juxtaposes 19th-century American naivete and practicality with European experience and guile, as the English Baroness Munster and her brother Felix journey to New England to visit their wealthy American cousins. The production received an Academy Award nomination for its costume design. *Principal cast:* Lisa Eichhorn, Robin Ellis, Lee Remick. (May 13, 1985; 90 min.)

Director: James Ivory
Producer: Ismail Merchant
Writer: Ruth Prawer Jhabvala
A Merchant/Ivory production
Source: Facets Video (home video)

El Norte

A teenage brother and sister flee Guatemala after their parents are slain. In the United States, *el norte*, they dream of finding a new life of freedom and opportunity. Filmed on location in Mexico and southern California, this feature film was nominated for an Academy Award for its screenplay. *Principal cast:* Zaide Silvia Guttierrez, David Villalpando. (May 20, 1985; 141 min.)

Director, writer: Gregory Nava
Producer, writer: Anna Thomas
Produced by Independent Productions
Source: Cinecom International; CBS/Fox (home video)

Three Sovereigns for Sarah

This three-part series depicts the mass hysteria surrounding the Salem witch trials in 17th-century New England. Vanessa Redgrave stars as Sarah Cloyce, a woman wrongly accused, who confronts her accusers and emerges triumphant. *Principal cast:* Kim Hunter, Patrick McGoohan, Vanessa Redgrave, Phyllis Thaxter. (May 27, June 3, and 10, 1985: 180 min.—3 x 60 min.)

Director: Philip Leacock
Producer, writer: Victor R. Pisano
Executive producers: Ben Melniker, Michael Uslan
Additional funding: National Endowment for the Humanities
A Night Owl production
Source: Prism Entertainment (home video)

Paper Angels

This adaptation of Genevieve Lim's stage play depicts the experience of Chinese immigrants entering the United States in the early 20th century. Set in the detention center on Angel Island in San Francisco Bay, a group of Chinese immigrants who have risked everything to journey to the United States wait in hope of being allowed into the country while being harassed by the detention center staff—a forecast of the treatment they may expect as aliens in the United States. *Principal cast:* Rosalind Chao, Joan Chen, Mike Genovese, James Hong, Beulah Quo, Victor Wong, Ping Wu. (June 17, 1985; 60 min.)

Director: John Lone
Producer: Ricki Franklin
Writer: Genevieve Lim
Executive producer: Phylis Geller
A production of KCET/Los Angeles
Source: Producer Services Group

Cat on a Hot Tin Roof

Jessica Lange is Maggie the Cat and Tommy Lee Jones is her forlorn husband, Brick, in this production of Tennessee Williams's classic play. During the birthday party of a wealthy southern patriarch, the secrets and passions of each family member are forced into the open. Presented in association with Showtime. *Principal cast:* David Dukes, Penny Fuller, Tommy Lee Jones, Jessica Lange, Kim Stanley, Rip Torn. (June 24, 1985; 142 min.)

Director: Jack Hofsiss
Producer: Phylis Geller
Executive producer: Lou LaMonte
Awards: Emmy Award: Outstanding Supporting Actress in a Limited Series or Special—Kim Stanley
A production of KCET/Los Angeles and the International Television Group
Source: Movies Unlimited (home video)

SEASON FIVE, 1986

The Rise and Rise of Daniel Rocket

This television production of Peter Parnell's stage play concerns Daniel Rocket's remarkable gift—the ability to fly. Beginning as a small boy, Daniel flies around the world for 20 years, only to return home and discover that his childhood love has wed another. *Principal cast:* Timothy Daly, James Eckhouse, Elizabeth Franz, Tom Hulce, Jane Jones, Valerie Mahaffey, Tom Robbins, Katie C. Sparer, Jesse Tendler, Jodi Thelen, Scott Waara. (January 20, 1986; 90 min.)

Director: Emile Ardolino
Producers: John H. Williams, Timothy Marx
Writer: Peter Parnell
A production of the Program Development Company
Source: PBS Video; Academy Entertainment (home video)

The Roommate

Orson Ziegler, a basketball star and aspiring M.D., arrives at Northwestern University in 1952 and finds he has to room with Henry Palamountain, "Hub," who is in every way his opposite. After an explosive confrontation, the staid Orson mellows, just a little. Adapted from John Updike's short story, *Christian Roommates*. *Principal cast:* Lance Guest, Barry Miller. (January 27, 1986; 90 min.)

Director: Nell Cox
Producer, writer: Morton Neal Miller
Executive producers: Morton Neal Miller, Richard Melman
A production of Rubicon Films and KTCA/St. Paul-Minneapolis

Valentine's Revenge

Set in 1898, this drama introduces us to the writer O. Henry, who, while serving time for embezzlement, weaves a tale for a dying fellow prisoner. He tells of a safecracker, Jimmy Valentine, whose plan for the greatest heist of his career is foiled by his affection for the banker's daughter. Based on O. Henry's short story *A Retrieved Reformation*. *Principal cast:* Victor Ertmanis, Wendy Lyon, Gerard Parkes, Gary Reineke, Marc Strange, Chris Wiggins. (February 3, 1986; 60 min.)

Director: Paul Saltzman
Producers: Simon Christopher Dew, Paul Saltzman
Writer: Paul M. Lally
Executive producers: Fred Rogers, Frank Doelger
Additional funding: National Endowment for the Humanities
A production of the Learning Corporation of America, Family Communications and Sunrise Films
Source: Coronet/MTI (educational); New World Entertainment (home video)

The Adventures of Huckleberry Finn

Mark Twain's classic novel is presented in this four-hour mini-series. Huck Finn and the runaway slave Jim travel down the Mississippi and venture across the ante-bellum South, meeting society's ne'er-do-wells, paupers and princes, discovering deeper values than those of the respectable society that cast them out. *Principal cast:* Jim Dale, Patrick Day, Frederic Forrest, Lillian Gish, Barnard Hughes, Richard Kiley, Butterfly McQueen, Geraldine Page, Sada Thompson, Samm-Art Williams. (February 10, 17, 24, and March 3, 1986; 240 min.—4 x 60 min.)

Director: Peter H. Hunt
Producer: Jane Iredale
Writer: Guy Gallo
Executive producer: William Perry
Additional funding: National Endowment for the Humanities
A production of the Great Amwell Company, WGBH/Boston and WGBY/Springfield
Source: Fries Distribution (educational); MCA Home Video

Tell Me A Riddle

This adaptation of Tillie Olsen's novella follows David and Eva, married for 47 years but now grown apart. Eva sinks into a deep melancholy, broken only by a visit to their granddaughter in San Francisco. The young girl's need for comfort in the aftermath of a break-up awakens Eva's tender and vital character. *Principal cast:* Brooke Adams, Melvyn Douglas, Lila Kedrova. (March 17, 1986; 90 min.)

Director: Lee Grant
Producers: Tony Wade, Mindy Affrime, Rachel Lyon, Susan O'Connell
Writers: Joyce Eliason, Alev Lytle
Executive producer: Michael Rosenberg
A Godmother Production

The Little Sister

Nicki Davis, a bright and attractive high school student confounds her parents by going steady with a juvenile delinquent. She is arrested by the police, and the trust that grows between her and her boyfriend's probation officer leads her to reveal the painful family secret she has hidden all her life. *Principal cast:* Laurel Berger, Roxanne Hart, Richard Jenkins, Jack Kehoe, Tracy Pollan, John Savage, Henry Tomaszewski. (April 7, 1986; 103 min.)

Director, writer: Jan Egleson
Producer: Steve Wax
Executive producers: Lindsay Law,
Kathleen Hammer
A production of the Little Sister
Partnership

The House of Ramon Iglesia

This television production of Jose
Rivera's play examines the emotional
and cultural conflict between a father
and son. After 19 years in the United
States, Ramon Iglesia decides to move
his family back to Puerto Rico. Faced
with difficulties selling the house, he
turns to his son for help and discovers
the young man's scorn for and resent-
ment of all things Puerto Rican. *Prin-*
cipal cast: Roberto Badillo, Marina
Durell, Annie Golden, Israel Juarbe,
Jaime Sanchez, Ray Serra. (March 31,
1986; 60 min.)

Director: Luis Soto
Producer: Laura Mola
Writer: Jose Rivera
An LFS production
Source: DeSoto Productions

A Flash of Green

The film adaptation of John D.
MacDonald's novel set on Florida's
Gulf Coast in 1961. A liberal small-
town newspaper man, Jimmy Wing,
finds himself in conflict: the woman he
loves is the leader of the local conser-
vationists; and he is fascinated by the
power of a shady politician with close
ties to developers seeking to exploit the
land. *Principal cast:* Blair Brown,
George Coe, Joan Goodfellow, Ed
Harris, Richard Jordan, Bob Murch.
(April 21, 1986; 120 min.)

Director, writer: Victor Nunez
Producer: Richard Jordan
Executive producer: Sam Gowan
A production of A Flash of Green, Ltd.
Source: Virgin Home Entertainment

Damien

An original production, staged as a
dramatic monologue by Father
Damien de Veuster, the Roman Catho-
lic priest who worked with lepers
confined to the Hawaiian island of
Molokai in the late 1800s, and who
himself contracted leprosy. The spirit
of the deceased Damien reminisces
about his childhood, his ministry in
the quarantined leper colony and his

faith in God and humanity. Terence
Knapp stars. (April 28, 1986; 90 min.)

Director, producer: Nino J. Martin
Writer: Aldyth Morris
A production of Hawaii Public
Television

Rocket to the Moon

In Clifford Odets's play set in New
York City in 1938, Ben Stark is a 39-
year-old Manhattan dentist married to
a possessive woman whom no one but
he seems to like. His father-in-law
thinks Ben is in a rut, due in part to
his bossy daughter. He suggests,
among other things, that Ben have an
affair with his secretary—plunging the
young man into doubt as to whether he
is really happy or if he might actually
need a change. *Principal cast:* Connie
Booth, Judy Davis, John Malkovich,
Eli Wallach. (May 5, 1986; 120 min.)

Director: John Jacobs
Producers: John H. Williams, Kirk
D'Amico
Writer: Wesley Moore
Executive producers: Jeremy
Wallington, Janet Walker
A production of the Program Develop-
ment Company
Source: PBS Video, VPI (educational)

Bernadette Peters (center, left) and Mandy Patinkin
(center, right) in Sunday in the Park with George,
Stephen Sondheim and James Lapine's Pulitzer
Prize-winning musical. Photo by Don Perdue.

A Case of Libel

In 1954, at the peak of communist hysteria, the well-known journalist, Quentin Reynolds, sued Westbrook Pegler, a right-wing columnist who had once been his friend, for libel. *A Case of Libel* exposes the soul of a man whose enormous ego and fiery self-assurance became the instruments of his destruction. Adapted from *My Life in Court* by Louis Nizer, the lawyer who represented Reynolds. *Principal cast:* Edward Asner, Lawrence Dane, Robin Gammell, Gordon Pinsent, Daniel J. Travanti. (May 12, 1986; 90 min.)

Director: Eric Till
Producer: John A. Delmage
Writer: Henry Denker
Executive producer: Gladys Rackmil
A Nederlander Television and Film production
Source: D.L. Daffner, Ltd. (educational); Viacom Enterprises (home video)

Painting Churches

In this adaptation of Tina Howe's 1983 Obie Award-winning drama, Mags Church is a successful artist who returns to New England after an absence of many years in order to paint a portrait of her aging parents. This bittersweet portrayal of the inner workings of a loving and talented family is full of warmth and humor. *Principal cast:* Roxanne Hart, Donald Moffat, Sada Thompson. (May 19, 1986; 86 min.)

Director: Jack O'Brien
Producer: Ricki Franklin
Writer: Tina Howe
Executive producers: Phylis Geller, David Loxton
A production of KCET/Los Angeles and WNET/Thirteen

Roanoak

This mini-series is the story of "The Lost Colony," where an entire English settlement disappeared without a trace over 400 years ago. It is told through the perspectives of the English artist John White and the young Indian hunter Wanchese. *Principal cast:* J. Kenneth Campbell, Hallie Foote, Victor Garber, John Horton, Tino Juarez, Patrick Kilpatrick, Joseph Runningfox, Will Sampson, Adrian Sparks. (May 26, and June 2, 9, 1986; 180 min.—3 x 60 min.)

Director: Jan Egleson
Producers: James K. McCarthy, Timothy Marx
Writers: James K. McCarthy, Dina Harris
Executive producer: Lindsay Law
Additional funding: National Endowment for the Humanities
A production of South Carolina ETV and First Contact Films
Source: PBS Video

Sunday in the Park with George

Stephen Sondheim's and James Lapine's musical celebration of the French pointillist painter Georges Seurat, juxtaposes Seurat's creation of his famous painting, *Sunday Afternoon on the Island of La Grande Jatte*, in 1884, with the self-examination of a young contemporary artist. Produced in association with Showtime. *Principal cast:* Mandy Patinkin, Bernadette Peters. (June 16, 1986; 144 min.)

Director: Terry Hughes
Stage director: James Lapine
Producer: Iris Merlis
Writer: James Lapine
Executive producers: Michael Brandman, Emanuel Azenberg
A Brandman production
Source: Lorimar Home Video, Image Entertainment

SEASON SIX, 1987

All My Sons

The television adaptation of Arthur Miller's play follows a crucial day in the life of the Kellers, a family caught in the aftermath of a swindle involving defective aircraft parts which led to the deaths of 21 Army pilots. It becomes clear that the father has escaped a jail conviction for fraud by making his partner the scapegoat. *Principal cast:* Joan Allen, Zeljko Ivanek, Michael Learned, Joanna Miles, Aidan Quinn, Alan Scarfe, James Whitmore. (January 19, 1987; 121 min.)

Director: Jack O'Brien
Producer: Iris Merlis
Writer: Arthur Miller
Executive producer: Michael Brandman
A Brandman production
Source: MCA/Universal (home video)

The Prodigious Hickey

At the prestigious Lawrenceville School circa 1905 adolescent pranks are orchestrated with military precision by boys with nicknames like "Gutter Pup" and "The Triumphant Egghead." The ringleader is William Hicks, alias "The Prodigious Hickey." Hickey concocts a scheme to help his roommate "Hungry Smeed" make a name for himself. Based on the *Lawrenceville Stories*, Owen Johnson's series that appeared in *The Saturday Evening Post* at the turn of the century. *Principal cast:* Stephen Baldwin, Zach Galligan, Josh Hamilton, Edward Herrmann, Robert Joy, Albert Schultz, Tony Van Bridge. (January 26, 1987; 55 min.)

Director: Robert Iscove
Producers: Ronald J. Kahn, Iain Paterson
Writer: Jan Jaffe Kahn
Executive producer: Jane Startz
A Ronald J. Kahn and Scholastic production
Source: Scholastic Productions

Anne Pitoniak (left) and Kate Wilkinson star in Mary Wilkins Freeman's short story, A Mistaken Charity. Photo by Bob Fletcher.

The Wide Net

An adaptation of Eudora Welty's story set in rural Mississippi in the 1930s. Hazel is the prettiest girl in the state, a fact not lost on her new husband, William Wallace. Hazel treats marriage as a game, and one night her husband, in frustration, stays out all night. He returns home to a note saying that Hazel intends to throw herself into the river—and he's not sure if it's another game or a bona fide threat. *Principal cast:* Tim Ransom, Kyra Sedgwick, Josef Somer, Barry Tubb. (February 2, 1987; 55 min.)

Director, writer: Anthony Herrera
Producers: Marcus Viscidi, Rachel McPherson
A production of the Wide Net Company and WGBH/Boston

Smooth Talk

A 15-year-old girl's passage from childhood to womanhood. Out of school for the summer, young Connie Wyatt rejects her mother and sister to seek encounters with boys at the movies and the mall, first accompanied by friends, then on her own. She meets, flees from, then is seduced by a sinister older man, as she seems to age many years in the course of one afternoon. Based on Joyce Carol Oates's short story *Where Are You Going, Where Have You Been? Principal cast:* Laura Dern, Treat Williams, Elizabeth Berridge, Levon Helm, Sarah Inglis, Mary Kay Place, Margaret Welch. (February 9, 1987; 94 min.)

Director: Joyce Chopra
Producer: Martin Rosen
Writer: Tom Cole
Executive producer: Lindsay Law
A Nepenthe production with Palmyra, Ltd.
Source: Facets Video (home video)

A Mistaken Charity

An adaptation of the short story by Mary Wilkins Freeman about two proud elderly sisters, Harriet and Charlotte, whose only ambitions are to remain in their home and have enough to eat. A neighbor, concerned at the deteriorating condition of their house, makes arrangements for the sisters to move to a "home." But Harriet and Charlotte plan an escape. *Principal cast:* Anne Pitoniak, Kate Wilkinson, Mary Louise Wilson. (February 16, 1987; 55 min.)

Director: C.R. Portz
Producer: Bette Craig
Writers: Lawrence DuKore, C.R. Portz
A Realizations production with South Carolina ETV

Dim Sum—A Little Bit of Heart

In *Dim Sum* Geraldine Tam, a graduate student, helps her bachelor uncle maintain his Chinatown bar and lives at home with her widowed mother. Geraldine is torn between her desire for independence and her obligations to her family. *Principal cast:* Kim Chew, Laureen Chew, Ida F.O. Chung, Cora Miao, Victor Wong. (March 2, 1987; 88 min.)

Director: Wayne Wang
Producers: Tom Sternberg, Wayne Wang, Danny Young
Writer: Terrel Seltzer
Executive producer: Vincent Tai
A CIM production
Source: Orion Classics; Pacific Arts Video (home video)

Victor Wong as Uncle Tam in Wayne Wang's film,
Dim Sum: A Little Bit of Heart.

Eleanor

A one-woman tribute to Eleanor
Roosevelt starring Lee Remick.
Adapted from Roosevelt's writings,
radio shows and news conferences, the
film captures her wisdom on such
issues as the fear and distrust of the
Soviet Union, political witch-hunting
and freedom of speech. Originally
staged at the Mark Taper Forum's
"Sundays at the Itchey Foot" literary
cabaret. (March 9, 1987; 56 min.)

Director: Mark Cullingham
Producer: Judith Rutherford James
Executive producer: Julian Fowles
Writer: Russell Vandenbroucke
A production of Taper Media Enter-
prises and KCET/Los Angeles

The Story of a Marriage

Horton Foote's screenplay is based on
stories of his parents' elopement and
the early years of their marriage. The
love between Elizabeth and Horace
Robedaux becomes a force that not
only sustains them but nourishes the
community in which they live. The
mini-series was theatrically released as
two feature films entitled *On
Valentine's Day* and *1918. Principal
cast:* William Converse-Roberts,
Hallie Foote, Matthew Broderick,
Horton Foote, Jr., Michael Higgins,
Steven Hill, Richard Jenkins, Jeanne
McCarthy, Rochelle Oliver. (April 6,
13 and 20, 1987; 8 hours, 20 min.)

*Directors: Howard Cummings, Ken
Harrison*
Producers: Lillian V. Foote, Ross

Milloy, Calvin Skaggs, Marcus Viscidi
Writer: Horton Foote
*Executive producers: Lewis Allen,
Lindsay Law, Ross Milloy, Peter
Newman*
An Austin/1918 Film productions
*Source: Angelika Films; Lorimar Home
Video, CBS/Fox (home video)*

Charley's Aunt

A new version of Brandon Thomas's
1890 comedy classic, one of the biggest
box office hits in theater history. The
play is the story of two Yale students
who invite their sweethearts to tea and
coerce a fellow student into chaperon-
ing them by impersonating their
"aunt" from Brazil. *Principal cast:*
Joyce Bulifant, Anne Francis, Victor
Garber, Vincent Gardenia, Charles
Grodin, Efrem Zimbalist, Jr. (May 11,
1987; 102 min.)

Director: William Asher
*Producers: Dennis D. Hennessey,
Richard Carothers*
Executive producer: Herb Rogers
*A production of Producers' Alliance in
conjunction with La Mirada Civic
Theatre*
*Source: MCA Home Video (home
video)*

Gal Young 'Un

In Florida's back woods during Prohi-
bition, Mattie Siles, a widow of means,
marries a young dandy named Trax.
Trax exploits Mattie's resources,
builds a still on her land and finally
brings home a young girl named Elly,
whom he claims is just a "gal young
'un with no place to go." Based on the
short story by Marjorie Kinnan
Rawlings. *Principal cast:* David Peck,
Dana Preu, J. Smith-Cameron. (May
18, 1987; 105 min.)

*Director, producer, writer: Victor
Nunez*
*A production of the Nunez Film
Company*
*Source: First Run Features; Academy
Entertainment (home video)*

House of Blue Leaves

The Tony Award-winning Broadway production of John Guare's 1970 play about a songwriter and all-round loser named Artie. When the Pope visits New York City, it touches off Artie's latent neuroses, as well as those of his friends and family. Artie and his girlfriend make plans to run away to Hollywood where he hopes to break into the movies. Their plans are complicated by Artie's wife, a deaf movie starlet, a band of marauding nuns, Artie's unbalanced son and a package containing a time bomb. *Principal cast:* Christine Baranski, Julie Hagerty, Swoosie Kurtz, John Mahoney, Richard Portnow, Ben Stiller. (May 25, 1987; 111 min.)

Director: Kirk Browning
Stage director: Jerry Zaks
Producer: Iris Merlis
Writer: John Guare
Executive producers: Michael Brandman, Gregory Mosher, Bernard Gersten
A Brandman production

Blue Window

It's been years since Libby threw a party, and this one isn't exactly a success. As the evening wears on her disparate friends begin to loosen up and learn a little about one another. When a tragic incident from Libby's past comes to light, it becomes clear that for Libby, simply hosting a party is a genuine triumph. *Principal cast:* Matt Craven, Randy Danson, Jane Galloway, Larry Joshua, Brad O'Hare, Maureen Silliman, Margo Skinner. (June 1, 1987; 79 min.)

Director: Norman Rene
Producers: Lindsay Law, Stan Wlodkowski
Writer: Craig Lucas
A Blue Window production

Dottie

Dottie is a widow who lives alone in Manhattan designing and selling greeting cards from her apartment. She suffers from agoraphobia and has not set foot out of her home in more than two years. When she learns that her sister Agnes, whom she hasn't seen in years, is dying, Dottie must journey see her, bringing each sister to an important crossroads in her life. *Principal cast:* Elizabeth Franz, Margaret Gibson, Betty Miller. (June 8, 1987; 79 min.)

Director: David Gelfand
Producers: David Gelfand, Frank Prinzi, Bruce Gelfand
Writer: Bruce Gelfand
A Dottie production

Waiting for the Moon

A dramatization of what Gertrude Stein's day-to-day relationship with Alice B. Toklas might have been like. The play freely maneuvers time, place and character to present a portrait of the writer in her own modernist terms, as Stein learns she is dying, proofreads a novel and stages a play with Toklas, entertains at Rue de Fleurus, learns she is not dying and considers adopting a child. *Principal cast:* Linda Bassett, Jacques Boudet, Linda Hunt, Bernadette Lafont, Andrew McCarthy, Bruce McGill. (June 15, 1987; 86 min.)

Director: Jill Godmilow
Producer: Sandra Schulberg
Writer: Mark Magill
Executive producer: Lindsay Law
A production of New Front Films, AB Films and the Laboratory for Icon and Idiom
Source: Skouras Pictures; CBS/Fox (home video)

Lee Remick as Eleanor Roosevelt in Eleanor: In Her Own Words. *Photo by Mitzi Trumbo.*

SEASON SEVEN, 1988

Strange Interlude

This production of Eugene O'Neill's Pulitzer Prize-winning drama stars Glenda Jackson as Nina Leeds, a manipulative, predatory woman who achieves her own fulfillment by mothering and, if need be, destroying the men in her life. *Principal cast:* Glenda Jackson, Kenneth Branagh, David Dukes, Jose Ferrer, Rosemary Harris, Ken Howard, Edward Petherbridge. (January 18, 19 and 20, 1988; 255 min.—3 x 85 min.)

Director: Herbert Wise
Producer: Philip Barry
Exectuive producer, writer: Robert Enders
A Bowden production with HTV, Ltd.
Source: Fries Entertainment (educational); Fries Home Video

The Return of Hickey

A sequel to season six's *The Prodigious Hickey*. William Hicks makes a triumphant return to the Lawrenceville Academy after having been expelled the previous semester. *Principal cast:* Stephen Baldwin, Zach Galligan, Josh Hamilton, Edward Herrmann, Robert Joy, Nicholas Rowe, Albert Schultz, Tony Van Bridge. (February 3, 1988; 55 min.)

Director: Allan Goldstein
Producers: Ronald J. Kahn, Martin Harbury
Writer: Jan Jaffe Kahn
Executive producers: Jane Startz, Kathryn Wallack
A Ronald J. Kahn and Scholastic production
Source: Ronald J. Kahn Productions, Scholastic Productions

Lemon Sky

The Pulitzer Prize-winning playwright Lanford Wilson traces a young man's responses after he rediscovers the father who abandoned him ten years earlier. The son rejoins his father, meets his father's new family and struggles to find his place in this new setting. *Principal cast:* Tom Atkins, Kevin Bacon, Lindsay Crouse. (February 10, 1988; 120 min.)

Director: Jan Egleson
Producer: Marcus Viscidi
Writer: Lanford Wilson
A Lemon Sky production with WGBH/Boston
Source: Public Television Playhouse

The Revolt of Mother

In 19th-century New England, Adam Penn builds a new barn on the site where 19 years earlier he had promised his bride he would build their home. His wife defies her husband by moving the children and the household into the barn, as the members of this traditional, puritanical farm family manage to communicate their needs to each other. Based on a short story by Mary Wilkins Freeman. *Principal cast:* Benjamin Bernouy, Katherine Hiler, Amy Madigan, Jay O. Sanders, Rob Walker. (February 17, 1988; 47 min.)

Director: Victor Lobl
Producer: Brian Benlifer
Writer: Cynthia Cherbak
Executive producer: Robert Geller
Additional funding: National Endowment for the Humanities
A production of Learning in Focus
Source: Coronet/MTI (educational); Monterey Home Video

Pigeon Feathers

A young farm boy becomes obsessed with his own mortality, causing him to question what he has been taught about God and the soul's eternal life. The boy turns to his father, mother, grandmother and others, seeking an understanding of death, heaven and religious certainty. Based on the short story by John Updike. *Principal cast:* Christopher Collet, Jeffrey DeMunn, Boyd Gaines, Caroline McWilliams, Lenka Peterson. (February 17, 1988; 40 min.)

Director: Sharron Miller
Producer: Brian Benlifer
Writer: Jan Hartman
Executive producer: Robert Geller
Additional funding: National Endowment for the Humanities
A production of Learning in Focus
Source: Coronet/MTI (educational); Monterey Home Video

Billy Galvin

Jack Galvin, a construction worker, although the embodiment of American machismo and blue-collar pride, wants to see his son Billy make a different life. But Billy, unable to express his love for his father, wants to emulate him. The conflict ends in reconciliation at young Galvin's wedding. *Principal cast:* Toni Kalem, Karl Malden, Joyce van Patten, Lenny von Dolen. (February 24, 1988; 100 min.)

Director, writer: John Gray
Producers: Sue Jett, Tony Mark
Executive producers: Stuart Benjamin, Howard L. Baldwin, William Minot, Lindsay Law
A production of the Galvin Company

Eugene O'Neill: Journey Into Genius

Eugene O'Neill's father, James O'Neill, was identified with the role he often played, the Count of Monte Cristo. This type-casting embittered the elder O'Neill, and he proclaimed the theater and his own career a sham. Eugene O'Neill struggled against this bitterness to express himself as a playwright, and his father's powerful presence haunted him throughout his life. *Principal cast:* Dylan Baker, Kate Burton, Chris Cooper, Jeffrey DeMunn, Kaiulani Lee, Matthew Modine, Deidre O'Connell, Kevin O'Morrison. (April 6, 1988; 60 min.)

Director, producer: Calvin Skaggs
Writer: Lanie Robertson
Additional funding: National Endowment for the Humanities
A Lumiere production with Connecticut Public Television

Suspicion

A remake of Alfred Hitchcock's psychological thriller. Lina is a rich, shy American woman who suspects that her debonair English husband is planning to murder her for her money. Her discovery of his scandalous past fuels her fears. *Principal cast:* Anthony Andrews, Jane Curtin, Michael Hordern, Jonathan Lynn. (April 20, 1988; 85 min.)

Director: Andrew Grieve
Producer: Barry Levinson
Writers: Barry Levinson, Jonathan Lynn
Executive producer: Patrick Dromgoole
A Hemisphere production
Source: Movies Unlimited (home video)

Long Day's Journey Into Night

The acclaimed Broadway revival of Eugene O'Neill's autobiographical masterpiece on the Tyrone family and its morass of love-hate relationships. James Tyrone is an embittered actor, his wife Mary is a morphine addict. The elder son Jamie is a dissipated drunkard who tries to prevent the younger son's decline into the same kind of life. Produced in association with Showtime. *Principal cast:* Peter Gallagher, Jack Lemmon, Bethel Leslie, Jodie Lynne McClintock, Kevin Spacey. (May 4, 1988; 169 min.)

Director: Jonathan Miller
Producer: Iris Merlis
Executive producers: Michael Brandman, Emanuel Azenberg
A Brandman production
Source: Facets Video (home video)

The Trial of Bernhard Goetz

On December 22, 1984, Bernhard Goetz shot four youths on the New York City subway after one of them hustled him for five dollars. Goetz claimed he acted in self-defense, becoming a folk hero to some, a paranoid vigilante to others. The film is based entirely on the Goetz trial transcripts. *Principal cast:* Michael P. Boatman, Dennis Boutsikaris, Peter Crombie, Paul D'Amato, Alan Feinstein, Dann Florek, Robert Libertini, Andrew Robinson, Larry B. Scott. (May 11, 1988; 135 min.)

Director, writer: Harry Moses
Producers: Harry Moses, James B. Freydberg, James Bigwood
A production of Litchfield Films
Source: Today Home Entertainment

Land of Little Rain

Mary Austin, a little-known American writer working at the turn of the century, found spiritual and artistic emancipation in her study of the Native American experience, becoming one of the first American writers to document the culture and heritage of the American southwest. *Principal cast:* Barbara Baxley, Helen Hunt, Peter McRobbie, Anne Pitoniak. (June 1, 1988; 59 min.)

Director: Evelyn Purcell
Writer: Doris Baizley
Executive producer: Brockman Seawell
A production of the Denver Center for the Performing Arts, Brockman Seawell and Mayport Productions

I Never Sang for My Father

Robert Anderson's autobiographical portrait follows the evolving relationship between an iron-willed, domineering father and the grown son who desperately wants to love him. The production was nominated for the Golden Globe Award. *Principal cast:* Harold Gould, Dorothy McGuire, Margo Skinner, Daniel J. Travanti. (June 15, 1988; 115 min.)

Director: Jack O'Brien
Producer: Iris Merlis
Writer: Robert Anderson
Executive producers: Michael Brandman, Jay Fuchs, Ricki Franklin, Phylis Geller
A production of Brandman Productions, Duet Productions, KCET/Los Angeles and Columbia Pictures Television

Dear American Playhouse,

On February 1, 1989, the nationally acclaimed play A Raisin In The Sun *aired in my area. I would like to say thank you for airing such an inspiring, exciting, and invigorating play.*

I enjoyed every second. . . and did not want it to come to an end. It brought back many memories of my childhood when I would listen to my elder relatives speak on those same issues. . . . What it meant to me was there is prejudice everywhere, be it racial, religious or otherwise.

A Raisin In The Sun was aired at a good time . . . when a lot of young black people are taking things so much for granted and have begun to forget what others before us had to struggle to achieve.

In closing I would like to again say thank you, and would very much like to see the theater version of A Raisin In The Sun.

P.A.P., Landover, Maryland

Native Son

Bigger Thomas is a poverty-stricken black youth whose "dream job" as the chauffeur for a wealthy white family turns into the instrument of his own destruction. Based on Richard Wright's 1940 novel, the story uncovers black frustrations and racial prejudice during the Great Depression. *Principal cast:* Carroll Baker, Matt Dillon, Victor Love, Elizabeth McGovern, Geraldine Page, Oprah Winfrey. (June 29, 1988; 111 min.)

Director: Jerrold Freedman
Producer: Diane Silver
Writer: Richard Wesley
Executive producer: Lindsay Law
A Diane Silver production
Source: Cinecom International Films; Facets Video (home video)

The Big Knife

Clifford Odets's 1949 play explores the struggle of a famous actor who realizes he irretrievably compromised his personal integrity when he fled the scene of a fatal accident many years earlier and allowed the movie studio he worked for to cover it up. The drama was one of the first incisive looks at the Hollywood movie industry and the greed and manipulation driving it. *Principal cast:* Betsy Brantley, Peter Gallagher, Stubby Kaye, Nehemiah Persoff, Irene Worth. (July 20, 1988; 120 min.)

Director, producer: John Jacobs
Writer: Kenneth Jupp
Executive producer: Johnny Goodman
A production of HTV, Ltd.

SEASON EIGHT, 1989

A Raisin In the Sun

The full-length version of Lorraine Hansberry's drama which opened on Broadway in 1959. The action revolves around a $10,000 life insurance benefit and the conflicting dreams it provokes among the members of a family. Underlying the action are Hansberry's prophetic themes: black identity, beauty, pride and liberation. *Principal cast:* Starletta DuPois, Danny Glover, Kimble Joyner, Joseph C. Phillips, Esther Rolle, Kim Yancey. (February 1, 1989; 161 min.)

Director: Bill Duke
Stage director: Harold Scott
Producer: Chiz Shultz
Executive producer: Robert Nemiroff
A production of Fireside Entertainment Corporation, KCET/Los Angeles, NBLA, WNET/Thirteen
Source: Image Entertainment, Fries Home Video

Ask Me Again

Elizabeth Leopold and Nelson Rodker have been thrown together from earliest childhood by their parents who hope for the perfect romantic alliance. But Elizabeth can't stand Nelson. Based on *An Old-Fashioned Story*, by Laurie Colwin. *Principal cast:* William Bogert, Cynthia Harris, Kathryn Hays, Leslie Hope, D.W. Moffett, Jeffrey Nordling, David O'Brien. (February 8, 1989; 79 min.)

Director: Deborah Reinisch
Producers: Stan Wlodkowski, Deborah Reinisch
Writer: Richard Greenberg
Executive producer: Lindsay Law
A production of DBR Films
Source: Public Television Playhouse

Stacking

In this feature film set in Montana in 1954, a mother and daughter try to come to terms with their dreams and with each other. While the father is hospitalized after an accident, the teenage daughter struggles to maintain the ranch that has been in the family for three generations; meanwhile her mother plans to escape from the ranch

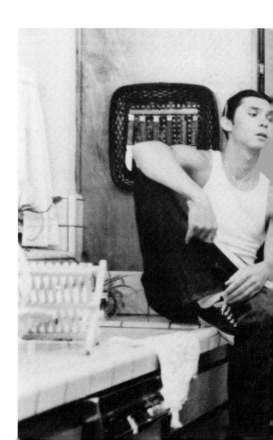

and the small town life that suffocates her. *Principal cast:* Ray Baker, Peter Coyote, Megan Follows, Frederic Forrest, Christine Lahti, Kaiulani Lee, Dan Morgan. (February 15, 1989; 86 min.)

Director, producer: Martin Rosen
Writer: Victoria Jenkins
Executive producer: Lindsay Law
A Nepenthe production
Source: Nelson Home Entertainment (home video)

My American Cousin

The award-winning Canadian film set in British Columbia in the summer of 1959 fixes on a golden moment in the life a 12-year-old Canadian girl, Sandy Wilcox. Her humdrum life is changed forever by a surprise visit from her 18-year-old cousin Butch, who is rebellious, hip and too handsome for his own good. *Principal cast:* Richard Donat, Camille Henderson, Margaret Langrick, Jane Mortifee, John Wildman. (February 22, 1989; 95 min.)

Director, writer: Sandy Wilson
Producer: Peter O'Brian
A production of Independent Pictures,
Borderline Productions and Spectrafilm
Source: Movies Unlimited (home video)

Love and Other Sorrows

In St. Louis in the 1950s, 16-year-old Ben tries to sort out his confusion about the meaning of love, while his widowed mother plots to marry off his beautiful older sister to a wealthy suitor. Adapted from the short story *First Love and Other Sorrows*, by Harold Brodkey. *Principal cast:* Sheila Ball, Christopher Collet, Elizabeth Franz, Spencer Garrett, Stephen Mailer, Haviland Morris, Tim Ransom. (March 1, 1989; 56 min.)

Director: Steven Gomer
Producer: Brian Benlifer
Writer: Dick Goldberg
Executive producer: Robert Geller
Additional funding: National Endowment for the Humanities
A production of Learning in Focus
Source: Coronet/MTI (educational)

Stand and Deliver

Based on the true story of Jaime Escalante, who left his high-paying job at an electronics corporation to teach computer science at Garfield High in East Los Angeles. He found a school ravaged by drugs and gangs, a math department run by shop and gym teachers and an unruly group of barrio kids. Yet Escalante broke through—inspiring and badgering his kids into succeeding at the most difficult of subjects: the calculus. Edward James Olmos was nominated for an Academy Award for his performance. *Principal cast:* Rosana DeSoto, Andy Garcia, Edward James Olmos, Lou Diamond Phillips. (March 15, 1989; 103 min.)

Director: Ramon Menendez
Producer: Tom Musca
Writers: Ramon Menendez, Tom Musca
Executive producer: Lindsay Law
An Eastside production
Source: Warner Brothers; Warner Home Video

The Silence at Bethany

Set in 1939, a time of upheaval throughout the world and among traditional Mennonites, a young man searches for the meaning of his beliefs. Conflicts between the church and the draft board led church members into alternative service and new experiences, bringing about a redefinition of the individual's relationship to the community. *Principal cast:* Tom Dahlgren, Richard Fancy, Dakin Matthews, Mark Moses, Susan Wilder. (March 22, 1989; 85 min.)

Director: Joel Oliansky
Producer: Tom Cherones
Writer: Joyce Keener
Executive producers: Lindsay Law, Joyce Keener
Additional funding: National Endowment for the Humanities
A Keener production

Edward James Olmos as the mathematics teacher Jaime Escalante and Lou Diamond Phillips as Angel in Stand and Deliver.

Dear AMERICAN PLAYHOUSE

My reason for writing to you is twofold. First I want to tell you how much I enjoyed this particular show [A Great Wall]. Although I regularly watch AMERICAN PLAYHOUSE, and think it is one of the best programs on any network or cable, this episode especially touched my heart. It was so well done that I forgot the cast was actors and, instead, felt more like I was watching a real family.

Second, because it may be months before this program is rerun (if at all), I am wondering whether this show is available on videotape. If so, could you please advise me how I might purchase it.

N.A.S., Gig Harbor, Washington

The Beginning of the Firm

The third in a trilogy of comedies about prep-school life at the prestigious Lawrenceville School in New Jersey in the early 1900s, this adventure begins in fall, 1906, with the arrival of an insufferable rich kid named Montague Skinner. The pranksters Hickey and Doc concoct a plan to take him down a peg. *Principal cast:* Stephen Baldwin, Zach Galligan, Josh Hamilton, Edward Herrmann, David Orth, Nicholas Rowe. (April 5, 1989; 56 min.)

Director: Allan A. Goldstein
Producers: Ronald J. Kahn, Martin Harbury
Writer: Jan Jaffe Kahn
Executive producers: Jane Startz, Kathryn Wallack
A Ronald J. Kahn and Scholastic production
Source: Ronald J. Kahn Productions; Scholastic Films Distribution

Life Under Water

The lush beaches of East Hampton, New York, are the setting for this sardonic comedy about a privileged adolescent seeking meaning and love. Kip is a bored and frustrated 20-year-old trying to break his ties to his divorced mother Jinx who is having an affair with a married man. Adapted from Richard Greenberg's one-act play. *Principal cast:* Joanna Gleason, Stephen McHattie, Haviland Morris, Sarah Jessica Parker, Keanu Reeves. (April 12, 1989; 56 min.)

Director, producer: H. Jay Holman
Writer: Richard Greenberg
A Life Under Water production
Source: Public Television Playhouse

A Great Wall

A moving, humorous feature film about a Chinese-born San Francisco computer executive who takes his American-born wife and son to the People's Republic of China to visit relatives he hasn't seen in 30 years. The film was shot on location in English and in Mandarin with English subtitles. *Principal cast:* Shen Guanglan, Sharon Iwai, Li QinQin, Peter Wang, Hu Xiaguang, Wang Xiao, Kelvin Han Yee. (April 19, 1989; 103 min.)

Director, writer: Peter Wang
Producer, writer: Shirley Sun
Executive producers: Wu Yangchian, Zhu Youjun, E.N. Wen
A W&S production
Source: Orion Classics; Pacific Arts Video (home video)

The Diaries of Adam and Eve

An adaptation of two works by Mark Twain: *Extracts of Adam's Diary* and *The First Authentic Mention of Niagara Falls.* This retelling of the first encounter between man and woman is by turns comic and lyrical. It stars Meredith Baxter Birney and David Birney and was taped during a live stage performance in Dallas, Texas. (April 26, 1989; 56 min.)

Director: William Woodman
Stage director, writer: David Birney
Producer: Norris J. Chumley
Executive producers: Meredith Baxter Birney, David Birney
A production of Magnetic Arts and Grail Productions
Source: Public Television Playhouse

The Meeting

This drama postulates a fictional meeting between Malcolm X and Martin Luther King, speculating about what might have happened had the two leaders met and joined forces before their assassinations in the 1960s. Based on the one-act play by Jeff Stetson. *Principal cast:* Paul Benjamin, Jason Bernard, John W. Smith, Michael Thoma, Dick Anthony Williams. (May 3, 1989; 70 min.)

Director: Bill Duke
Producer: Ricki Franklin
Writer: Jeffrey Stetson
Executive producer: Hillard Elkins
A production of KCET/Los Angeles, Hillard Elkins Entertainment, Yagya Productions and Jeffrey Stetson

Sam Waterston (left) as the American negotiator and Robert Prosky as his Soviet counterpart in Lee Blessing's A Walk in the Woods. *Photo by Peter Cunningham.*

A Walk in the Woods

This adaptation of Lee Blessing's stage play was inspired by the meeting between U.S. arms negotiator Paul Nitze and Soviet delegate Yuli Kvitsinsky at the 1982 arms control talks in Geneva. Their exchange marked a new level of shared concern by the superpowers to ease the threat of mutually assured destruction. Produced on Broadway in 1988 by American Playhouse, Lucile Lortel and the Yale Repertory Theater. *Principal cast:* Robert Prosky, Sam Waterston. (May 10, 1989; 105 min.)

Director: Kirk Browning
Stage director: Des McAnuff
Producers: Lindsay Law, Nondas Voll
Writer: Lee Blessing
A production of Public Television Playhouse

Big Time

A portrait of three young professionals and their fast-paced, unfulfilled lives: Fran, a fashion model who yearns to become a serious actress; Michael, a successful investment banker who keeps and supports Fran; and Paul, a commercial photographer who is Michael's friend and Fran's lover. The film takes an inventory of the moral and personal tolls levied on the "yuppie" generation. *Principal cast:* Dennis Boutsikaris, Alexander Chirkov, Paul Guilfoyle, Roxanne Hart, Adrian Pasdar, Mia Sara. (May 17, 1989; 85 min.)

Directors: Jan Egleson, Howard Cummings
Producer: Marcus Viscidi
Writer: Keith Reddin
Executive producers: Lindsay Law, David Stern
A production of Advocate Productions, Lemon Sky Productions and WGBH/Boston

The Thin Blue Line

The 1988 feature film reconstructs the events surrounding the murder of a Dallas police officer in 1976. As a result of evidence uncovered in the film, Randall Dale Adams, the man wrongfully convicted of the crime, was released from prison after 13 years. The film consists of dramatic reconstructions and interviews with the principals in the case: Adams, homicide detectives, defense attorneys, the judge and David Harris, who from his own evidence may be the murderer. Music by Philip Glass. (May 24, 1989; 120 min.)

Director: Errol Morris
Producer: Mark Lipson
Executive producer: Lindsay Law
A Third Floor production
Source: HBO Video (home video)

Ollie Hopnoodle's Haven of Bliss

According to Jean Shepherd, the summer vacation is an American ritual "as important as the Fourth of July, or your first car or prom night." One family's unforgettable summer vacation—and the series of minor disasters that threaten to ruin it—is reported in *Ollie Hopnoodle's Haven of Bliss.* *Principal cast:* Jason Clarke Adams, Dorothy Lyman, Jerry O'Connell, Jean Shepherd, James B. Sikking. (May 31, 1989; 85 min.)

Director: Dick Bartlett
Producer: Olivia Tappan
Writer: Jean Shepherd
Executive producer: Fred Barzyk
A production of WGBH/Boston, Pholly, Inc., and the Disney Channel

Imagining America

Four short films communicate particular views of America. *This Ain't Bebop* by Ralph Bakshi is an homage to the Beat Generation, evoking the spirits of Allen Ginsberg and Jack Kerouac. *Reflections of a Native Son* by Mustapha Khan introduces a 15-year-old South Bronx youth and the multiple voices in his life: his friends (some of them drug dealers), his mother and the older, more experienced men who act as his guardians. *Get Your Kicks on Route 66* by Ed Lachman tells of the famous highway and the people who have traversed it from St. Louis to San Bernardino. *Tribe* by Matt Mahurin is about life, love and death as enacted in the "tribal rites" of Americans—from a Harlem church, to a game show set, to a Golden Gloves boxing match, to a famous music club. (June 7, 1989; 50 min.)

Producer: John H. Williams
A production of Vanguard Films
Source: Public Television Playhouse

Belizaire the Cajun

Belizaire Breaux is a village healer in the Louisiana bayous in the late 1850s. Vigilantes sweep down on the Cajun camp, accusing Belizaire's cousin, Hypolite Leger, of theft and murder. Belizaire uses his wiles to help rescue Hypolite but finds himself caught up in the intrigues of the local sheriff, who is playing each side off against the other. *Principal cast: Armand Assante, Robert Duvall, Stephen McHattie, Will Patton, Loulan Pitre, Michael Shoeffling, Gail Youngs.* (June 14, 1989; 103 min.)

Director, writer: Glen Pitre
Producers: Allan L. Durand,
Glen Pitre
Executive producer: James
B. Levert, Jr.
A production of Cote Blanche
Feature Films
Source: CBS/Fox (home video)

Rachel River

The people of Rachel River, Minnesota, are a hardy and resilient lot, very proud of their Scandinavian roots. They include Mary Graving, who has a weekly radio show; Harriet White, the stoic wife of a farmer; and Marlen, the not-too-bright deputy sheriff. Adapted from three short stories by Carol Bly. *Principal cast: Jon De Vries, Jo Henderson, Zeljko Ivanek, Viveca Lindfors, Craig T. Nelson, Alan North, James Olson, Pamela Reed.* (June 21, 1989; 90 min.)

Director: Sandy Smolan
Producer: Timothy Marx
Writer: Judith Guest
Executive producer: Lindsay Law
A production of Rachel River Films

Armand Assante stars as Belizaire Breaux, a Cajun healer embroiled in a local power struggle, in Belizaire the Cajun.

SEASON NINE, 1990

Sensibility and Sense

This adaptation of Richard Nelson's stage play examines three people initially drawn together by their left-wing politics and their dedication to literature. Fifty years later, they have all become prominent intellectuals. Despite a lifetime of professional association, involvements and jealousies, they find they have never really known one another. *Principal cast:* Tom Aldredge, Trini Alvarado, Jeffrey Demunn, Jean Simmons, Lori Singer, Eric Stoltz, Elaine Stritch, Lili Taylor. (January 24, 1990; 137 min.)

Director: David Jones
Producer: Timothy Marx
Writer: Richard Nelson
A TSM production
Source: Public Television Playhouse

Women and Wallace

In this dark comedy, a boy struggles with his warped attitude toward women, the result of his mother's suicide. After failed attempts at relationships with eight women Wallace learns to stop using humor as a defense that forestalls his potential for happiness. The play is a semi-autobiographical work, written by Jonathan Marc Sherman at age 18. *Principal cast:* Joan Copeland, Shaie Dively, Erica Gimpel, Joanna Going, Josh Hamilton, Mary Joy, Debra Monk, Cynthia Nixon, Jill Tasker. (January 31, 1990; 80 min.)

Director: Don Scardino
Producer: Nondas Voll
Writer: Jonathan Marc Sherman
Executive producer: Lindsay Law
A production of Public Television Playhouse and KCET/Los Angeles

The Wizard of Loneliness

A precociously cynical 12-year-old boy adjusts to his new surroundings in a small town in Vermont during World War II. After the death of his mother and his father's departure for the European front, young Wendall Oler begins to discover himself as he becomes involved in the complexities of the small town his grandparents, aunts and uncles inhabit. *Principal cast:* Dylan Baker, Lance Guest, Lukas Haas, Josh Hamilton, Anne Pitoniak, John Randolph, Lea Thompson. (February 7, 1990; 110 min.)

Director: Jenny Bowen
Producers: Philip Porcella, Thom Tyson
Writer: Nancy Larson
Executive producer: Lindsay Law
A production of Wizard Productions and Virgin Vision
Source: Skouras Pictures; Virgin Home Entertainment (home video)

Richard Thomas, Sada Thompson (center) and Sylvia Sidney (right) in the Emmy Award-winning program, Andre's Mother.

Zora is My Name!

An adaptation of Ruby Dee's play about the novelist and southern folklorist Zora Neale Hurston that draws on Hurston's life and the characters in her stories. Born in Eatonville, Florida, at the turn of the century, Hurston is best known for her portrayals of black life in the rural South in the 1930s and 1940s in such books as *Jonah's Gourd Vine* and *Their Eyes Were Watching God*. *Principal cast:* Oscar Brown, Jr., Olu Dara, Ruby Dee, Louis Gossett, Jr., Leontine Guilliard, Paula Kelly, Otis Sallid, Count Stovall, Lynn Whitfield, Flip Wilson. (February 14, 1990; 90 min.)

Director: Neema Barnette
Producer: Iris Merlis
Writer: Ann Wallace
A production of KCET/Los Angeles and Emmalyn II Production Company
Source: PBS Home Video

In a Shallow Grave

This first work by the novelist James Purdy to be adapted for the screen is set in 1944. Garnet Montrose, grotesquely disfigured by fire at Guadalcanal, has been released from a veterans' hospital and returns to live in isolation on his family's Virginia farm. He hires a drifter who acts as a go-between for Garnet and his pre-war sweetheart. A strange love triangle develops. *Principal cast:* Michael Beach, Michael Biehn, Patrick Dempsey, Maureen Mueller. (February 21, 1990; 115 min.)

Director, writer: Kenneth Bowser
Producers: Kenneth Bowser, Barry Jossen
Executive producers: Marilyn Haft, Lindsay Law
A King Nine production
Source: Skouras Pictures; Warner Home Video

Andre's Mother

Terrence McNally's drama about denial and acceptance is set at a memorial service for a young gay man named Andre who has recently succumbed to AIDS. His mother, Katherine, must deal with the loss of her son and with her denial of Andre's homosexuality. The decisive confrontation comes when Andre's lover Cal insists that Katherine recognize the bond of love and sorrow they both share. *Principal cast:* Sylvia Sidney, Richard Thomas, Sada Thompson, Richard Venture. (March 14, 1990; 48 min.)

Director: Deborah Reinisch
Producers: Sarah Green, Deborah Reinisch
Writer: Terrence McNally
Awards: Emmy Award: Outstanding Writing in a Limited Series or Special
A production of DBR Films

The Wash

Masi Matsumoto, a member of a West Coast Japanese-American community, reluctantly leaves an unhappy 40-year marriage and finds a new lease on life when she meets a loving and caring widower. Yet the ties that bind are not so easily dissolved, and Masi returns once a week to visit her husband when she picks up his laundry. *Principal cast:* Shizuko Hoshi, Mako, Nobu McCarthy, Sab Shimono, Patti Yasutake, Marion Yue. (March 21, 1990; 85 min.)

Director: Michael Toshiyuki Uno
Producer: Calvin Skaggs
Writer: Philip Kan Gotanda
Executive producer: Lindsay Law
A production of the Wash Company
Source: Skouras Pictures

Triple Play

Three films commissioned by Chanticleer Films' Discovery Program for first-time directors. Richard Kletter's *Teach 109,* based on an idea by Isaac Asimov, is about a robot used as a teaching aid in a medical school who becomes romantically attached to a student. *Ray's Male Heterosexual Dance Hall* by Bryan Gordon parodies the social maneuvers of the race to get ahead, as a young man tries to get a job through the connections he makes at a neurotically competitive dance hall. *Homesick* by Johanna Demetrakas concerns an elderly man and his teenage grandson's discovery that he is faking senility to stay at a senior citizens' home where he has a sweetheart and a life of his own. (March 28, 1990; 90 min.)

A production of Chanticleer Films
Source: Fox/Lorber Associates; JCI Video (home video)

Break of Dawn

The true story of Pedro J. Gonzalez, America's first Spanish-language radio and recording star, who was born in Mexico and moved to Los Angeles in the 1920s. After working as a laborer and dockworker, he landed a job at radio station KMPC and went on to become the host of an early morning show. His activism in fighting deportations of Mexican-Americans enraged the authorities, and he was sent to jail on false charges of rape. *Principal cast:* Oscar Chavez, Kamala Lopez, Maria Rojo, Maria Rubell, Peter Henry Schroeder, Pepe Serna. (April 11, 1990; 100 min.)

Director, writer: Isaac Artenstein
Producer: Jude Pauline Eberhard
A production of Cinewest Productions and Break of Dawn Partners
Source: Platform Releasing (home video)

Prisoners of Inertia

A newlywed couple in Manhattan have grown so self-absorbed that the decision to go to brunch consumes an entire morning. Once out of their apartment's cocoon, however, they are lured to Hoboken, and a 24-hour adventure begins. *Principal cast:* Mark Boone Junior, John C. McGinley, Amanda Plummer, Christopher Rich. (April 25, 1990; 85 min.)

Director, writer: Jeffrey Noyes Scher
Producers: Zanne Devine, Deirdre Gainor
Executive producer: Julie Kempner
A production of Northwinds Entertainment
Source: Northwinds Entertainment; Studio Entertainment (home video)

Michelle St. John (left) and Kim Bruisedhead-Fox portray two members of the Blackfoot tribe in Where the Spirit Lives.

Eat a Bowl of Tea

Based on Louis Chu's 1961 novel, the film is set in 1949 after the repeal of the anti-Chinese immigration laws. A young man returns to China after World War II to find a wife and brings her back to their pressure-filled life in New York's Chinatown. Desperately seeking to save the marriage, the wife turns to a Taoist priest who gives her some advice and a special packet of bitter tea. *Principal cast:* Cora Miao, Lau Siu Ming, Eric Tsang Chi Wai, Russell Wong, Victor Wong. (May 2, 1990; 105 min.)

Director: Wayne Wang
Producer: Tom Sternberg
Writer: Judith Rascoe
Executive producer: John K. Chan
A Tea production
Source: Columbia Pictures

All God's Dangers

Theodore Rosengarten's Pulitzer Prize-winning oral history, *All God's Dangers: The Life of Nate Shaw*, is staged as a one-person show starring Cleavon Little. Shaw, a fiercely independent Alabama sharecropper rebels against racial injustice during the Depression. Based on more than 120 hours of taped interviews with an actual sharecropper named Ned Cobb. (May 9, 1990; 85 min.)

Director: Michael Hadley
Stage director: William Partlan
Producers: Jennifer Hadley, Michael Hadley
Writers: Theodore Rosengarten, Jennifer Hadley, Michael Hadley
A Hadley production
Source: Public Television Playhouse

Sidewalk Stories

A critically acclaimed feature film dealing with urban homelessness, rendered as a black-and-white silent comedy in the style of Charles Chaplin. The Artist lives by day among other street artists and performers and by night, in an abandoned tenement. By choosing to make a silent film, the director Charles Lane gives dramatic impact to the voicelessness of the homeless. *Principal cast:* Nicole Alysia, Trula Hoosier, Charles Lane, Darnell Williams, Sandye Wilson. (May 16, 1990; 97 min.)

Director, producer, writer: Charles Lane
Executive producers: Howard M. Brickner, Vicki Lebenbaum
A Rhinoceros production
Source: Palm Pictures

The Bloodhounds of Broadway

This 1920s gangster farce, adapted from four short stories by Damon Runyon, takes place on New Year's Eve, 1928, as Broadway's colorful characters celebrate the coming year in grand style with clandestine crap games, bootleg hooch, femmes fatales and raucous parties in art deco palaces. *Principal cast:* Matt Dillon, Jennifer Grey, Rutger Hauer, Harriet MacKyle, Madonna, Dinah Manoff, Randy Quaid, Josef Sommer. (May 23, 1990; 85 min.)

Director, producer: Howard Brookner
Writers: Howard Brookner, Colman deKay
Executive producer: Lindsay Law
A production of Speakeasy Films
Source: Columbia Pictures (home video)

Where the Spirit Lives

Set in 1937 in the Rocky Mountains, this is the story of a Blackfoot girl named Amelia who is taken from her home and relocated by the government to an English-speaking settlement. With the help of a compassionate school teacher who befriends her, Amelia finds the courage to live in a civilization she finds both foreign and hostile. *Principal cast:* David Hemblen, Heather Hess, Ann-Marie MacDonald, Michelle St. John, Ron White. (June 6, 1990; 96 min.)

Director: Bruce Pittman
Producers: Heather Goldin, Mary Young Leckie
Writer: Keith Ross Leckie
Executive producer: Paul Stephens
An Amazing Spirits production
Source: Atlantis Releasing; Studio Entertainment (home video)

An Enemy of the People

In Arthur Miller's adaptation of Henrik Ibsen's classic play, a small town doctor discovers that the mineral springs that give his village its fame and fortune are poisoned. He attempts to convince the town officials of the danger the springs pose to public health, but he is ostracized and labeled crazy. *Principal cast:* William Anton, Richard Easton, John Glover, George Grizzard, Byron Jennings, Valerie Mahaffey, James Morrison, Nina Siemaszko, Robert Symonds. (June 13, 1990; 96 min.)

Director: Jack O'Brien
Producer: David Griffiths
Executive producer: Samuel J. Paul, III
A production of KCET/Los Angeles

Separation

A two-character play about a British playwright, Joe Green, who suffers from severe neuroses and phobias, and an American actress, Sarah Wise, who has a rare, debilitating neurological disease. When Joe calls from London to give Sarah permission to star in an off-off Broadway production of his play, they begin an ongoing relationship, conducted primarily by telephone, that forces each of them to face up to difficult truths about themselves and each other. Based on the stage play by Tom Kempinski. *Principal cast:* Rosanna Arquette, David Suchet. (June 27, 1990; 80 min.)

Director: Barry Davis
Producers: Mark Forstater, Paddy Higson
Writer: Tom Kempinski
Executive producer: Bill Bryden
A Mark Forstater production, London

Geena Davis stars as a secret agent in
The Hit List.

TRYING TIMES

TRYING TIMES is a collection of original comedies written by contemporary American playwrights on the problems of survival in the age of anxiety. Neither a sitcom nor a collection of sketches, each half hour features a character whose main objective is to survive a personal challenge familiar to us all. The series had its premiere in October, 1987. The Endowment began its support of TRYING TIMES in its second season, fall, 1989.

Executive producer: Phylis Geller
Producer: Jon S. Denny
Additional funders include: Corporation for Public Broadcasting, public television stations
A production of KCET/Los Angeles and Qualli Productions in association with JSD Entertainment and CCC of America
Source: PBS Video

SEASON TWO, 1989

Hunger Chic

Enid and David are a self-absorbed yuppie couple whose hermetically sealed world is suddenly disrupted by the arrival of a very flamboyant household helper, Emma St. John. When Enid accuses Emma of stealing her earrings, Emma seeks revenge—using a touch of magic. *Principal cast: Griffin Dunne, Carrie Fisher, Danitra Vance. (October 12, 1989; 30 min.)*

Director: Buck Henry
Writer: George C. Wolfe

The Hit List

An ordinary suburban man, Bill Grieber, returns home one night to find his wife and children missing and a beautiful stranger named Daphne in their place. Daphne informs Bill that his name has appeared on a computer printout of potential targets of terrorist assassinations and that she has been sent to protect him. *Principal cast: Geena Davis, Peter Riegert. (October 19, 1989; 30 min.)*

Director: Michael Lindsay-Hogg
Writer: A.R. Gurney, Jr.

Death and Taxes

Howard, an orthopedic shoe salesman and part-time saxophone player, decides to confess his unreported income to the IRS. He is referred to a beautiful six-foot-tall Wall Street tax lawyer, Agripina Gravanescu-Smith. Though representing Howard, she falls for an aggressive IRS agent, and Howard flees to South America to avoid his penalties. Sentenced to death for lousy sax playing, he is saved from a firing squad at the very last minute. *Principal cast: Sally Kirkland, John Polito, Peter Scolari. (October 26, 1989; 30 min.)*

Director: Jon S. Denny
Writer: Albert Innaurato

The Sad Professor

Jed, a talented young professor, suddenly finds himself discontented and haunted by recurring dreams of a bride. Convinced she is the love of his life, he is stunned when he discovers her identity: she is one of his colleagues, the chain-smoking, bulldozing misanthrope Hilde Bundt. The two embark on a most unlikely affair, with unexpected results. *Principal cast: Stockard Channing, Linda Purl, Judge Reinhold. (November 2, 1989; 30 min.)*

Director: Christopher Guest
Writer: Richard Greenberg

The Boss

A 63-year-old widow, Edna, finds employment at the neighborhood fast-food franchise, Burger Guy, but her naturally cheerful attitude is soon dampened by her tyrannical 18-year-old boss, Bill. Perplexed by his attitude, she dreams of escaping to Italy. Meanwhile, Burger Guy is slated for demolition to make room for a water slide. At that moment, Edna and Bill discover that they both dream of escaping, and they set out to forge new, more exciting lives. *Principal cast: Corey Feldman, Jean Stapleton. (November 9, 1989; 30 min.)*

Director: Alan Arkin
Writer: Marilyn Suzanne Miller

A Good Life

Buddy gave up cigarettes seven years ago, but has never lost his craving. Reflecting on his life, he considers the possibility of smoking again. His wife is perplexed as to why. Buddy reminisces about how and why he gave up cigarettes and the role smoking played in his life. Will Buddy succumb once again to this deadly addiction? *Principal cast: Robert Klein, Sheila McCarthy. (November 16, 1989; 30 min.)*

Director: Sheldon Larry
Writer: Terence McNally

VISIONS

VISIONS pioneered original American dramas commissioned for public television. The idea for the series emerged in the March, 1973, seminar, American Television Drama, cosponsored by the Theatre Communications Group, the Ford Foundation and the Endowment and held in Tarrytown, New York. There, John Houseman delivered a position paper, *TV Drama in the U.S.A.*, and a call for proposals from the nation's public television stations ensued. In 1974 the New Drama Project, a proposal by KCET/Los Angeles, with Barbara Schultz as executive producer, was funded by the Endowment, the Corporation for Public Broadcasting and the Ford Foundation.

VISIONS was the first major television series funded by the Arts Endowment. Its 32 programs were a proving ground for drama on public television as well as for talented actors, directors and writers. The tone of the series was serious, examining personal problems and social issues with a deliberate pace far removed from the forced urgency of commercial television. VISIONS presented topics such as the choice between career and family, dramas by and about racial and ethnic minorities and dramatizations of little-known events of recent history.

During its lifespan, 1976 to 1980, such themes and the uncensored language that conveyed them with veracity and credibility were unwelcome on some public television stations, and eventually the series was not renewed. Two years later, serious drama reemerged on public television, this time to remain—in the form of AMERICAN PLAYHOUSE.

Executive producer: Barbara Schultz
Additional funders include: Ford Foundation,
Corporation for Public Broadcasting
A production of KCET/Los Angeles

SEASON ONE, 1976 - 1977

Two Brothers

A drama about a physician with a mental illness whose older brother attempts to get help for him. The younger brother self-diagnoses his illness, prescribing himself increasing doses of drugs and finally overdoses. Narrated by his older brother, the film examines the surviving brother's feelings of guilt and helplessness. *Principal cast:* Sarah Cunningham, Stephen Elliott, Judd Hirsch, Zina Jasper, Tom Rosqui, Diane Shalot, David Spielberg. (October 21, 1976; 90 min.)

Director: Burt Brinckerhoff
Writer: Conrad Bromberg

The War Widow

A gentle and lonely young woman whose husband is fighting in France during World War I finds herself increasingly attracted to another woman, a young photographer. *Principal cast:* Katharine Bard, Pamela Bellwood, Frances Lee McCain, Barbara Cason, Nan Martin, Tim Matheson, Stephanie Retsek, Maxine Stuart. (October 28, 1976; 90 min.)

Director: Paul Bogart
Writer: Harvey Perr

El Corrido

A group of farm workers see their lives paralleled in a ballad about a Mexican bracero—from his illegal entry into the United States to his death in the slums of a city barrio. They enact the drama with songs, dance, humor, irony and pathos. Features El Teatro Campesino Company. *Principal cast:* Felix Alvarez, San Juan Bautista, Daniel Valdez, Luis Valdez. (November 4, 1976; 90 min.)

Director: Kirk Browning
Writer: Luis Valdez

The Gold Watch

In the hysteria that follows the Japanese attack on Pearl Harbor, a family of Japanese truck farmers living in the Pacific Northwest are forced off their land and into an internment camp. *Principal cast:* Jesse Dixon, Shizuko Hoshi, Mako. (November 11, 1976; 90 min.)

Director: Lloyd Richards
Writer: Momoko Iko

Liza's Pioneer Diary

Set in 1848, a 20-year-old Kentucky bride crosses the Plains with her young husband and his family in a wagon train. *Principal cast:* Dennis Redfield, Ayn Ruyman. (November 18, 1976; 90 min.)

Director, writer: Nell Cox

The Great Cherub Knitwear Strike

The story of the love between a young girl at her first job as a clerk in a knitwear factory and a young firebrand labor reformer who leads a strike during the Great Depression. *Principal cast:* Adam Arkin, Leon Askin, Kathy Beller. (November 25, 1976; 90 min.)

Director: George Tyne
Writer: Ethel Tyne

Life Among the Lowly

Set around the time of the Civil War, the film concerns a man who is haunted by his past. Once a slave trader, he ends his life a madman in an alms house in Rhode Island. *Principal cast:* Robert Black, Richard Kneeland, Marguerite Lenert. (December 2, 1976; 90 min.)

Director: Adrian Hall
Writers: Adrian Hall, Richard Cumming

Pennsylvania Lynch

A drama about an Hungarian immigrant family living in 1911 in a small Pennsylvania town whose 12-year-old son witnesses the lynching of a black man. *Principal cast:* Tom Atkins, Bo Brundin, Lelia Goldoni, Lenka Peterson, Bill Whitaker. (December 9, 1976; 90 min.)

Directors: Jeff Bleckner, Rich Bennewitz
Writer: David Epstein

Scenes from the Middle Class

Two hour-long plays, one about a black family on the way up the economic ladder, the other about a white family on the way down. *Monkey in the Middle* is about a middle-aged black woman whose marriage to a physician begins to disintegrate when they move into a mansion in "the best part of town." *Principal cast:* Mary Alice, Thalmus Rasulala. *Winter Tour* is the story of a wealthy young girl's rude awakening to the reality that she must depend on her own resources when her father loses his executive position and her mother refuses to face the family crisis. *Principal cast:* Patricia Barry, Jean Rasey, Wayne Tippet. (December 16, 1976; 120 min.)

Director: Rick Bennewitz
Writer, Monkey in the Middle: Betty Patrick
Writer, Winter Tour: David Trainer

Phantom of the Open Hearth

A comedy about growing up in the 1950s in a midwestern steel mill town, seen through the eyes of a teenage boy. Ralph is working in his first job delivering mail at the mill and looking forward to the prom. The smallest events take on a sense of ritual, drama and suspense as Ralph wonders whether he will be smiled on or not by the "phantom of the open hearth," whose glance, according to steel-mill lore, brings either good fortune or bad. *Principal cast:* Barbara Bolton, James Broderick, David Elliott, Roberta Wallach. (December 23, 1976; 90 min.)

Directed and produced by: Fred Barzyk, David Loxton
Writer: Jean Shepherd
A coproduction of the Television Laboratory at WNET/Thirteen and the WGBH New Television Workshop

The Tapestry/Circles

Two works written by Alexis DeVeaux. *The Tapestry* is a play about a serious young black woman who, after years of study, scholarships and hard work, is about to take her final law school exams. She finds her past experience and her present friends pressuring her to give it all up. *Principal cast:* Gloria Jones Schultz, Glynn Turman, Ebony Wright. *Circles* is a story about a young girl who dreams of becoming a dancer and touring in Africa. The strict and bitter grandmother with whom she lives in Harlem constantly tries to instill her own ideas of "common sense" in her grandchild. *Principal cast:* Raymond Allen, Ruth Beckford-Smith, Tamu. (December 30, 1976; 90 min.)

Director: Maya Angelou
Writer: Alexis DeVeaux

The Gardener's Son

Set in the Deep South during Reconstruction, this is a drama of two families—a millworker's and the millowner's—examining the class hatred and animosity between the families. *Principal cast:* Kevin Conway, Brad Dourif, Jerry Hardin. (January 6, 1977; 90 min.)

Director: Richard Pearce
Writer: Cormac McCarthy

Prison Game

A take-off on game shows with an unusual twist. One of the three contestants has murdered her husband—the challenge is to guess which one. Through game-show questions and answers and dramatic flashbacks, the audience explores the lives of three very different women—a young Puerto Rican housewife, a bored suburbanite, and a middle-aged working-class wife—and the events leading up to the murder. *Principal cast:* Peter Bonerz, Edith Diaz, Bo Kaprell, Neva Patterson, Marvin Someon, Jessica Walter, Cara Williams. (January 13, 1977; 90 min.)

Director: Robert Stevens
Writer: Susan Yankowitz

SEASON TWO, 1977 - 1978

Iowa

A young woman living in New York searches for identity and meaning. She visits her family, originally from the Midwest, who now live in California. Her parents react with indifference or hostility to her questioning and her struggle to understand death. Not until she is reunited with her grandmother, living in a nursing home, does she begin to find understanding and peace. *Principal cast:* John-Anthony Bailey, Alma Beltran, Peggy Feury, Carol Fox, Nora Heflin, Bethel Leslie, Warren Stevens, Ellen Travolta. (October 2, 1977; 90 min.)

Director: Rick Bennewitz
Writer: Murray Mednick

Freeman

A young black man, an only son, refuses to give up his dreams and submit to the practicalities of everyday life. The drama studies the relations within the family and the anxiety over his unrealistic hopes in a world of compromised values. *Principal cast:* Chip Fields, Lou Gossett, Pauline Myers, Richard Ward, Dick Anthony Williams (October 9, 1977; 90 min.)

Director: Lloyd Richards
Writer: Phillip Hayes Dean

Alambrista!

The odyssey of a young Mexican who enters the United States illegally to work and make money for his wife and newborn child who remain behind. Pursued by the authorities and subsisting in depressed and debilitating conditions, Roberto Ramirez works as a laborer at various jobs across California's agricultural belt. The death of his father, who spent his adult life as a laborer and alien in the United States, provokes a realization of the futility of this kind of life, and he returns to Mexico. *Principal cast:* Domingo Ambriz, Ned Beatty, Trinidad Silva. (October 16, 1977; 120 min.)

Director, writer: Robert Young
Producer: Irwin Young

Alan Feinstein and Carol Kane in Fans of the Kosko Show.

The Dancing Bear

An actor in Los Angeles finds himself out of work for the first time in many years. Separated from his wife and child and depressed by the stress of the job search, he insists that there is nothing he will not do to get work, until he encounters an arrogant young director whose demands cross his sense of dignity. *Principal cast:* Charles Durning, Tyne Daly, Burt Brinckerhoff. (October 23, 1977; 90 min.)

Director: Burt Brinckerhoff
Writer: Conrad Bromberg

Over/Under/Sideways/Down

A drama about a rebellious assembly-line worker, his marriage and his dreams of leaving his job and becoming a baseball player. *Principal cast:* Sharon Goldman, Robert Viharo. (October 30, 1977; 90 min.)

Directors: Steve Wax, Eugene Corr
Writers: Peter Gessner, Eugene Corr

Pleasantville

The story of an old woman living in a tumble-down house whose grand-daughter comes to stay with her just as she is losing the fight to save the house from being torn down for a new highway. *Principal cast:* Gale Sondergaard, Suzanne Weber. (November 6, 1977; 90 min.)

Directed and written by: Ken Locker, Vicki Polon

You Can Run But You Can't Hide

A troubled Vietnam veteran works out his anger with the help of the friends he makes after joining a street theater group. *Principal cast:* Tom Lagrua, Joseph Stern, Robert Symonds, Deborah White (November 13, 1977; 90 min.)

Director: Rick Bennewitz
Writer: Brother Jonathan Ringkamp

All I Could See from Where I Stood

A drama about a teenage girl desperate to get away from a home life made miserable by an alcoholic mother. *Principal cast:* Richard Gilliland, Season Hubley, Louise Latham, Biff McGuire. (November 20, 1977; 90 min.)

Director: Burt Brinckerhoff
Writer: Elizabeth Clark

Nanook Taxi

An Eskimo man is unable to choose between a primitive life of isolation and the westernized life of the nearest town. The film looks at a people and culture in transition through a modern-day Eskimo hunter in the Canadian northwest who goes to the city to earn extra money as a cab driver. Johanassie Salomonie stars. (November 27, 1977; 90 min.)

Director, writer: Edward Folger
Producer: Jeffrey Hayes

Secret Space

A 12-year-old boy discovers the Jewish religion and begins to study it in earnest—much to the surprise of his liberal atheist parents. *Principal cast:* Virginia Graham, Jon Matthews, Phyllis Newman, Lester Rawlins, Sam Schacht. (December 4, 1977; 90 min.)

Director, writer: Rosalyn Regelson
Producer, writer: Roberta Hodes
Source: Ergo Media

SEASON THREE, 1978 - 1979

Charlie Smith and the Fritter Tree

A dramatized biography of America's oldest citizen, the 135-year-old Charlie Smith. His life, from slave to cowboy to juke joint owner, spans two-thirds of America's history and provides insights into many of the myths and fantasies of American life and folklore. Filmed on location in Texas and New Orleans. *Principal cast:* Glynn Turman, Richard Ward, Mary Alice, Donny Cooper, Richard Dysart, Morgan Freeman, Julius Harris. (October 9, 1978; 90 min.)

Directors: David Loxton, Fred Barzyk
Writer: Charles Johnson
A coproduction of the Television Laboratory at WNET/Thirteen and the WGBH New Television Workshop

Escape

An absurdist play about a linguistics teacher and a student tunneling their way out of a midwestern university campus, an attempt to break out of the reality that confines them. The attempt fails, and as they return to reality, the teacher, who had dominated the action, is upstaged by the student, who takes control. *Principal cast:* Robin Gammell, Marc Singer. (October 16, 1978; 90 min.)

Director: Robert Stevens
Writer: Jonathan Reynolds

Fans of the Kosko Show

While awaiting a showdown with drug-dealing mobsters, Kosko, a charismatic disc jockey, reflects on the remarkable events that have led to his current predicament. *Principal cast:* Eileen Brennan, Alan Feinstein, Carol Kane, Charles Siebert. (October 23, 1978; 90 min.)

Director: John Desmond
Writer: David Epstein

Blessings

A poor Jewish woman decides that her 12-year-old son should have a bar mitzvah. Although she taxes the patience of relatives and rabbis, her tenacity pays off and the ceremony itself affords a glimpse of human potential. *Principal cast:* Bobby Crisman, Marilyn Chris, Leonard Frey, Viola Harris, Lee Wallace. (October 30, 1978; 90 min.)

Director: Arvin Brown
Writer: Murray Mednick

Blackout

A New York surgeon neglects his family life in order to develop his successful career. He learns that his wife has been diagnosed with breast cancer at the same time as a citywide blackout strikes, and he is forced to face up to the troubled relationships he has left in his wake. *Principal cast:* Barbara Barrie, Naomi Foner, Joseph Maher, Kathryn Walker. (November 13, 1978; 90 min.)

Director: Rick Bennewitz
Writer: Naomi Foner

Ladies in Waiting

Fourteen women find relief from their demanding jobs as waitresses in their steady exchange of wit and gossip in the locker room and bathroom, the setting of the play. As the play opens, they speculate about who will get the lucrative station of the senior waitress, who is about to retire. *Principal cast:* Ronee Blakely, Sally Kirkland, Annette O'Toole, Annie Potts, Susan Tyrell, Joyce Van Patten, Elizabeth Wilson. (January 8, 1979; 90 min.)

Directors: Oz Scott, Michael Lindsay-Hogg
Writer: Patricia Resnick

Shoes/String

Shoes is the story of three youths and the value they place on money. As they discuss their plans to buy expensive shoes and clothes, their boss tries to give them advice on planning and saving money. One youth becomes so angry that he pulls a gun on the man. *Principal cast:* John-Anthony Bailey, Bill Cobbs, Corkey Ford, Gary Veney, Bill Walker. In *String*, a man loses his wallet at a community picnic and an older, reclusive man who is considered odd by his neighbors is accused of stealing it after he is seen picking up a piece of string from the ground. *Principal cast:* Stymie Beard, Theodore Wilson. (January 12, 1980; 90 min.)

Director: Oz Scott
Writer, Shoes: Ted Shines
Writer, String: Alice Childress

It's the Willingness

The story of an Appalachian family in eastern Kentucky in 1929 who face the poverty, hunger and frustration of the Great Depression as they gather for a delayed memorial service for the mother who died two years earlier. *Principal cast:* R.G. Armstrong, Monnoe Bartlett, Guy Boyd, Stephanie Faracy, George Harn, Mary Beth Hurt, Christopher Lloyd. (January 19, 1980; 90 min.)

Director: Gordon Davidson
Writer: Marsha Norman

He Wants Her Back

A young architect seesaws between brilliance and failure as he and his wife clash over his utopian ideals and her belief in compromise. The action takes place over the course of their daughter's first ten years. The story is told from the viewpoints of all three family members. *Principal cast:* Susan Anspach, Joe Cortese, Cindy Hiller, Katherine Lardner. (January 26, 1980; 120 min.)

Director: Kaye Braden
Producers: Kaye Braden, Bill Braden
Writer: Stanton Kaye

DRAMA SPECIALS

The Mahabharata: The Great Story of Mankind

The mini-series adapted from Jean-Claude Carriere's dramatization of the Indian Sanskrit epic. The very basis of India's religion, history and thought, *The Mahabharata* has a spiritual import akin to *The Bible*, a literary vitality comparable to *The Iliad* and story-telling impact as captivating as *The Arabian Nights*. Composed over a period of 1,000 years, the epic tells of a protracted struggle between two wings of a royal family. Its many sub-plots are parables, posing essential moral and philosophical questions. *Principal cast:* Miriam Goldschmidt, Corine Jaber, Mireille Maalouf, Helene Patarot, Mallika Sarabhai, Tam-Sir (March 25 - 27, 1991; mini-series: six hours—3 x 120 min.; film version: 150 min.)

Director: Peter Brook
Screenplay: Peter Brook, Jean-Claude Carriere, Marie Helene Estienne
Source: RM Associates

Rockaby

Presented here is the life-cycle of the play *Rockaby* by Samuel Beckett. The film follows the British actress Billie Whitelaw and the American director Alan Schneider from the first reading of the one-person play through the complete premiere performance, recording segments from rehearsals, their exchanges over interpretation, their reactions to this play and their observations on staging Beckett's work in general. The play had its premiere at the State University of New York on the occasion of Beckett's 75th birthday. (May 28, 1984; 60 min.)

Directed and produced by: D.A. Pennebaker, Chris Hegedus
Source: Pennebaker Associates

Chapter 6:

CHILDREN'S DRAMA

WONDERWORKS

Anne Shirley (Megan Follows) and Marilla Cuthbert (Colleen Dewhurst) in Kevin Sullivan's adapation of Anne of Green Gables, *the classic tale by Lucy Maud Montgomery.*

WONDERWORKS

With its premiere in 1984, WONDERWORKS became the first primetime series specifically for pre-teens and their families, as developed by its executive producer, Jay Rayvid. An alternative to typical children's fare—hackneyed sit-coms and cartoon superheroes—WONDERWORKS filled the gap in quality television programming for young people. At once entertaining and educational, productions such as *Booker* and *Anne of Green Gables* have become classics, frequently drawing audiences of 3 and 4 million. WONDERWORKS presents drama, comedy and fantasy, adaptations of classic works of children's literature, dramatizations of history and original television dramas. Many programs dramatize issues that children may experience at close hand—divorce, racial prejudice, adoption, physical handicaps. Productions originating in the United States and around the world represent the best that first-rate directors, producers, actors and writers can create for young audiences.

Senior executive producer: Jay Rayvid
Executive producers: Lee Polk (seasons 1 - 3); Dale Bell (seasons 5 - 6)
Additional funders include: Corporation for Public Broadcasting, public television stations
A production of public television's Children's and Family Consortium, headed by QED Communications, Pittsburgh, and including KCET/Los Angeles; KTCA/St. Paul-Minneapolis; South Carolina ETV and WETA-TV/Washington, D.C.

SEASON ONE, 1984 - 1985

Booker

This award-winning film follows the transition from slavery to freedom through the eyes of the young Booker T. Washington (1856 - 1915) as he struggles to learn to read. No teacher will break the law to teach him before the Civil War, and after the war's end he finds he must work to support his family. His determination convinces his family that he must be given the opportunity to learn. *Principal cast:* James Bond III, LeVar Burton, Shelley Duvall, Marian Mercer, Shavar Ross. (October 1, 1984; 40 min.)

Director: Stan Lathan
Producer: Avon Kirkland
Writers: Charles Johnson, John Allman
Additional funding: National Endowment for the Humanities
A New Images production
Source: Coronet/MTI (educational)

How to Be a Perfect Person in Just Three Days

The ultimate klutz, 12-year-old Milo Crimpley bumps into and breaks most everything in his path. One day he stumbles upon Dr. Silverfish who can teach people "how to be a perfect person in just three days." Silverfish devises some unorthodox exercises for our young hero who follows them to the letter despite his family's criticism and his schoolmates' derision. In the process Milo learns a valuable lesson about perfection. Based on a book by Stephen McManus. *Principal cast:* Hermione Gingold, Ilan Mitchell-Smith, Wallace Shawn. (October 8, 1984; 60 min.)

Director: Joan Micklin-Silver
Producer: Mark R. Gordon
Writer: Bruce Harmon
A production of Highgate Pictures
Source: Public Media Video (home video); Films Inc., Video (educational)

Who Has Seen the Wind?

This two-part adaptation of W.O. Mitchell's novel examines the adult world through the eyes of a ten-year-old child. In rural Saskatchewan during the Depression, Brian encounters bitterness, prejudice and hypocrisy, in contrast to the kindness and quiet dignity of his father, whose death brings the boy face to face with his most difficult crisis. *Principal cast:* Jose Ferrer, Doug Junor, Brian Painchaud, Helen Shaver. (October 15 and 22, 1984; 120 min.—2 x 60 min.)

Director, producer: Allan W. King
Writer: Patricia Watson
A production of Allan King Associates
Source: Janus Films

Boys and Girls

Male and female roles are dramatized in this Academy Award-winning short film set in southern Ontario in the 1940s. When her younger brother becomes old enough to take on the outdoor chores, Margaret's parents make it clear that she must begin to perform "female" duties in the kitchen—a role she rebels against. Based on the short story by Alice Munro. *Principal cast:* Clare Coulter, Megan Follows, David Fox, Ian Heath. (October 22, 1984; 25 min.)

Director: Don McBrearty
Producers: Janice Platt, Seaton McLean, Michael McMillan
Writer: Joe Wiesenfeld
Awards: Academy Award: Outstanding Short Film
A production of the Learning Corporation of America with Atlantis Films, Ltd.
Source: Atlantis Releasing

The Boy Who Loved Trolls

Twelve-year-old Paul keeps the dreams of childhood alive through his search for a troll. One day he discovers the troll Ofoeti under a bridge. In order for it to survive, however, Ofoeti must find a child every 100 years who believes in trolls. The child must choose to stay with the troll forever, never to grow up. When Paul arrives, Ofoeti has less than a day left. Based on the play *Ofoeti* by John Wheatcroft. *Principal cast:* Susan Anton, Matt Dill, Sam Waterston, Max Wright. (October 29, 1984; 60 min.)

Director: Harvey Laidman
Producers: Jay Rayvid, Bob Walsh, Jim DeVinney
Writer: Jim DeVinney
A production of WQED/Pittsburgh
Source: Public Media Video (home video); Films Inc., Video (educational)

Young Arthur (Peter Billingsley) and the 266-pound Henrietta in The Hoboken Chicken Emergency.

The House of Dies Drear

This two-part mystery based on the book by Virginia Hamilton centers on the Walter Small family, who move into an Ohio house that once belonged to the abolitionist Dies Drear, murdered 100 years earlier while helping slaves escape to freedom by means of the underground railroad. Eerie occurrences cause the family to wonder if the house is haunted; they must decide whether to flee or to remain in the house that had meant freedom for their forebears. *Principal cast:* Gloria Foster, Moses Gunn, Howard E. Rollins, Jr., Shavar Ross, Joe Seneca, Clarence Williams, III. (November 5 and 12, 1984; 120 min.—2 x 60 min.)

Director: Allan Goldstein
Producer: Chiz Schultz
Writer: Richard Wesley
A production of the Children's Television Workshop

The Hoboken Chicken Emergency

When young Arthur Bobowicz brings home the "best poultry bargain on earth," a 266-pound chicken named Henrietta, fear and panic break out in Hoboken, New Jersey. The mayor courageously tries to calm his citizens, and fear turns to fondness as a series of chaotic, comical adventures shows everyone that the hefty Henrietta is just a lovable chick. Based on the book by D. Manus Pinkwater. *Principal cast:* Peter Billingsley, Arlene Golonka, Gabe Kaplan, Clive Revill, Dick Van Patten. (November 19, 1984; 60 min.)

Director: Peter Baldwin
Producer: Martin Tahse
Writers: Arthur Alsberg, Don Nelson
A Martin Tahse production
Source: Public Media Video (home video); Films Inc., Video (educational)

Islands

Lacey is a self-centered suburban teenager who feels her parents don't understand her. She has been expelled from school and runs with a gang that has had clashes with the police. When her parents go to Europe for the summer, they leave Lacey with Maureen Davis, a middle-aged friend who lives as a recluse on an island. A deep relationship develops between the girl and the older woman. *Principal cast:* Louise Fletcher, Ingrid Veninger. (November 26, 1984; 60 min.)

Director: Rene Bonniere
Producers: Robert McDonald, Seaton McLean
Writer: Ken August
A production of the Learning Corporation of America with Atlantis, Ltd.
Source: New World Entertainment (home video)

All Summer in a Day

This short story by Ray Bradbury takes place on a planet where the sun has not shone in nine years. Scientists are predicting that the sun will make a rare and brief appearance again. Margot, a girl who once lived on earth, tries to explain sunlight to the other children who have great difficulty imagining it. *Principal cast:* Edith Fields, Reesa Mallen, Jerry Marshak, Bridget Meade, Keith Mitchell, Tammy Simpson. (December 3, 1984; 30 min.)

Director: Ed Kaplan
Producer: Karl Epstein
Writer: S. Murdock Donaldson
A production of the Learning Corporation of America
Source: Coronet/MTI (educational)

Danny's Egg

Australia is the home of the emu, the swift running, flightless bird related to the ostrich. One day young Danny discovers a large black egg and decides to care for it, creating a makeshift incubator, protecting it from school bullies and scavenger snakes. During a special event honoring Danny's parents, a baby emu chick hatches from the egg. Stars Ken Talbot. (December 3, 1984; 30 min.)

Director, writer: David Haythornwaite
Producer: Michael Midlam
A production of PBL Productions, Australia

The Box of Delights

In this three-part story, Kay Harker, a sleepy schoolboy taking the train home for Christmas holidays, encounters Old Cole Hawlings who gives him a mysterious "box of delights" for safekeeping from the villain, Abner Brown. The box's "old" magic and Brown's "new" magic lead Kay into magical adventures: a kidnapping in King Arthur's camp, a Peter Pan-type fantasy and a flight back in time. The award-winning British film is based on the book by John Masefield. *Principal cast:* Devin Stanfield, Robert Stephens, Patrick Troughton. (December 10, 17, 24, 1984; 180 min.—3 x 60 min.)

Director: Rennie Rye
Producer: Paul Stone
Writer: Alan Seymour
A production of the British Broadcasting Corporation and Lella Productions
Source: Lionheart Television International

Hide and Seek

Hacker, a computer whiz-kid, writes a computer program that grows more powerful over several years until it develops a will of its own and takes over a nuclear power plant. Hacker and his friend Jessica are called in to neutralize the rogue program, entangling themselves in a web or intrigue and danger. Based on the book *Adolescence of "1"* by Thomas J. Ryan. *Principal cast:* Bob Martin, Ingrid Veninger. (January 7, 1985; 60 min.)

Director: Rene Bonniere
Producer: Alan Burke
Writer: Barrie Wexler
A production of the Canadian Broadcasting Corporation
Source: CBC Television

And the Children Shall Lead

The arrival of civil rights activists in a sleepy Mississippi town divides a black family. The father, long an advocate of equality for blacks, begins to waver as he sees that the town's whites, his employers, threaten to fire those who question the status quo. As the family's two young daughters come to challenge the Jim Crow separation of races, they find the decision to do so is not an easy one. *Principal cast:* Levar Burton, Danny Glover, Denise Nicholas, Pam Potillo. (January 14, 1985; 60 min.)

Director: Michael Pressman
Producers: Topper Carew, Henry Johnson
Writers: Emma Pullen, Ilunge Adell
A production of the Rainbow Television Workshop
Source: Public Media Video (home video); Films Inc., Video (educational)

Jen's Place

Fourteen-year-old Jen returns from summer camp to find her parents have separated and haven't consulted her about custody. She fights back by hiring a child-advocacy lawyer and finds she must make some hard decisions. *Principal cast:* Megan Follows, Michael Kirby, Diana Le Blanc. (January 21, 1985; 60 min.)

Directed and produced by: Glen Salsman, Rebecca Yates
Writers: John Lazarus, M. Glassbourg
A production of Cineflics Film with the Canadian Broadcasting Corporation
Source: Beacon Films (educational)

Run Rebecca, Run!

A feisty girl is held captive by an illegal immigrant seeking sanctuary in Australia. The relationship between the two moves from hostility to friendship, as the girl ultimately helps the man gain Australian citizenship. *Principal cast:* Simmone Buchanan, Mary Ann Severne, John Stanton. (January 28, 1985; 60 min.)

Director: Peter Maxwell
Producer: Bredon Lunney
Writer: Charles Stamp
A production of Independent Productions, Australia
Source: FilmWorld Entertainment

Bridge to Terabithia

A story of the friendship between two 11-year-olds in a rural farming community. Jesse is a sensitive, quiet farm boy who builds a private world with Leslie, an imaginative, independent tomboy. Based on the book by Katherine Paterson. *Principal cast:* Julie Beaulieu, Julian Coutts, Annette O'Toole. (February 4, 1985; 60 min.)

Director: Eric Till
Producer: Bill Novodor
Writer: Nancy Sackett
A Twenty-Minute production with Kicking Horse Productions, Canada
Source: Public Media Video (home video); Films Inc., Video (educational)

Words by Heart

This two-part program is an adaptation of the award-winning book by Ouida Sebestyen. Young Lena and her family are the only blacks living in a small midwestern community at the turn of the century. The story of their strength, courage and love in the face of prejudice is affecting and inspiring. *Principal cast:* Robert Hooks, Charlotte Rae, Alfre Woodard. (February 11 and 18, 1985; 120 min.—2 x 60 min.)

Director: Bob Thompson
Producer: Martin Tahse
Writer: Frank Dandridge
A Martin Tahse production
Source: Public Media Video (home video); Films Inc., Video (educational)

Clown White

A story about hearing-impaired children, in which a deaf boy closes himself off to everyone until a mime helps bring him out of his world of silence. The music for the story was composed by the guitarist Bruce Cockburn. *Principal cast:* Mark Christopher Dillon, Saul Rubinek, Lorene Yarnell. (February 25, 1985; 60 min.)

Director: Paul Shapiro
Producer: Martin Harbury
Writers: Jeffrey Cohen, Paul Shapiro
A Martin-Paul production, Canada
Source: Coronet/MTI (educational)

Tale of a Tiger

A young model airplane enthusiast stumbles upon a set of authentic plans for a World War I fighter plane. The owner of the plans is a cantankerous old pilot. With the help of three friends, the two build a plane from the plans and realize their dream. *Principal cast:* Caz Lederman, Grant Navin, Gordon Poole. (March 4, 1985; 60 min.)

Director, writer: Rolf de Heer
Producer: James Vernon
A production of The Producers' Circle, Australia

Two Alone

Two short stories are presented. In *Just an Overnight Guest*, an only child's life changes when her parents take in an abandoned child. *Principal cast:* Rosalind Cash, Richard Roundtree. *The Cap* is about a young baseball fan's turbulent relationship with his father. *Principal cast:* Jennifer Dale, Michael Ironside, Roger Michael, Nicholas Podbrey. (March 31, 1985; 60 min.)

Director, writer: Robert Duncan
Producers: Seaton McLean, Michael McMillan, Janice Platt, Andy Thomson
A production of Atlantis Films, National Film Board of Canada, Telefilm and the Global Television Network
Source: National Film Board of Canada

SEASON TWO, 1985 - 1986

Konrad

A two-part comedy/fantasy in which eight-year-old Konrad, an "instant child" created in a factory, is delivered by mistake to Bertie Bartolotti, an eccentric, disorganized, endearing woman. The factory tries to recall Konrad, fearing his environment is unsuitable, but by then the boy has become very attached to his friends and his colorful adopted mother. *Principal cast:* Ned Beatty, Huckleberry Fox, Polly Holliday, Max Wright. (October 7 and 14, 1985; 120 min.—2 x 60 min.)

Director: Nell Cox
Producer: Elliot Friedgen
Writer: Malcolm Marmorstein
A production of Sunn Classics, a division of Taft Entertainment Company

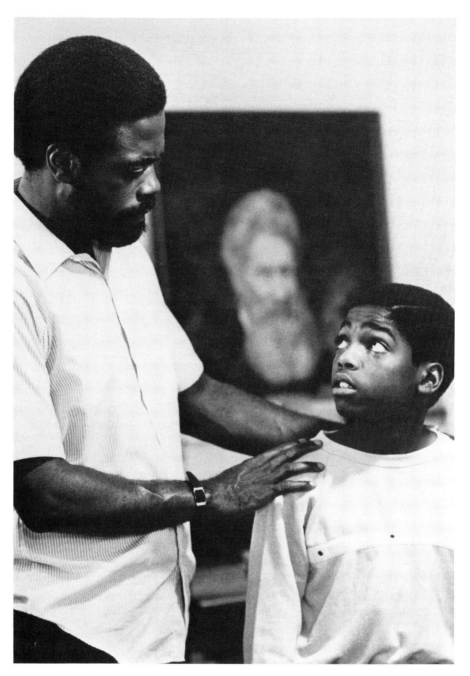

Walter Small (Howard Rollins) reassures his son (Shavar Ross) that their Ohio home is not haunted in The House of Dies Drear.

Happily Ever After

An animated program about Molly Conway, a carefree child with a colorful imagination and a big problem— her parents no longer get along. Molly tries to keep them from separating, but her plans backfire. With the help of friends and her teacher, she comes to realize she can still live "happily ever after." Narrated by Carol Burnett. *Cast voices:* Carrie Fisher, Cassandra Coblentz, Henry Winkler, Rhea Perlman, Danny DeVito, Danny Colby. (October 21, 1985; 60 min.)

Animation: Bill Melendez
Writer: Bill Scott
Producers: Henry Winkler, Roger Birnbaum, Linda Balahoutis, M. Katzenberg
A JZM/Bill Melendez production

The Fire in the Stone

This adaptation of the Australian author Colin Thiele's work centers on Ernie, a teenager who dreams of striking it rich in order to reunite his mother and father, an irresponsible daydreamer. He discovers an opal mine, but before he can claim the stones, they are stolen. Ernie and his friends become impatient with the local law and decide to get the valuables back themselves. *Principal cast:* Alan Cassell, Andrew Gaston, Linda Hartley, Ray Meagher, Theo Pertsindis, Paul Smith. (October 28, 1985; 60 min.)

Director: Gary Conway
Producer: Pamela Vanneck
Writer: Graeme Roetsveid
A production of South Australian Film Corporation
Source: Movies Unlimited (home video)

Seal Morning

A two-part drama based on Rowena Farre's book set on the west coast of England. A young girl, Rowena, comes to live with her aunt Miriam, whom she hardly knows. She has difficulty adjusting, but their discovery and adoption of an orphaned baby seal bring them closer. One day, Rowena meets Dr. Bernard Lacy, a visiting Canadian scientist. He hires Miriam as his research assistant and discovers he has more in common with her than with his fiancee. *Principal cast:* Holly Aird, David Birney, Jack Carr, Jane Lapotaire. (November 4 and 11, 1985; 120 min.—2 x 60 min.)

Director, producer: David Cobham
Writer: Rosemary Anne Sisson
A production of Central Independent Television and Primetime, England

The Canterville Ghost

An adaptation of Oscar Wilde's short story. An American family spends the summer in Canterville Chase, a mansion once inhabited by Sir Simon de Canterville and now haunted by his ghost. The parents and the two sons contrive several traps to snare it. The young daughter befriends the ghost, and through her caring and trust, it finds peace. *Principal cast:* Richard Kiley, Mary Wickes. (November 18, 1985; 60 min.)

Director: William F. Claxton
Producers: Joseph Maurer, Bradley Wigor, Sascha Schneider
Writer: B.W. Sandefur
A Helios production
Source: Public Media Video (home video); Films Inc., Video (educational)

Miracle at Moreaux

In occupied France during World War II, a nun and the group of children she cares for risk their lives to harbor a group of Jewish children escaping from the Nazis. Based on a true story as recounted in the book *Twenty and Ten* by Claire Huchet Bishop. *Principal cast:* Robert Joy, Ken Pogue, Loretta Swit. (December 2, 1985; 60 min.)

Director: Paul Shapiro
Producers: Janice Platt, Seaton McLean, Jim DeVinney, Zilla Clinton
Writers: Paul Shapiro, Geoffrey Cohen
A production of Atlantis Films, Ltd. with WQED/Pittsburgh
Source: Public Media Video (home video); Films Inc., Video (educational)

Buster's World

Young Buster is an aspiring magician and a lively dreamer whose faith and optimism sparkle in the midst of the realities of everyday life. *Principal cast:* Mads Bugge-Anderson, Katarina Stenbeck. (December 16, 1985; 60 min.)

Director: Bille August
Producer: Nina Crone
Writer: Bjarn Reuter
A production of Crone Films and the Danish Film Institute
Source: Crone Films

Maricela

A young Salvadoran girl must find her place in American society when she and her mother come to work for a wealthy family in Malibu, California. Through that search, she reaffirms her own Hispanic identity. *Principal cast:* Carlina Cruz, Irene de Bari, Linda Lavin, Lisa Marie Simmon. (January 13, 1986; 60 min.)

Director: Christine Burrill
Producer: Richard Soto
Writer: Nancy Audley
A production of Richard Soto Productions and KCET/Los Angeles

The Boy Who Never Was

An action-adventure story about a boy, the son of an African ambassador, who, along with his father, is kidnapped. The boy escapes and, in trying to free his father from the terrorists, is caught in a web of international intrigue and mistaken identity. *Principal cast:* Paul Atlantis, Christian Bullock, Gordon Hagen. (January 27, 1985; 60 min.)

Director: Frank Godwin
Produced and written by: H. MacLeod, Robertson Godwin, Frank Godwin
A production of Satori/Monument Films, England
Source: FilmWorld Television

Hockey Night

When 14-year-old Kathy Yarrow moves to the small town of Huntsville, she tries to fit in the best way she knows how, by joining the all-star boys' hockey team. The drama depicts her struggle to be accepted as a girl on the boys' team and, on a more basic level, as a newcomer among established high school groups. *Principal cast:* Megan Follows, Rick Moranis, Ingrid Veninger. (February 3, 1986; 60 min.)

Director: Paul Shapiro
Producer: Martin Harbury
Writers: Paul Shapiro, Jack Blum
A Martin-Paul production, Canada
Source: Family Home Entertainment (home video)

The Lone Star Kid (The Youngest Mayor in the United States)

At age 11, Brian Zimmerman was voted mayor of Crabb, Texas, an unincorporated area near Houston. Shocked and frustrated after seeing a person die in a car accident because no ambulance was available, Brian soon became active in preventing the annexation of the town by Houston. He was voted into office, helped secure additional city services and promoted the development of the town. Based on a true story. *Principal cast:* Charlie Daniels, James Earl Jones, Chad Sheets. (February 10, 1986; 60 min.)

Director: Anson Williams
Producer: Barbara Hiser
Writers: Anson Williams, Barbara Hiser
Executive producers: Anson Williams, Ron Howard, Fred Tatashore
A Major H/ Anson Williams Production with New World Television

Anne of Green Gables

A four-part adaptation of the classic tale by Lucy Maud Montgomery. An orphan girl, Anne Shirley, escapes the sadness of her life through literature, poetry and the imaginary world she creates. An elderly couple, a brother and sister, take her into Green Gables, their home in Nova Scotia. It becomes Anne's home, and the awkward and aloof girl blossoms into a paragon of charm, forthrightness and virtue. *Principal cast:* Colleen Dewhurst, Megan Follows, Richard Farnsworth. (February 17 and 24, March 3 and 10, 1986; 240 min.—4 x 60 min.)

Director: Kevin Sullivan
Producers: Kevin Sullivan, Ian McDougall
Writers: Kevin Sullivan, Joe Wiesenfeld
Emmy Award: Outstanding Children's Program; Peabody Award
A production of Sullivan Films with WONDERWORKS, *the Canadian Broadcasting Corporation, City TV and ZDF/Germany*
Source: Direct Cinema; Buena Vista

On Loan

Lindy is a Vietnamese girl who was adopted by an adoring Australian couple as an infant. Just as she is entering her teens, her Australian parents are contacted by Lindy's natural father who wants to visit and possibly take her with him. *Principal cast:* Quang Chinh Dinh, Marrillac Johnston, TranTuy Phoung. (March 17, 1986; 60 min.)

Director: Geoffrey Bennett
Producers: Patricia Edgar, Jane Scott
Writer: Anne Brooksbank
A production of the Australian Children's Television Foundation, Australian Film Commission, Film Victoria and the New South Wales Film Corporation
Source: Australian Children's Foundation

SEASON THREE, 1986 - 1987

Walking on Air

Danny dreams of being able to fly despite his disability—he is unable to walk. One day, during physical therapy he discovers the exhilarating feeling of weightlessness that swimming brings. Taking his dream one more step, Danny fights friends, family and NASA so that he and other friends with disabilities can become part of the space program. Based on the short story by Ray Bradbury. *Principal cast:* Jordan Marder, Lynn Redgrave. (January 17, 1987; 60 min.)

Director, writer: Ed Kaplan
Producer: Ricki Franklin
A production of KCET/Los Angeles
Source: Public Media Video (home video); Films Inc., Video (educational)

The Wild Pony

After her husband dies in an accident, Mrs. Fellows arranges to marry Frank Chase, who was present at the accident and feels partly responsible for her husband's death. She sees the marriage simply as a means of survival for her and her children, but Chase soon grows to love them. Over her objections, he buys the son a wild pony. As they work together to break the pony, a bond of love grows between them all. Based on the book, *Year of the Black Pony*, by Walt Morey. *Principal cast:* Josh Byrne, Art Hindle, Marilyn Lightstone, Kelsey McLeod. (January 24, 1987; 60 min.)

Director: Kevin Sullivan
Producer: Eda Lishman
Writers: Eda Lishman, Kevin Sullivan
A production of Huntington Films/ Pony Film Productions, Canada

Hector's Bunyip

Hector is the youngest member of a large and unusual foster family. His best friend is an invisible creature, a giant he calls his "bunyip." A misunderstanding prompts the child welfare agency to put Hector in a new home. But before they can act, Hector disappears—apparently kidnapped by his bunyip. *Principal cast:* Scott Bartle, Robert Coleby, Tushka Hose, Barbara Stephens. (January 31, 1987; 60 min.)

Director: Mark Callan
Producers: James Davern, Helen Boyd
Writer: Judith Colquhoun
A production of JNP Films, Ltd.,
Australia
Source: Public Media Video (home
video); Films Inc., Video (educational)

Ride a Northbound Horse

An orphan boy buys a horse to join a cattle drive, but the horse is stolen by a dishonest peddler. The boy joins the cattle drive as the cook, and with the help of friends, outwits the peddler to get his horse back. Based on a book by Richard Wormser *Principal cast:* Andy Devine, Jack Elam, Carroll O'Connor, Michael Shea. (February 7, 1987; 60 min.)

Director: Robert Totten
Producer: Tom Leetch
Writer: Herman Graves
Executive producer: Ron Miller
A Walt Disney production

The Mighty Pawns

A group of inner-city kids forms a chess team with the help of a maverick teacher. Despite the temptations and setbacks of their environment, the team goes on to prove itself. Based on a true story. *Principal cast:* Rosalind Cash, Terence Knox, Alphonso Ribero, Teddy Wilson, Paul Winfield. (February 14, 1987; 60 min.)

Director: Eric Laneuville
Producers: Mary Rawson, Jay

Rayvid, Wayne Morris
Writer: Stewart Bird
A production of WQED/Pittsburgh
Source: Public Media Video (home
video); Films Inc., Video (educational)

A Little Princess

This three-part adaptation of the classic book by Francis Hodgson Burnett is the story of Sara Crewe, a little rich girl forced into a life of poverty when her father dies penniless. Once the prized pupil at her boarding school, Sara is forced to become a servant to the coldhearted school mistress and the classmates who had always been jealous of her. *Principal cast:* Nigel Havers, Amelia Shankley. (February 21, 28 and March 7, 1987; 180 min.—3 x 60 min.)

Director: Carol Wiseman
Producers: Nick Elliott, Colin Shindler
Writer: Jeremy Burnham
A production of London Weekend
Television for WONDERWORKS
Source: Public Media Video (home
video); Films Inc., Video (educational)

The Last War Horse

An Australian family joins forces with a Japanese businessman and his grandson when they discover they are being cheated by an unscrupulous land developer. *Principal cast:* Graham Dow, Olivia Martin, Katsu Masumoto, Richard Singer, Kristin Veriga. (March 14, 1986; 60 min.)

Director: Robert Meillon
Producers: James Davern, Helen Boyd
Writer: Colin Free
A production of JNP Films, Ltd.

The Haunting of Barney Palmer

Barney Palmer fears he has inherited his family's magical powers when he finds himself haunted by the spirit of his great uncle. In fact, his older sister is guarding a shocking secret. Based on a book *The Haunting* by Margaret Mahy. *Principal cast:* Alexis Banas,

Ned Beatty. (March 28, 1987; 60 min.)

Director: Yvonne Mackay
Producer: Dave Gibson
Writer: Margaret Mahy
A production of The Gibson Group,
New Zealand

Top Kid

In 1947, Gary is a ten-year-old boy loved by his teachers but beleaguered by his classmates. He becomes a local celebrity when he appears on a children's quiz show, but is faced with a moral dilemma when he must decide whether to cheat on the show or to give up his newfound fame and fortune. *Principal cast:* Michelle Fawdon, Harold Hopkins, Emil Minty. (April 4, 1987; 60 min.)

Director: Carl Schultz
Producers: Patricia Edgar, Jane Scott
Writer: Bob Ellis
A production of the Australian
Children's Television Foundation
Source: Australian Children's Televi-
sion Foundation

The Revolt of Job

In Hungary during World War II, an elderly, childless Jewish couple illegally adopt a Gentile boy and share with him not only their material possessions, but their spiritual values. The film was nominated for an Academy Award in the Best Foreign Film category. *Principal cast:* Heidi Temessy, Forenc Zenthe, Gabor Feher. (April 11, 1987; 60 min.)

Directors: Imre Gyongyossy, Barna
Kabay
Writers: Imre Gyongyossy, Barna
Kalbay, Katalin Petenyi
Producers: Mafilm Tarsalus Studio,
Starfilm, ZDF/Germany, MTV,
Marcropus Film
A production of Sefel Films, Canada
Source: Sefel Corporation

Daniel and the Towers

A streetwise Hispanic boy forms an unlikely friendship with Simon Rodea, the eccentric Italian immigrant who singlehandedly built Los Angeles's Watts Towers. The story was inspired by actual events. *Principal cast:* Miguel Alamo, Alan Arbus, Michael McKean, Carmen Zapata. (April 18, 1987; 60 min.)

Director: Paul Schneider
Producer: Judith James Rutherford
Writers: Camille Thomasson, Jessica Nelson, Stephen Tolkin
A production of Taper Media Entertainment

Room to Move

Carol, a dedicated track athlete, befriends Angie, a dancer whose punk look makes her the object of ridicule. Through Angie, Carol develops a love of dancing and finds that she must make a choice between continuing her track training or devoting herself to dance. *Principal cast:* Alyssa Cook, Niccole Kidman. (April 25, 1987; 60 min.)

Director, writer: John Duigan
Producers: Patricia Edgar, Julie Overton, Richard Mason
A production of ITC Entertainment with the Australian Children's Television Foundation
Source: Australian Children's Foundation

The Horse Without a Head

A suspenseful comedy of errors about an inept band of robbers whose plans to steal three mailbags filled with money are thwarted by a series of mishaps and several encounters with a group of mischievous children. Based on the book *One Hundred Million Francs* by Paul Berna. *Principal cast:* Jean-Pierre Aumont, Herbert Lom, Leo McKern. (May 2, 1987; 60 min.)

Director: Don Chaffey
Producer: Hugh Atwood
Writer: I.E.B. Clarke
A Walt Disney production
Source: Walt Disney Home Video

Quest Beyond Time

In this science-fiction fantasy, a teenager is propelled into the future to help save a tribe afflicted with a mysterious fatal illness. *Principal cast:* Daniel Cordeaux, Tim Elliott, Rebecca Rigg, Roger Ward. (May 9, 1987; 50 min.)

Director: Stephen Wallace
Producers: Richard Mason, Julia Overton
Writer: Tom Morphett
A production of the Australian Children's Television with the Australian Film Commission and New South Wales Film Commission
Source: Australian Children's Foundation

Almost Partners

A feisty girl forms an unlikely alliance with a world-weary detective to track down the thieves who have stolen her grandmother's urn, which contains her grandfather's ashes. *Principal cast:* Royana Black, Paul Sorvino, Mary Wickes. (May 16, 1987; 60 min.)

Director: Alan Kingsberg
Producer: Gary Weiner
Writers: Gary Weiner, Alan Kingsberg
A production of South Carolina ETV and Kingsberg/Weiner
Source: Public Media Video (home video); Films Inc., Video (educational)

Colour in the Creek

In this two-part presentation set in Depression-era Australia, a boy and his family try their luck at gold prospecting in a small bedraggled settlement. Though life is hard, the boy finds adventure, friendship and unexpected rewards. *Principal cast:* Hugh Clairmont-Simpson, Dennis Miller, Pascale Moray, Judy Morris, Ken Talbot. (May 23 and 30, 1987; 120 min.—2 x 60 min.)

Director: Rob Stewart
Producer: Mike Midlam
Writer: Sonia Borg
A production of PBL Productions and Revcom Television, Australia
Source: Lionheart Television International

December Rose

A two-part presentation in which a chimney sweep stumbles into murder and intrigue when he arrives to clean chimneys in an elegant townhouse in Victorian London. He comes into possession of a mysterious locket, then finds himself pursued by ruthless men who will stop at nothing to get it back. A kindly seaman offers to help—endangering both their lives. *Principal cast:* Judy Cornwell, Tony Haygarth, Patrick Malahdie. (June 6 and 13, 1987; 120 min.—2 x 60 min.)

Director: Renny Rye
Producer: Paul Stone
Writer: Leon Garfield
A production of British TV/Friday Productions and Alpine Pictures, Ltd.

SEASON FOUR, 1987 - 1988

The Fig Tree

An adaptation of a short story by Katherine Anne Porter. Six-year-old Miranda's mother died when she was an infant. The girl has become obsessed with death and is stricken by phobias. She turns to her maternal grandmother, who displays no understanding of her condition. With the passage of time and the attentions of an eccentric great aunt, Miranda comes to resolve her anxieties. *Principal cast:* Olivia Cole, William Converse-Roberts, Karron Graves, Doris Roberts, Teresa Wright. (October 10, 1987; 60 min.)

Director: Calvin Skaggs
Producer: Terry Benes
Writer: Stephanie Keys
Additional funding: National Endowment for the Humanities
A production of KERA/Dallas and Lumiere Productions
Source: Public Media Video (home video); Films Inc., Video (educational)

The Littlest Horse Thieves

In this two-part presentation set in a Yorkshire mining town at the turn of the century, three children hatch a bold scheme to rescue a group of ponies from the slaughterhouse. *Principal cast:* Peter Barkworth, Maurice Colbourne, Alistair Sim, Susan Tebbs. (October 17 and 24, 1987; 120 min.—2 x 60 min.)

Director: Charles Jarrott
Producer: Ron Miller
Writer: Rosemary Anne Sisson
A Walt Disney production

The Paper Boy

In Depression-era Australia, a boy sells newspapers on the street corner after his father loses his job, becoming the sole breadwinner in the family. The boy comes to see his father as ineffective, and after clashing with him, he leaves home to live on the street. *Principal cast:* Tony Llewellyn-Jones, Christopher Schlusser, Linden Wilkenson. (November 7, 1987; 60 min.)

Director: Paul Cox
Producers: Patricia Edgar, Jane Ballantyne
Writer: Bob Ellis
A production of the Australian Children's Television Foundation
Source: Australian Children's Television Foundation

Sam Rodia (Allan Arbus) befriends young Daniel (Miguel Alamo) as they work together to complete the Watts Towers in Daniel and the Towers.

Isaac Littlefeathers

Isaac Littlefeathers, a Native American boy, is abandoned by his mother and taken in by an elderly Jewish man. Through the man's love Isaac learns to overcome prejudice and to accept both his old and new worlds. *Principal cast:* Bryan Fustukian, Lynda Mason Green, Scott Hylands, Lou Jacobi, William Korbut. (November 14, 1987; 60 min.)

Director: Les Rose
Producers: Barry Pearson, William Johnston
Writers: Les Rose, Barry Pearson
Executive producers: Gerald M. Soloway, Ronald Lillie
A production of Lauron International, Canadian Broadcasting Corporation and Pearson-Rose Films
Source: Oasis Pictures

Home at Last

From 1854 to 1929, the Children's Aid Society sent more than 100,000 children on "orphan trains" from the slums of New York City to new homes in the west. Set in the early 1900s, Billy is a street-wise New York City urchin sent to a foster home. Uprooted from his harsh but familiar surroundings, Billy has great difficulty adjusting to life on the farm and to the family of Swedish immigrants that takes him in. *Principal cast:* Adrien Brody, Frank Converse, Caroline Lagerfelt, Sascha Radetsky. (January 9, 1988; 60 min.)

Director, writer: David DeVries
Producer: Chris Brigham
A production of David DeVries Films

Taking Care of Terrific

Enid Crowley, a girl who hates her name and everything else about her boring existence, becomes the full-time babysitter to a sheltered little boy. Spending their days in the park, the two start to enjoy themselves, having some hilarious adventures with a bag lady and an itinerant saxophone player. Based on the book by Lois Lowry. *Principal cast:* Benjamin Barrett, Jackie Burroughs, Melvin Van Peebles, Joanne Vannicola. (January 16, 1988; 60 min.)

Director: Jim Purdy
Producer: Barbara Joy Laffey
Writer: Kenneth Cavender
A production of WETA-TV/Washington, D.C., with Paragon Pictures

Frog

Arlo, a shy yet gifted young science student, discovers that his pet frog Gus is really a 600-year-old prince. Arlo and Gus make a pact: If Arlo can find a girl to kiss Gus and restore his former self, Gus promises to teach Arlo confidence and help him get to know the girl of his dreams. *Principal cast:* Shelley Duvall, Elliot Gould, Scott Grimes, Amy Lynne, Paul Williams. (January 23, 1988; 60 min.)

Director: David Grossman
Producer: Bridget Terry
Writers: David Arata, Mark Herder
A Platypus production

Golden Pennies

A two-part program in which an immigrant family struggles to build a new life in a rugged Australian gold mining community, as a young boy comes to terms with his stepfather. *Principal cast:* Mickaela Abay, Carol Drinkwater, Gerard Kennedy, Bryan Marshall. (January 30 and February 6, 1988; 120 min.—2 x 60 min.)

Director, producer: Oscar Whitbread
Writer: Graeme Farmer
A production of Revcom, Central Television, Australian Broadcasting, with Bayerischer Rundfunk, Societe Radio Canada and Lionheart Television
Source: Lionheart Television International

Anne of Green Gables—The Sequel

In this award-winning, two-part sequel, Anne Shirley has grown into a lovely young woman and is employed at a girl's boarding school where her impetuosness and imagination lead to comical misadventures. She finds she has to match wits with the icy principal and with a class of girls determined to drive her to distraction. Based on the books *Anne of Avonlea, Anne of the Island* and *Anne of the Windy Poplars* by Lucy Maud Montgomery. *Principal cast:* Frank Converse, Jonathan Crombie, Colleen Dewhurst, Megan Follows, Patricia Hamilton, Dame Wendy Hiller. (March 5 and 12, 1988; 240 min.—2 x 120 min.)

Director, producer, writer: Kevin Sullivan
A production of Sullivan Films, Canada
Source: Direct Cinema; Buena Vista

A Waltz Through the Hills

In this two-part drama, a boy resolves to travel to England with his younger sister after the death of their mother in order to keep them from being separated. To get to the boatyards in Perth however, they must make a secret, dangerous journey through the wilds of the Australian outback. Based on the book by G.M. Glaskin. *Principal cast:* Ernie Dingo, Andre Jansen, Tina Kemp, Dan O'Herlihy. (April 23 and 30, 1988; 120 min.—2 x 60 min.)

Director: Frank Arnold
Producers: Paul Barron, Roz Barrystone
Writer: John Goldsmith
A production of Barron Films and Primetime Television
Source: Public Media Video (home video); Films Inc., Video (educational)

Hiroshima Maiden

Following World War II, a group of young Japanese women called the "Hiroshima maidens" were brought to live with American families while undergoing plastic surgery for scarring caused by the atomic bomb. This is the story of one such woman and the impact she has on her American family, particularly the young son. *Principal cast:* Susan Blakely, Stephen Dorff, Richard Masur, Tamlyn Tomita. (May 14, 1988; 60 min.)

Director: Joan Darling
Producer: Jean O'Neill
Writer: Ken Cavander
An Arnold Shapiro production
Source: Public Media Video (home video); Films Inc., Video (educational)

Places Not Our Own

A young girl moves with her family to a remote part of Ontario in 1929. The father continues north in search of work, and the family tries to subsist in the new town where they are made unwelcome because of they are considered "half-breeds." The children struggle to be allowed to attend school, encountering scorn and prejudice once they enter, despite their best efforts. *Principal cast:* Dianne Debassige, Tantoo Martin-Cardinal. (May 21, 1988; 60 min.)

Director: Derek Mazur
Producer: Norma Bailey
Writer: Sandra Birdsell
A production of the National Film Board of Canada
Source: National Film Board of Canada

Gryphon

Young Ricky Guerra is a tough Hispanic boy whose outlook changes when the enchanting Ms. Ferenszi becomes the substitute teacher of his class. His newfound desire to learn and study prompts the scorn of his classmates, who criticize and shun him. Soon, however, they all fall under the spell of Ms. Ferenszi's magic. *Principal cast:* Alexis Cruz, Sully Diaz, Amanda Plummer. (May 28, 1988; 60 min.)

Director: Mark Cullingham
Produced and written by: Carl Haber, Manuel Arce
A production of Max Mambru Films, Ltd.
Source: Public Media Video (home video); Films Inc., Video (educational)

SEASON FIVE, 1988 - 1989

Necessary Parties

A two-part story about a 15-year-old boy whose parents intend to divorce. Chris Mills refuses to accept his parents' decision and sets out to fight it. An eccentric part-time lawyer and mechanic helps Chris plead his right to intervene in the divorce action as a "necessary party." *Principal cast:* Adam Arkin, Alan Arkin, Barbara Dana, Mark Paul Gosselaar, Julie Hagerty, Donald Moffat, Geoff Pierson. (November 5 and 12, 1988; 120 min.—2 x 60 min.)

Director: Gwen Arner
Producer: Otto Salomon
Writer: Barbara Dana
A production of the Corelli Company
Source: Public Media Video (home video); Films Inc., Video (educational)

The Silent One

In New Zealand, a Maori boy who can neither speak nor hear develops a friendship with a giant white tortoise. The village sees the boy as possessed of an evil spirit and the source of misfortune; the tortoise they see as a demon. This superstition pits the boy's parents against the rest of the village, and they try to keep the tortoise and the boy separate in the hope it will save them. *Principal cast:* Pat Evison, George Henare, Rongo Tupatea Kahu, Telo Malase, Anzac Wallace. (November 19, 1988; 60 min.)

Director: Yvonne MacKay
Producer: Dave Gibson
Writer: Ian Mune
Executive producer: David Compton
A production of Gibson Film Productions, New Zealand
Source: VidAmerica, Inc. (home video)

Born to Run

In New South Wales in the early 1900s, young Teddy Boyd saves his family from financial ruin when he turns a foundling colt into a champion harness racehorse. *Principal cast:* Robert Bettles, Tom Farley, Andrew McFarland, Julieanne Newbould, Mary Ward. (November 26, 1988; 60 min.)

Director: Don Chaffey
Producer: Jerome Courtland
Writer: Ed Jurist
A production of Samson Productions, Ltd. and Walt Disney Productions
Source: Buena Vista

Miracle Down Under

In Australia in 1868, an imaginative young boy with a penchant for making up stories mistakes a ne'er-do-well, sometime goldminer for Father Christmas. His faith in Christmas touches his family, neighbors and even Father Christmas. *Principal cast:* Andrew

Dear WONDERWORKS:

Our family has just discovered the fine program WONDERWORKS. *We were delighted with the* Chronicles of Narnia *series and are hoping that the further adventures in that series will also be broadcast. Thank you for adding to the small number of quality TV programs for families.*

Sincerely,

K.R.H., Spokane, Wash.

Dear WONDERWORKS:

I saw your production of Sweet 15 *on Albuquerque's educational channel, KNME, it was a beautiful and sensitive treatment of a very [relevant] topic. I am a bilingual program director in Albuquerque schools and all my students are recent arrivals in the U.S. The program treats themes that are of enormous relevance in their lives. I would like to purchase a copy of the program on videotape so that I may show it in class . . . .*

Sincerely yours,

M.E.L., Albuquerque, N.M.

Ferguson, Bill Kerr, Dee Wallace Stone, Charles Tingwell, John Waters. (December 3, 1988; 120 min.)

Director: George Miller
Producers: Peter Beilby, Robert Le Tet
Writer: Jeff Peck
A production of Entertainment Media and Disney, Australia, for WONDERWORKS
Source: Buena Vista Home Video

The Chronicles of Narnia: The Lion, the Witch and the Wardrobe

Based on C.S. Lewis's classic tales, this three-part story follows the adventures of four children in the fantasy land of Narnia, where the cruel white witch and the great white lion Aslan vie for power over the realm and its magical talking creatures. Nominated for an Emmy Award. *Principal cast:* Sophie Cook, Richard Dempsey, Barbara Kellerman, Jeffrey Perry, Jonathan R. Scott, Sophie Wilcox. (January 14, 21 and 28, 1989; 180 min.—3 x 60 min.)

Director: Marilyn Fox
Producer: Paul Stone
Writer: Alan Seymour
A production of the British Broadcasting Corporation and WONDERWORKS
Source: Public Media Video (home video); Films Inc., Video (educational)

Runaway

The saga of a motherless 13-year-old boy who lives for 121 days in the subway tunnels of New York City and survives against the odds of poverty, fear and despair. Based on the book *Slake's Limbo* by Felice Holman. (February 4, 1989; 60 min.)

Director: Gilbert Moses
Producer: Peggy Zapple
Writer: Lonne Elder, III
Executive producers: William L. Wallace, William Baynes
A production of WQED/Pittsburgh and Pacificon
Source: Public Media Video (home video); Films Inc., Video (educational)

Young Charlie Chaplin

A three-part dramatization of Chaplin's early struggles to overcome a childhood marked by deprivation and want. By creating a world of fantasy, young Charlie develops the resources that sustain him through his unhappy youth to become the world's most beloved actor. The film was nominated for an Emmy Award in 1989. *Principal cast:* Joe Geary, Ian McShane, Twiggy. (February 11, 18 and 25, 1989; 180 min.—3 x 60 min.)

Director: Baz Taylor
Producer: Colin Shindler
Writer: Jeremy Burnham
Executive producer: Alan Horrox
A production of Thames Television, England

Captain Johnno

In an Australian fishing village in the 1950s, a young hearing-impaired boy, misunderstood at home and at school and isolated by the provincial small-mindedness of his town, befriends an Italian immigrant fisherman, who is an outcast because of his poor English. Together the two create a world of their own and transcend language barriers. *Principal cast:* Michele Fawdon, Joe Petruzzi, Rebecca Sykes, Damian Walters, John Waters. (April 8 and 15, 1989; 60 min., 50 min.)

Director: Mario Andreacchio
Producer: Jane Ballantyne
Writer: Rob George
Executive producer: Patricia Edgar
A production of the Australian Children's Television Foundation
Source: Revcom International

Two Daddies?

The animated sequel to *Happily Ever After* from season two continues the story of Molly Conway and her discovery that there is life after divorce. This time Molly must come to terms with the new man in her mother's life. Cast voices: Henry Winkler, Carrie Fisher, Rhea Perlman, Richard Masur, Danny DeVito. (April 22, 1989; 60 min.)

Director: Bill Melendez
Producer: Linda Balahoutis
Writers: Ron Friedman, Malcolm Marmorstein, Linda Balahoutis
Executive producer: Henry Winkler
A Molly production—Bill Melendez Productions, JZM Productions and Linda Balahoutis Productions

Jacob Have I Loved

Louise, a young girl who lives on a tiny island in the Chesapeake Bay, has always felt that her sister was the favored child, so she sets out to find her own special place in this small world. Based on the book by Katherine Paterson. *Principal cast:* Bridget Fonda, John Kellog, Evan Mirand, Jenny Robertson. (April 29, 1989; 60 min.)

Director, writer: Victoria Hochberg
Producer: Richard Heus
Executive producer: Ricki Franklin
A production of KCET/Los Angeles
Source: Public Media Video (home video); Films Inc., Video (educational)

Good Old Boy

Based on the life of the writer and editor Willie Morris, this two-part story tells of a young boy's coming of age in Yazoo, Mississippi, during the summer of 1942. Adapted from Morris's book *Good Ole Boy: A Delta Boyhood. Principal cast:* Richard

Farnsworth, Ryan Francis, Maureen O'Sullivan, Anne Ramsey. (May 6 and 13, 1989; 120 min.—2 x 60 min.)

Director, producer: Tom Robertson
Writer: Paul Cooper
A Multi-Media production

SEASON SIX, 1989 - 1990

Sweet 15

The story of a Mexican-American girl, Marta, who eagerly awaits her *quinceañera*, the Mexican "sweet 15" birthday celebration. Her family requires her to perform volunteer work in the community to prepare for womanhood. While working at the local immigration office, she discovers that her father is an illegal alien, who has hidden the fact. She sets out to gather the paperwork necessary for her father to become a legal alien under the temporary immigration amnesty law. *Principal cast:* Jenny Gago, Karla Montana, Tony Plana,

After saving the magical land of Narnia from the White Witch, Aslan the lion and the four children reign over the kingdom in this adaptation of the C.S. Lewis classic, The Lion, the Witch and the Wardrobe.

Susan Ruttan, Jerry Stiller. (January 13 and 20, 1990; 120 min.—2 x 60 min.)

Director: Victoria Hochberg
Producer: Richard Soto
Writer: Sharon Weil
A Richard Soto production
Source: Public Media Video (home video); Films Inc., Video (educational)

The Chronicles of Narnia: Prince Caspian and The Voyage of the Dawn Treader

A three-part presentation based on books two and three of *The Chronicles of Narnia* by C.S. Lewis. This is the second installment about the adventures of four children in the mythical land of Narnia. *Principal cast:* Sophie Cook, Richard Dempsey, Jean Marc Perrett, Jonathan Scott, David

Thwaite, Samuel West, Sophie Wilcox. (January 27, February 3 and 10, 1990; 180 min.—3 x 60 min.)

Director: Alex Kirby
Producer: Paul Stone
Writer: Alan Seymour
A production of the British Broadcasting Corporation and WONDERWORKS
Source: Public Media Video (home video); Films Inc., Video (educational)

Traitor in My House

In Richmond, Virginia, during the Civil War, a teenage girl finds herself disagreeing with her friends over the question of slavery, which she feels to be wrong. She discovers that the aunt with whom she lives is a spy. Her aunt is arrested, and she alone can help a Union soldier hidden in the house escape. Based on a true story. *Principal cast:* Charles Dutton, Angela Goethals, Mary Kay Place. (March 10, 1990; 60 min.)

Director: Nell Cox
Produced and written by: Rosemary Puglia-Ritvo, Laverne Berry
Executive producer: Ira H. Klugerman
Additional funding: National Endowment for the Humanities
A production of the Educational Film Center

Danny the Champion of the World

Based on the popular book by Roald Dahl in which a boy helps his father rescue a flock of pheasants from the shooting party a mean-spirited and social-climbing land developer is planning to hold. *Principal cast:* Robbie Coltrane, Cyril Cusack, Michael Hordern, Jeremy Irons, Samuel Irons, Lionel Jeffries, Jean Marsh. (March 17, 1990; 90 min.)

Director: Gavin Miller
Producer: Eric Abraham
Writer: John Goldsmith
A production of Portobello for Thames Television. A Disney coproduction with WONDERWORKS

Princess Kate

Fourteen-year-old Kate discovers she was adopted as an infant and despite her adoptive parent's wishes sets out to find her natural mother. Although her expectations of her natural mother prove far from reality. The new relationship she forms helps her to define her identity and find her place in the world. *Principal cast:* Alan Cassel, Justine Clarke, Myra Noblet, Lyndel Rowe. (March 24 and 31, 1990; 120 min.—2 x 60 min.)

Director: George Ogilvie
Producer: Antonia Barnard
Writers: Kristen Williamson, David Williamson
Executive producer: Patricia Edgar
A production of the Australian Children's Television Foundation

Caddie Woodlawn

A young girl comes of age on the Wisconsin prairie in the 1860s. As Caddie approaches womanhood, her mother insists she give up her tomboyish ways and take on the responsibilities of a female member of a pioneer household. But only through her own adventures does Caddie discover and learn to accept what it means to be a young woman. Based on the book by Carol Ryrie Brink. *Principal cast:* Season Hubley, Emily Schulman, James Stephens, Parker Stevenson. (April 21 and 28, 1990; 120 min.—2 x 60 min.)

Director: Giles Walker
Producer: Richard John David
Writers: Joe Wiesenfeld, Richard John David
Executive producers: George McQuilkin, Noel Resnick
A production of Churchill Entertainment. A Disney coproduction with WONDERWORKS
Source: Churchill Films (educational, home video)

African Journey

A three-part presentation in which 16-year-old Luke Novak goes to Africa to spend four months with his father. From the day he arrives, Luke finds himself at odds with Themba Mafosa, a 16-year-old African boy who is his opposite in every way. But their common experiences eventually unite them in a powerful and inspiring friendship. *Principal cast:* Jason Blicker, Alan Jordan, Jeses Mungoshi, Pedzisai Sithole, Eldinah Tshated. (May 5, 12 and 19, 1990; 180 min.—3 x 60 min.)

Director: George Bloomfield
Producers: Paul Stephens, Mark Winemaker
Writers: David Eames, Keith Leckie
A production of the Film Works and Atlantis Films, Ltd.

The Finding

Ten-year-old Alex doesn't celebrate his birthday; he and his family happily celebrate his "finding day," the day he was found as an abandoned infant. But his world is torn apart when he receives a mysterious inheritance that holds a clue to his past. *Principal cast:* James Adler, Moira Listen, Miriam Margolyes, Roger Rees, Alison Steadman. (May 26, 1990; 60 min.)

Director, producer: Carol Wiseman
Executive producer: Alan Horrox
Writer: Stephen Wakelam
A production of Thames Television

Chapter 7:
FOLK ART

Norteño, or Tex-Mex, music is explored in Chulas
Fronteras, *one of the films on the series,*
SOUTHBOUND.

AMERICAN PATCHWORK

SOUTHBOUND

VISIONS OF PARADISE

FOLK ART SPECIALS

AMERICAN PATCHWORK

The artistry of America's masters of folk arts performance rivals that of their acclaimed and regularly televised colleagues in the formal arts. The annual Endowment-supported National Heritage Awards, hosted by Charles Kuralt, bestows recognition on these national treasures. But how to bring them to television? The eminent ethnomusicologist, Alan Lomax, who produced and hosts this series, has spent a lifetime seeking out the masters of folk styles, winning their confidence and eliciting peak performances from them, all the while exploring the relationship between these arts and their society. Lomax continues a tradition of recording America's least-known and most authentic folk artists established by his father, John Lomax, in the early 20th century; between them they have documented more than a century's worth of American voices. AMERICAN PATCHWORK presents the originators of uniquely American genres—blues, Cajun and zydeco, gospel—connecting them in a family tree reaching back to Europe and Africa and ahead to the evolving sounds of popular music.

Executive producer: Alan Lomax
Additional funders include: Corporation for Public Broadcasting, public television stations, Rock Foundation
A production of the Association for Cultural Equity, North Carolina Public Television and the Program Service of the University of North Carolina Public Television

Jazz Parades: Feet Don't Fail Me Now

The great New Orleans jazz composer Jelly Roll Morton was one of the first to point out that jazz first flourished in the brass band parades staged by black organizations on such occasions as wakes and Mardi Gras. In New Orleans to this day jazz is supported by black neighborhood organizations, and it lives on in dance halls, parades and rehearsals. Roaming the back streets of New Orleans, the film uncovers local customs, dance and musical performances and demonstrates a resemblance between them and practices in the French-speaking Caribbean and West Africa. (July 6, 1990; 60 min.)

Director, producer, writer: Alan Lomax

Cajun Country: Don't Drop the Potato

Exploring French-speaking western Louisiana and the roots of America's Cajun folk culture, the film travels from a Mardi Gras celebrated on horseback near Mamou, Louisiana—a reminder that the earliest Cajun settlers established cattle ranches on the swampy plains of Louisiana—to a round-up in the swamps. Film footage taped in France introduces us to distant relations of the Cajuns, and we find that they too are swamp-dwelling, ballad-singing cattlemen whose lifestyle focuses on seafood and "letting the good times roll." (July 13, 1990; 60 min.)

The Land Where Blues Began

"The land where the blues began" is the Mississippi River Delta region. The origin of the blues, America's most original song-form, is shown in its social, cultural and emotional background. Older blues singers recount their experiences as prisoners in chain-gangs, as laborers working on levees and in the fields, or traveling far from home in search of work. Their experiences explain the traditional blues lyrics, and the work chants they recre-

frontier artistic life. The influence of Afro-American culture and urban musical forms on this creative stream culminates in two modern phenomena: balletized square dancing and red-hot country music. (July 27, 1990; 60 min.)

Director: Alan Lomax
Producer: Mike Dibb
A production of the Association for Cultural Equity and Channel Four/ Great Britain

Dreams and Songs of the Noble Old

Creativity after the age of 70 is docu-mented in the lives and performances of several outstanding folk artists. Many traditional communities still venerate the elderly as repositories of the wisdom and artistic skills of their societies. Viewers are introduced to a black female cultural leader from the Sea Islands off the southeastern coast, a mountain fiddler and moonshiner, several Mississippi blues players, Cajun musicians, a Kentucky ballad singer and the Preservation Hall Jazz Band. (August 3, 1990; 60 min.)

Director: Mike Dibb
A production of The Association for Cultural Equity and Channel Four/ Great Britain

Stanley Hicks presents story and dance on Appalachian Journey. Photo by Joe Wilson.

ate evoke the chords and harmonies now familiar in dozens of popular blues variants. Originally broadcast in February, 1980. (July 20, 1990; 60 min.)

Director, writer: Alan Lomax
A production of The Association for Cultural Equity and Mississippi Educational Television with John Bishop and Worth Long

Appalachian Journey

The Appalachian Mountains are a creative heartland that has shaped America's westward moving pioneer culture from a mixture of English, Scottish and Irish origins. The early ballads, the tall tales, the hand-made toys and the banjo and dulcimer tunes we encounter here evoke the typical

SOUTHBOUND

In 11 films SOUTHBOUND presents the musical styles of the South. Directed by independent filmmakers, the films present the breadth of regional styles—sacred and secular-from Appalachian mountain ballads to the music of the Louisiana bayou, the Mississippi Delta and the Texas border. The filmmakers travel to locations across the south—to fairs and festivals, musicians' homes, dance halls and churches—presenting the unique physical and social environments in which each style took root. Hamper McBee, a raconteur, ballad singer and former moonshiner, hosts the series.

Producers: Sol Korine, Blaine Dunlap
Additional funders include: Lyndhurst Foundation, Tennessee Arts Commission
A production of the Tennessee Folklore Society and the Georgia Educational Network

Mouth Music

Demonstrates the distinctive modes that the human voice, the most influential of all musical instruments, takes on in southern folk music and folk culture. These modes span traditional *a cappella* performance styles as well as unique expressive vocal forms that have evolved as part of daily life, work and play: hollerin', jump-rope rhymes, "eephing," nonsense songs, auctioneering, drill sergeant's patter and others. (May 28, 1981; 30 min.)

Producers: Blaine Dunlap, Sol Korine, Charles Wolfe

Gravel Springs Fife and Drum/ Give My Poor Heart Ease

Two films on black folk styles and the blues. *Gravel Springs Fife and Drum* pays a visit to the folk musician Othar Turner, in whose fife and drum music the rhythms and harmonies of West African styles can be identified. *Give My Poor Heart Ease* tells the story of the blues in personal accounts, recollections and performances by B.B. King, Son Thomas, inmates of Mississippi's Parchman Prison, musicians in a Leland juke joint, a barber from Clarksdale and a salesman in a Beale Street clothing store. (June 4, 1981; 30 min.)

Directors: Bill Ferris, Judy Peiser
A production of the Center for Southern Folklore
Source: Center for Southern Folklore

Hamper McBee: Raw Mash

A portrait of a Tennessee ballad singer, storyteller and moonshiner, Hamper McBee. The film follows McBee as he works, socializes, talks about his music and sings some of his favorite ballads, continuing a tradition brought to the United States by colonists from the British Isles centuries ago. (June 11, 1981; 30 min.)

Producers: Blaine Dunlap, Sol Korine

Give the World a Smile

To explore the sounds and the roots of white gospel music, the film takes us to the home of an old-fashioned, church-going farm family in North Carolina, the Schuylers, where we listen to them perform and learn about their life and beliefs. (June 18, 1981; 30 min.)

Director, producer: Gretchen Robinson

Fannie Bell Chapman

Fannie Bell Chapman is a gospel singer and faith healer from the southwest Mississippi town of Centerville in whose music the vital black gospel

A Mississippi gospel singer, family leader and faith healer is portrayed in Fannie Bell Chapman: Gospel Singer.

tradition flourishes. Chapman performs and discusses the importance of the church and gospel music in her life as she goes about her daily work of healing the sick. (June 25, 1981; 30 min.)

Producers: Bill Ferris, Bobby Taylor, Judy Peiser
A production of the Center for Southern Folklore
Source: Center for Southern Folklore

This Cat Can Play Anything

Emmanuel "Manny" Sayles, a master of the jazz banjo, demonstrates his signature plectrum banjo style in an original composition, *Give Me that Old New Orleans Jazz* and on stage at Preservation Hall in Jelly Roll Morton's *Whinin' Boy Blues* and the traditional *St. James Infirmary*. Also appearing is the fiddle player Papa John Creach. (July 2, 1981; 30 min.)

Producers: Andrew Kolker, Eddie Kurtz
Executive producer: Stevenson Palfi

Spend It All

Self-reliance, stubbornness and a zest for living define the Cajun culture of southern Louisiana, the cradle of a unique traditional music style. Seen in performance are the Balfa brothers: Dewey, Rodney, Will and Drew;

Nathan Abshire and Marc Savoy. (July 9, 1981; 30 min.)

Director, producer: Les Blank
Source: Flower Films

Chulas Fronteras

The border region shared by Texas and Mexico has produced a unique ethnic folk style, *norteño*, and many great musicians. The film surveys several outstanding *norteño* musicians of the older and younger generations: Lydia Mendoza, Flaco Jimenez, Los Alegres de Teran, Eugenio Abrego and Rumel Fuentes. (July 16, 1981; 30 min.)

Producers: Les Blank, Chris Strachwitz
Source: Brazos

Gimble's Swing

The film examines the current state of western swing, the popular hybrid of jazz and southern string music introduced by Bob Wills and his Texas Playboys in the 1930s. Featured is the music of Johnny Gimble, with appearances by the guitarist Jim Boyd, the fiddler Cliff Bruner, the electric guitarist Eldon Shamblin, the banjo player Marvin Montgomery, the Texas Playboys and Asleep at the Wheel. (July 23, 1981; 30 min.)

Producer: Ken Harrison

Showdown at the Hoedown

Across the south, fiddlers' conventions attract hundreds of fiddlers and thousands of onlookers. The film pays a visit to the Smithville Fiddlers' Contest to witness the competition between the senior fiddle champ Frazier Moss and Paul Chrisman, a young contender. (July 30, 1981; 30 min.)

Producers: Blaine Dunlap, Sol Korine

VISIONS OF PARADISE

These films portray five contemporary American artists, all of whom are self-taught and who began practicing their art in their later years. Compelled by idiosyncratic visions, they have peopled their homes with sculptures and paintings of characters and landscapes of their youth. Each artist obsessively fulfills his or her desire to materialize the figures of memory and imagination. The series, which has appeared on several local stations, has not been broadcast nationally.

Directed and produced by: Irving Saraf, Allie Light
Additional funders include: L.J. Skaggs Foundation
A PTV production
Source: Light/Saraf Films

Possum Trot: The Life and Work of Calvin Black

Calvin Black, a visionary artist of the Mojave desert, created over 80 wooden, near life-sized dolls, each endowed with its own personality, function and costume. He also built a theater where the dolls "perform." The film shows the figures moving in the desert wind, frozen on stage, coming to life on film on the stage of the Bird Cage Theater, as Black had perhaps imagined. Calvin Black died in 1972, and his wife Ruby in 1980. *Possum Trot*, the name Ruby and Cal gave to their desert home, is the only filmed document of their lives. (30 min.)

Hundred and Two Mature: The Art of Harry Lieberman

Harry Lieberman, at age 102, shares his art, philosophy and love of life as he describes his transformation from a retired businessman into an artist. He relates the original stories of his paint-

ings that depict scenes from 80, 90 or 95 years back, from the Eastern European village where he was raised and from Talmudic lore. A resident of Great Neck, New York, Lieberman began painting at age 80. (30 min.)

Grandma's Bottle Village: The Art of Tressa Prisbrey

Tressa Prisbrey built her first bottle house to hold her collection of 17,000 pencils. This was the beginning of the Bottle Village in Simi Valley, California. The 84-year-old Grandma Tressa is a vivacious tour guide through the brilliant houses of the bottle village, each crammed with scavenged and found objects. The village includes Cleopatra's Bedroom, the Round House, Pencil House, Doll House and the marvelous mosaic of the village sidewalks, each composed of artifacts from the first half of the 20th century. Prisbrey died in 1988. (30 min.)

The Monument of Chief Rolling Mountain Thunder

Chief Rolling Mountain Thunder lives with his young wife and small children in *The Monument*, a concrete and stone house with powerful forms and arches he built and decorated. His overwhelming sculptures, "spirits of

the living," portray Indian heroes, family and friends. The film captures the tragedy of Chief Thunder's life, his painful isolation, the beauty of his work and his creative process. (30 min.)

The Angel that Stands by Me: Minnie Evans's Paintings

Minnie Evans is an 88-year-old black painter from Wilmington, North Carolina, where she has created a world of mythical animals, religious symbols and natural beauty. We see the sources of Evans's art—in particular Airlie Garden, with its magnificent azaleas and swans, where Evans worked as gatekeeper for 27 years and where she did most of her paintings. Scenes from her African Methodist church illuminate her religious fervor and its emergence in her art, and she relates her personal history at a family reunion of six generations. (30 min.)

FOLK ART SPECIALS

Amazing Grace: A Bicentennial Celebration of American Song

A bicentennial project celebrating the American character through song, as it presents itself in the ethnic, national, regional, economic, political and social elements that make up culture in the United States. Over 90 kinds of song are included: a barn dance and sing at a Pennsylvania farm; a prisoners' song in a Knoxville, Tennessee; jail and rock-breaking by a chain gang; music by cowboys; sodbuster songs and folk ballads from Arkansas and Kansas. Also included are songs from an after-hours get-together with Lena Horne; an Allman Brothers Band rock concert; blues from Chicago's streets and bars and Aaron Copland in his studio. (October, 1976; 90 min.)

Director, producer: Allan Miller
A production of the Music Project for Television and WNET/Thirteen
Source: Pyramid Films

The four original Weavers, Lee Hays, Pete Seeger, Fred Hellerman and Ronnie Gilbert, filmed by the director Jim Brown in Wasn't That a Time!

Dry Wood/Hot Pepper

Dry Wood is a film about the Creole musician Alfonse "Bois Sec" Ardoin, his family and their music. A rural Mardi Gras is celebrated by the butchering of the hog, the women's preparation of the feast and the men's party. *Hot Pepper* presents the late Clifton Chenier, zydeco king and blues accordionist, and his Red Hot Louisiana Band performing in the bayous of Louisiana and in country dancehalls. The film also shows the musicians' instruments being made and the farming fields where rhythms were perhaps picked up in the process of planting and harvesting. (Date of release: 1976; 30 min.; 60 min.)

Director: Les Blank
Source: Flower Films

Quilting Women

A tribute to the quilting art and the countless women who practice it, filmed at Little Cowan Creek in Letcher County, Kentucky. Stills of previous generations of women quilting in parlors and on front porches give way to footage of today's women buying yards of material, cutting and piecing the patchwork tops and gathering with friends and relations for the final quilt construction. The film shows an array of beautifully intricate designs stitched in coverlets. Fiddles and dulcimers provide musical accompaniment. (Date of release: 1976; 30 min.)

Director: Elizabeth Barret
Source: Appalshop

Say Amen, Somebody

Visiting church sanctuaries and gospel conventions in St. Louis and Chicago, *Say Amen, Somebody* sets down in word and song the history of modern gospel music of the postwar period. The exuberant sound of urban gospel, with its unique interplay of the soloist's call and choir's response, evoked group participation that rocked theaters during the film's theatrical run in 1983. Those interviewed include Thomas A. Dorsey, the former blues singer who became a gospel song writer, and Willie Mae Ford Smith, a gospel singer for most of

her life. Zella Jackson Price, the Barrett Sisters and the O'Neal Twins also perform. (September 25, 1985; 100 min.)

Director: George T. Nierenberg
Producers: George T. Nierenberg, Karen Nierenberg
Additional funding: National Endowment for the Humanities
Source: Pacific Arts Video

Sourwood Mountain Dulcimers

Among the world's oldest musical instruments, dulcimers have been played in the southern mountains since the time of the earliest white settlers. I.D. Stamper, a master dulcimer maker and player, and John McCutcheon, one of the most talented members of the next generation of dulcimer players, play together, swap tunes and discuss musical traditions and history. (Date of release: 1976; 30 min.)

Director: Gene DuBey
Source: Appalshop

The Weavers: Wasn't That a Time!

The members of the 1950s folk group, the Weavers, get together for a concert in 1981 at Carnegie Hall. Equally compelled by the love of music as by their social conscience, the four Weavers, Ronnie Gilbert, Lee Hays, Fred Hellerman and Pete Seeger, look back on the music that made them popular and got them blacklisted in the 1950s. They discuss the origins of their music in socialist idealism and trade unionism, their hopes that it would somehow make a difference and the place this music holds in the contemporary

American cultural scene. Also appearing in the film are Arlo Guthrie, Don McLean, Holly Near and Peter, Paul and Mary. (March 5, 1983; 80 min.)

Director: Jim Brown
Producers: Jim Brown, Harold Leventhal, George Stoney
Writer: Lee Hays
Source: Devillier and Donegan; United Artists Home Video

We Shall Overcome

We Shall Overcome has evolved from an Afro-American gospel hymn, to a union organizing song, to the Civil Rights movement's theme song, to the definitive protest song known around the world. Its life history exemplifies the folk tradition and its relation to sociopolitical movements. Appearing are Peter, Paul and Mary, Pete Seeger, Joan Baez, the Freedom Singers, the Moving Star Hall Singers, Guy Carawan, Bernard Lafayette, the American Baptist College Choir, Jamila Jones, Dorothy Cotton, Miles Horton, Andrew Young, Bernice Johnson Reagon, Julian Bond, Bishop Desmond Tutu. First broadcast on the 25th anniversary of the 1963 March on Washington. Narrated by Harry Belafonte. (August 27, 1988; 90 min.)

Director: Jim Brown
Producers: Jim Brown, Ginger Brown, George Stoney, Harold Leventhal
Awards: Emmy Award
Source: Resolution, Inc./California Newsreel

Chapter 8:

AMERICAN ARTISTS

*Ansel Adams and Georgia O'Keeffe in a scene from
Ansel Adams Photographer.* Photo by John Huszar.

AMERICAN MASTERS

DOCUMENTARY SPECIALS

AMERICAN MASTERS

When Sacha Guitry filmed Renoir and Degas in 1915, the moving image enhanced our acquaintance with their persons. In this tradition, AMERICAN MASTERS has recorded the most gifted exemplars of our arts through documentary portraits by fellow (media) artists. The film or video portrait involves complex relationships between the subject's most intimate possession—his or her own image and substance—and the filmmaker who represents that self to wider audiences. The myths and misinterpretations visited on every major figure presents the film/video biographer with problems of discrimination, tact and understanding. As produced by Susan Lacy, the 46 portraits by 39 media artists made over four years are "subject-friendly." They do not debunk or criticize through ironic commentary. The results, always interesting, vary in their interpretive depth, and the iconic title of "master" is sometimes loosely applied. Mastery is a social agreement which correlates with age and wide acceptance, and most of these portraits are of artists crowned, as it were, by their careers. But an attempt has been made to record artists at mid-career when their ideas are evolving and their struggles with their work and for an audience are sharper. The audience for each of these programs averaged 2.6 million in 1990.

The value of these film biographies increases each year. The series will provide the future with a window through which our great artists can be seen and heard. Despite the prevalence of critical devices devoted to separating the artist from the art, the basic curiosity about the artist, which can be grotesquely distorted by celebrity, always remains. In these portraits, it is handled with respect and insight.

Executive producer: Susan Lacy
Senior producer: Harlene Freezer
Producer: Diane Dufault
Additional funders include: Public television stations, Corporation for Public Broadcasting, Marilyn M. Simpson Charitable Trust, Rosalind P. Walter, Marjorie Carr Adams Charitable Trust, Giorgio Armani (seasons 4 and 5)

SEASON ONE, 1986

Private Conversations: On the Set of Death of a Salesman

A record of the artistic collaboration that took place in mounting Arthur Miller's *Death of a Salesman*. The film shows the interaction between the playwright, Arthur Miller; the director, Volker Schloendorff, and the cast—Dustin Hoffman as Willy Loman, Kate Reid as Linda Loman and John Malkovich as Biff Loman—and sheds light on the crafts of writing, acting, theater and filmmaking. (June 23, 1986; 90 min.)

Director, producer: Christian Blackwood
Source: Castle Hill Productions; Karl/Lorimar Home Video (home video)

Philip Johnson: A Self-Portrait

An extended interview with the architect Philip Johnson by the writer and art critic Rosamond Bernier. Johnson, 80 years old at the time of the film, won some of his most substantial commissions late in his career, including those for New York City's AT&T Building, Transco Tower and Times Square renovation project and Houston's Republic Bank. (June 30, 1986; 60 min.)

Billie Holiday listens to playbacks in the recording studio, New York City, 1959. Photo © 1959. by Milt Hinton.

Director: John Musilli
Producer: Stephan Chodorov
Writer: Rosamond Bernier
A Camera Three production with the ASDA Foundation and AMERICAN MASTERS
Source: Camera Three Productions

Katherine Anne Porter: The Eye of Memory

This film portrait of the author of *Ship of Fools* and *Noon Wine* illuminates the writer and her work through interviews with Eudora Welty, Robert

Penn Warren, Paul Porter and Joan Givner and with dramatizations of three of her short stories set in central Texas, *The Grave*, *The Witness* and *The Circus*. (July 7, 1986; 60 min.)

Director: Ken Harrison
Producer: Calvin Skaggs
Additional funding: National Endowment for the Humanities
A production of KERA/Dallas-Fort Worth, Lumiere Productions and AMERICAN MASTERS
Source: KERA/Dallas-Fort Worth

Unknown Chaplin

A three-part portrait of Charlie Chaplin, the master of screen comedy, using outtakes from Chaplin's films to show the creative thinking that shaped his work. *My Happiest Years*, covers the early period Chaplin spent with the Mutual Film Company. *The Great Director*, documents Chaplin's early efforts as an independent filmmaker. *Hidden Treasures*, features the movies Chaplin made for fun. Scenes from films that were later abandoned and sequences cut from such masterpieces as *City Lights* and *Modern Times* are shown. James Mason narrates. (July 14, 21 and 28, 1986; 180 min.—3 x 60 min.)

Directors: Kevin Brownlow, David Gill
Awards: Emmy Award: Outstanding Informational Series; Peabody Award; Special Peabody Award
Produced in association with Thames Television
Source: HBO Video, Image Entertainment (home video)

Billie Holiday: The Long Night of Lady Day

The joy and pain of Billie Holiday's troubled life and career, featuring renditions of such seminal songs as *Don't Explain, Foolin' Myself, Fine and Mellow* and the powerful musical story of a lynching, *Strange Fruit*. Footage from the mid-1930s to the late 1950s illustrates Holiday's career. Interviews with: Artie Shaw, Leonard Feather, John Hammond and Milt Gabler. (August 4, 1986; 90 min.)

Director: John Jeremy
Producer: Alan Yentob
Contact: Angus Trowbridge, TCB Releasing, Ltd. (rights holder)

James Levine: The Life in Music

The film communicates the extraordinary command of technical skills and of varied musical styles possessed by James Levine, the artistic director of the Metropolitan Opera. Footage showing Levine rehearsing and conducting, serving as piano accompanist at recitals and in performance at the Salzburg and Bayreuth Festivals. Interviews with: Placido Domingo, Jean-Pierre Ponelle, Leonie Rysanek and Lynn Harrell. Joanne Woodward hosts the film. (August 11, 1986; 60 min.)

Director, producer: Peter Weinberg
Executive producer: Susan Lacy
A production of Unitel and AMERICAN MASTERS
Source: ITTC

Aaron Copland: A Self-Portrait

A television autobiography tracing the life of one of America's most influential composers and an indefatigable champion of American music. First aired in October, 1985 in honor of Copland's 85th birthday, it features a wealth of Copland's music, plus interviews with Leonard Bernstein, Ned Rorem, Michael Tilson Thomas and Agnes de Mille. (August 18, 1986; 60 min.)

Director: Allan Miller
Producer: Ruth Leon
Writer: Vivian Perlis
Executive producer: Susan Lacy
Source: Producer Services Group (educational)

Thomas Eakins: A Motion Portrait

The great painter's period is recreated through documentary footage and through dramatizations of key events in his life, as Kevin Conway plays Eakins. The program features rare archival interviews with two women who posed for the artist at the turn of the century. Eakins paintings and his pioneering motion studies are examined. Sam Waterston narrates the film. (August 25, 1986; 60 min.)

Director: Theodor Timreck
Producer: Richard Kilberg
Executive producer: Susan Lacy
A production of Spofford Films, ASDA

William Wyler directing Bette Davis, from Directed by William Wyler.

Foundation and AMERICAN MASTERS
Source: Metropolitan Museum of Art; HomeVision (home video)

Georgia O'Keeffe

Based on interviews in her New Mexico home, the film provides a rare glimpse of the painter's life. O'Keeffe discusses her art and the New Mexico landscape that inspired her; photographs by Ansel Adams, Alfred Steiglitz and Edward Steichen illustrate her career and personal history. The award-winning documentary was first broadcast on the artist's 90th birthday in 1977. (September 1, 1986; 60 min.)

Director, producer: Perry Miller Adato
Source: Films, Inc.; HomeVision (home video)

Eugene O'Neill: A Glory of Ghosts

This two-part film traces the life and work of the playwright, exploring the themes that engaged him throughout his career. A cast that includes Zoe Caldwell, Blythe Danner, Tony LoBianco and Jason Robards portrays the people who influenced O'Neill's life and enacts scenes from eight of the plays, including *The Iceman Cometh, Long Day's Journey into Night, Anna Christie* and *The Hairy Ape.* Joanne Woodward hosts. (September 8, 1986; 150 min.—60 and 90 min.)

Director: Perry Miller Adato
Producers: Perry Miller Adato, Megan Calloway
Executive producers: Susan Lacy, Jac Venza
Additional funding: National Endowment for the Humanities
Contact: WNET/Thirteen (rights holder)

SEASON TWO, 1987

Isaac in America: A Journey with Isaac Bashevis Singer

The Yiddish-language writer and recipient of the 1978 Nobel Prize for Literature offers his wisdom, irony and charm. The peculiarity of writing in Yiddish in the late 20th century is a theme that recurs throughout the film. Singer explains, saying, "First, I like to write ghost stories . . . and nothing fits a ghost better than a dying language. The deader the language, the more alive is the ghost. Ghosts love Yiddish—they all speak it!" Nominated for an Academy Award in 1986. (July 6, 1987; 60 min.)

Director: Amram Nowak
Producer: Kirk Simon
Executive producer: Manya Starr
Additional funding: National Endowment for the Humanities
A production of Amram Nowak Associates, AMERICAN MASTERS and the ASDA Foundation
Source: Direct Cinema (educational)

Directed by William Wyler

Over 50 years, Wyler directed such classic films as *Ben Hur, Funny Girl, Jezebel, The Little Foxes* and *Wuthering Heights*. This documentary on the master of the multiple "take" features a candid interview with Wyler conducted by his daughter Catherine shortly before his death. Film clips, archival footage and home movies contribute to the portrait. Interviews with: Bette Davis, Greer Garson, Lillian Hellmann, Audrey Hepburn, Charlton Heston, John Huston, Laurence Olivier, Gregory Peck, Ralph Richardson, Barbra Streisand, Billy Wilder. (July 13, 1987; 60 min.)

Director: Aviva Slesin
Producer: Catherine Tatge
Writer: A. Scott Berg

Executive producer: Catherine Wyler
A Topgallant production with AMERICAN MASTERS

Rubinstein Remembered: A 100th Anniversary Tribute

This film memorial to the great concert pianist, illustrated by clips of Arthur Rubinstein (1887 - 1982) in concert and in interviews, presents a man whose musical talent was matched by a talent for living. For his 100th, the people of Lodz, Poland, Rubinstein's birthplace, invited his widow and son John Rubinstein to their city for a memorial concert, conducted by John. (July 20, 1987; 60 min.)

Director, producer: Peter Rosen
A Peter Rosen production with ProServ Television and Clasart Films
Source: HomeVision, Video Artists International (home video)

Nik and Murray

The careers and longtime collaboration of Alwin Nikolais and Murray Louis—Nik and Murray—are explored in a montage of dance performances and conversations conducted on streets, stages and dance studios. Nikolais, modern dance's pioneer of multimedia, is the choreographer, composer and designer for his company, Nikolais Dance Theater. Louis, who made his reputation as a performer in Nikolais's company, formed his own company, the Murray Louis Dance Company in 1953. Excerpts from Nikolais's works: *Illusive Visions, Contact, Tensile Involvement, Fusion* and *Antechamber*; and from Louis's: *Harmonica Suite, Schubert, Frail Demons, The Disenchantment of Pierrot* and *The Station*. (July 27, 1987; 60 min.)

Director, producer: Christian Blackwood
A Christian Blackwood production with WDR, Cologne
Contact: Christian Blackwood Productions (rights holder)

George Gershwin Remembered

The life and career of the composer is reviewed. Born Jacob Gershvin into an impoverished Jewish family in Brooklyn, Gershwin became one of America's most original composers. Includes material from the Gershwin family photo albums and home movies; footage from Gershwin's performances and rehearsals; clips from his many shows and movies; reminiscences by friends and coworkers Frances Godowsky, Kitty Carlisle Hart, Ed Jablonski, Mabel Shirmer and Kay Swift; and insights into Gershwin's genius by Leonard Bernstein, Michael Feinstein, Linda Ronstadt, Michael Tilson Thomas and Virgil Thomson. (August 24, 1987; 90 min.)

Director, writer: Peter Adam
Executive producers: Susan Lacy, Kirk D'Amico, John Williams
A production of the Program Development Company, the British Broadcasting Corporation, AMERICAN MASTERS and Unitel
Source: VPI (laser disk)

Maurice Sendak: 'Mon Cher Papa'

"What interests me is the creative process," Sendak reports, "[or] how you get yourself to work." After the death of his father 15 years ago, Sendak adopted the composer Mozart, whom he calls "mon cher papa," as his creative mentor. Sendak's brilliance was widely acknowledged with the publication of the great children's illustrated book, *Where the Wild Things Are*. His later successes include *The Night Kitchen* and *Outside Over There*. In the 1980s, Sendak began designing sets for operas and ballets. He considers set design as illustration on a grand scale and a very special kind of collaboration. (August 31, 1987; 60 min.)

Dear AMERICAN MASTERS:

I have recently viewed your AMERICAN MASTERS series parts one and two on Ellington and Armstrong. I was very impressed with the content and artistic quality of these productions.

I teach a history of American jazz at — Community College and would like to know if these materials are available on video cassette? They would be enormously helpful in such a class . . . .

Thank you for your time and for the series.

Sincerely,

J.P.Z., White Bear Lake, Minn.

Director, producer: Christopher Swann
Executive producer: Susan Lacy
A production of RM Arts and AMERICAN MASTERS
Contact: RM Associates (rights holder)

The Negro Ensemble Company

The story of the company's troubled, but ultimately triumphant history. Founded in 1967 by Robert Hooks, Gerald Krone and Douglas Turner Ward to present works about the black experience and to give young black actors a place to perform, the Negro Ensemble Company has produced over 200 new plays; provided a theatrical home for more than 4,000 cast and crew members including such renowned black actors as Louis Gossett Jr., Sherman Hemsley and Phylicia Rashad; and won more than 40 major awards. Ossie Davis narrates. (September 14, 1987; 60 min.)

Director, producer: Richard Kilberg
Executive producer: Susan Lacy

An RKB production with AMERICAN MASTERS
Contact: Films for the Humanities

Unanswered Prayers: The Life and Times of Truman Capote

The flamboyant author of *In Cold Blood, Breakfast at Tiffany's* and *Music for Chameleons*, was considered one of the great American writers during his lifetime. This documentary recounts Capote's youth in New Orleans and his early years in New York City, and it gives special focus to the last phase of his life, when his flamboyant lifestyle made him one of high society's "glitterati," drawing on Capote's unfinished *Answered Prayers*, interviews with friends and footage from his outrageous television appearances. (September 21, 1987; 60 min.)

Director, producer: Andrew Harries
A production of RM Arts and AMERICAN MASTERS
Contact: RM Associates (rights holder)

The composer George Gershwin completes the score of Porgy and Bess, from the documentary George Gershwin Remembered.

The Ten-Year Lunch: The Wit and Legend of the Algonquin Round Table

A celebration of the legendary group of artists and critics who lunched daily at the Algonquin Hotel in New York City during the 1920s. The core of the group included Dorothy Parker, Robert Benchley, Harold Ross, Heywood Broun, Alexander Woollcott, George S. Kaufman, Marc Connelly, Edna Ferber, Robert Sherwood and Franklin Pierce Adams. The film introduces the Round Tablers as young hopefuls, outspoken and outrageous, and follows them through the 1920s, a decade whose style they embodied and helped create. Participating in the documentary are Marc Connelly, Margalo Gillmore, Ruth Gordon, W. Averell Harriman and Helen Hayes. Heywood Hale Broun hosts the film. (September 28, 1987; 60 min.)

Director, producer: Aviva Slesin
Writers: Peter Foges, Mary Jo Kaplan
Executive producers: Aviva Slesin, Stephen Samuels
Awards: Academy Award: Best Feature Documentary
A production of Aviva Films and AMERICAN MASTERS
Source: Direct Cinema (educational)

Buster Keaton: A Hard Act to Follow

The genius of early film comedy is the subject of this profile. Part one centers on a 1964 interview with Keaton. It reconstructs Keaton's childhood as a member of his parents' traveling medicine show and his first film work with Roscoe "Fatty" Arbuckle. Featured are scenes from *Our Hospitality*, *Sherlock Jr.* and *The Navigator*. Part two follows Keaton's career from its zenith in the mid-1920s with films such as *Seven Chances*, *Battling Butler* and *The General*, to its decline in the mid-1930s. Part three chronicles Keaton's difficult years in the 1930s and 1940s,

the revival of interest in his work in the 1950s and his death in 1966. (November 18 and 25, 1987; 180 min.—3 x 60 min.)

Produced and written by: Kevin Brownlow, David Gill
Executive producer: Susan Lacy
Awards: Emmy Awards: Outstanding Informational Series; Outstanding Achievement in Writing; Special Peabody Award
A production of Thames Television in association with Raymond Rohauer, curator of the Keaton Archives
Source: HBO Video, Image Entertainment (home video)

SEASON THREE, 1988

Lillian Gish: The Actor's Life for Me

"The first lady of the silent screen" is the subject of this retrospective of a career that has spanned the 20th century. With an extended interview and footage from her performances in such classics as *The Birth of a Nation* (1915), *Broken Blossoms* (1919) and *Way Down East* (1920), directed by D.W. Griffith, for Gish, "the father of film." The profile emerges as a portrait of both Gish and her favorite director. (July 11, 1988; 60 min.)

Director, producer: Terry Sanders
Executive producers: Susan Lacy, Freida Lee Mock
Awards: Emmy Award: Outstanding Informational Special
A production of American Film Foundation and AMERICAN MASTERS
Source: American Film Foundation (educational)

A Duke Named Ellington

The life and career of one America's greatest musicians, conductors and composers, Edward Kennedy "Duke" Ellington (1899 - 1974). Part one chronicles Duke Ellington's early

professional experience in Harlem and in Hollywood, from the 1920s through the early 1950s. Interviews with Willie "The Lion" Smith, Ben Webster, Clark Terry and Adelaide Hall; commentary by Ellington; performances of *Creole Rhapsody* and *Take the A-Train* and segments of European performances. Part two commences in 1956 with the Ellington band's legendary performance at the Newport Jazz Festival, marking a new direction for the group and for American jazz. This program explores Ellington's longer works, a ballet written with Alvin Ailey, his relationship with his co-composer and arranger Billy Strayhorn and his influence on contemporary musicians. Performances include *Mood Indigo* and *Black, Brown and Beige*. (July 18 and 25, 1988; 120 min.—2 x 60 min.)

Director, producer: Terry Carter
Coproducer, writer: Leonard "Skip" Malone
Executive producer: Susan Lacy
A production of the Council for Positive Images and AMERICAN MASTERS
Contact: Council for Positive Images (rights holder)

Andre Kertesz of the Cities

The final year of the life of the master photographer as he travels from New York City back to Budapest (the city of his youth) and then to Paris (where he developed his signature style of photojournalism). Kertesz's journey illustrates how each of these cities influenced his vision and how each represents a distinct period in his career. Classic images from Kertesz's opus are often contrasted with similar scenes from the present. (August 8, 1988; 60 min.)

Director, producer: Teri Wehn-Damasch
A TF 1 production with AMERICAN MASTERS

Dear AMERICAN MASTERS:

I recently saw a wonderful TV show on our PBS station about the life of Louis Armstrong with an interview by Dave and Iola Brubeck.

Is there any way I could use that film for a class I teach in music, Jazz History, next semester.

I would be willing to rent or pay mailing costs. It was such a fine show and would be so meaningful for my students.

W.L.B., Marietta, Ohio

Aretha Franklin: The Queen of Soul

Aretha Franklin's life reflects the essence of soul, the unique African-American blend of gospel passion and pop lyrics. Daughter of the black leader and Detroit minister, the Reverend C.L. Franklin, from her earliest years Franklin was grounded in gospel and acquainted with the leading black entertainers. Surging to the top of the charts in 1967, she became a symbol of black advancement, and staged recording comebacks in the 1970s and 1980s. The film probes the roots of Aretha's style in gospel music, the unique expression she brought to soul and the effect of her career on her personal life. Excerpts from three decades of performances. Interviews with: Ray Charles, Eric Clapton, John Hammond, Whitney Houston, Keith Richards, Smokey Robinson, Dionne Warwick and Jerry Wexler. (August 22, 1988; 60 min.)

Director: Kathy Neukum
Producer: Kirk D'Amico
Executive producers: John H. Williams, Susan Lacy
Writer: Nelson George
A production of the Program Development Company, AMERICAN MASTERS and the British Broadcasting Corporation
Source: Pacific Arts Video, Image Entertainment (home video)

Rivera in America

The Mexican muralist Diego Rivera reintroduced classic fresco painting to the architecture of public buildings and spaces. In the 1930s, Rivera created major works in San Francisco, Detroit and New York, which served as an inspiration for Roosevelt's WPA program. The film explores the works Rivera created in the United States and the public controversy their political content provoked. (August 29, 1988; 60 min.)

Director, producer: Rick Tejada-Flores
Executive producer: Susan Lacy
A production of Alturas Films and AMERICAN MASTERS
Contact: Alturas Films (rights holder)

Saint Gaudens: Masque of the Golden Bowl

A dramatized portrait of the sculptor Augustus Saint Gaudens that takes place on a summer's day in 1905 as Saint Gaudens is feted by the residents of the Cornish Art Colony in New Hampshire. Saint Gaudens reflects on his life and the development of his career: as a young artisan, as a student painter under John LaFarge and as a struggling sculptor working with another young renegade, Stanford White. *Principal cast:* James Hurdle, Elizabeth Franz, Kevin Conway and Richard Ramos. (September 5, 1988, 60 min.)

Director, producer: Theodor Timreck
Writer: Will N. Goetzmann
Producer: Joe Babas
A production of Spofford Films
Source: Metropolitan Museum of Art, HomeVision (home video)

SEASON FOUR, 1989

Broadway's Dreamers: The Legacy of The Group Theatre

In the summer of 1931 three young idealists, Harold Clurman, Cheryl Crawford and Lee Strasberg, recruited 28 actors to form a permanent ensemble dedicated to dramatizing the times in which they lived. This ensemble, The Group Theatre, changed American theater, and its influence persists in film and television to this day. The actress and director Joanne Woodward, a student of Sanford Meisner, one of the original members of The Group Theatre, hosts the program. She interviews surviving members, including the director and acting teacher Bobby Lewis and the director Elia Kazan. (June 26, 1989; 90 min.)

Director: David Heeley
Producers: Joan Kramer, David Heeley, Joanne Woodward
Writer: Steve Lawson
Executive producers: Jac Venza, Susan Lacy
Awards: Emmy Award: Outstanding Informational Special
A production of WNET/Thirteen
Contact: WNET/Thirteen (rights holder)

Harold Clurman: A Life of Theatre

One of American theater's leading innovators, Clurman was a founder of The Group Theatre. This documentary contains footage from Ibsen's *The Lady from the Sea* (broadcast here for the first time), a clip of Julie Harris in *The Member of the Wedding* and interviews with Clurman's friends and associates: Arthur Miller, Lee Strasberg, Elia Kazan, Karl Malden, Roy Scheider and Julie Harris. Includes selections from Clurman's lecture series, The Shape of the Theater. Meryl Streep narrates. (July 3, 1989; 60 min.)

Directed and produced by: Tom Klein, Alan Kaplan
A Famous production with the Media Arts Program of the Eugene O'Neill Theater Center

Stella Adler: Awake and Dream!

The film profiles one of the great teachers of the American stage and screen whose students include Warren Beatty, Candice Bergen, Marlon Brando and Robert de Niro. The daughter of Jacob Adler, one of the legends of the Yiddish stage, Adler studied under Constantin Stanislavsky and was an active member of The Group Theatre in the 1930s. Adler talks about her life and work; interviews with Karl Malden, John Abbot and Bobby Lewis. Frank Langella narrates the film. (July 10, 1989; 60 min.)

Director: Merrill Brockway
Producer: Catherine Tatge
Writer: Glenn Berenbeim
Executive producers: Jack Willis, Susan Lacy
A production of WNET/Thirteen and the Center for Documentary Media
Source: RM Associates

Celebrating Bird: The Triumph of Charlie Parker

One of jazz's great innovators, the saxophonist Charlie Parker was known for his revolutionary approach to improvisation and for a lifestyle that led to his death at 34. Such Parker master recordings as *Koko, Yardbird Suite, Lover Man, Just Friends* are highlighted, as Dizzy Gillespie, Louis Armstrong, Count Basie, Jimmy Dorsey and Thelonious Monk appear in performance and discuss Bird's music, his fatal addiction and his lasting impact on jazz. Based on the biography by Gary Giddins. (July 17, 1989; 60 min.)

Codirector, writer: Gary Giddins
Codirector, editor: Kendrick Simmons

A production of Toby Byron/ Multiprises
Source: Sony Music Video Enterprises, Pioneer Artists/Pioneer Signature (home video)

Satchmo

As trumpeter, singer and bandleader, Louis "Satchmo" Armstrong is known throughout the world. This documentary on his life and career reveals the depth of Armstrong's sometimes underrated artistry, a genius masked by commercial success. *Ain't Misbehavin', Skeleton in the Closet, Jeepers Creepers* and *Hello Dolly* appear in footage from his Hollywood and television appearances. Home movies from the 1930s and 1960s complement interviews with Tony Bennett, Dave and Iola Brubeck, Dexter Gordon, Wynton Marsalis. Based on the biography by Gary Giddins. (July 31, 1989; 90 min.)

Director, writer: Gary Giddins
Producer: Toby Byron
Executive producers: Fritz Diekmann, Jerry Durkin, Claus Hallig, Susan Lacy, Debbie Newman
A production of Toby Byron/ Multiprises, CBS Music Video Enterprises, Beta Taurus Films and WNET/ Thirteen
Source: Sony Music Video Enterprises (home video)

James Baldwin: The Price of the Ticket

The life, works and beliefs of the author and civil rights activist. Baldwin narrates the film, telling his own story. For the author, the writer's life was the "price" he had to pay to

Celebrating Bird: The Triumph of Charlie Parker. Photo by Toby Byron/Multiprises.

escape poverty. Archival footage from over 100 sources and nine different countries melds interviews and eloquent public speeches with cinema-verite glimpses of the writer's life. Interviews with: his brother David, his biographer David Leeming, Maya Angelou, Amiri Baraka, Ishmael Reed, William Styron, Bobby Short. (August 14, 1989; 90 min.)

Director: Karen Thorsen
Producers: Karen Thorsen, William Miles
Executive producers: Susan Lacy, Albert Maysles
Additional funding: National Endowment for the Humanities
A production of Nobody Knows Productions, Maysles Films, WNET/Thirteen and AMERICAN MASTERS
Source: California Newsreel (home video, educational)

Simply Simon: A Neil Simon Retrospective

Neil Simon's 22 produced plays and 17 movies in 28 years have garnered more Academy Award and Tony nominations than those of any other writer. Beyond these laurels of public approval, the film examines Simon's artistic growth, particularly in *Chapter Two*, *Brighton Beach Memoirs* and *Broadway Bound*. Interviews with: his producer Emmanuel Azenberg, Sid Caesar, Linda Lavin, Jack Lemmon, Marsha Mason, Walter Matthau, Carl Reiner, Herbert Ross, Gene Saks. (August 21, 1989; 60 min.)

Director: Amram Novak
Producer: Manya Starr
Executive producer: Susan Lacy
Source: RM Associates

Jasper Johns: Ideas in Paint

Jasper Johns, the painter and printmaker, emerged on the art scene in the late 1950s. The film includes conversations with the artist as well as footage of Johns at work in his studio.

Interviews with: Leo Castelli, Frank Stella, Richard Serra, John Cage, Merce Cunningham, Barbara Rose. (September 11, 1989; 60 min.)

Director, producer: Rick Tejada-Flores
Executive producers: David Othmer, Susan Lacy
A production of WHYY/Philadelphia and WNET/Thirteen
Source: RM Associates

Mort Sahl: The Loyal Opposition

For four decades Mort Sahl satirized and entertained U.S. presidents from Eisenhower to Bush, breaking new ground in stand-up comedy with his combination of political awareness and uninhibited commentary. (September 18, 1989; 90 min.)

Director, producer: Robert B. Weide
Executive producer: Susan Lacy

W. Eugene Smith: Photography Made Difficult

The war in the South Pacific, a country doctor in Colorado, the victims of mercury poisoning in a Japanese fishing village—these were captured in emotionally charged photographs by W. Eugene Smith (1918 - 1978). Smith's evocative portraits reveal his subjects in ways that touch the conscience of the viewer. This troubled and complex figure combined a passion for social justice with a compulsion to create photographic works of art. More than 600 of Smith's photos are shown. (September 25, 1989; 90 min.)

Director: Gene Lasko
Producer: Kirk Morris
Coproducer: Marthe Smith
Writer: Jan Hartman
Executive producers: Greg Andorfer, Susan Lacy
Awards: Emmy Award: Outstanding Individual Achievement in Informational Programming
Additional funding: National Endow-

ment for the Humanities
A production of WES FORee Productions, WQED/Pittsburgh and WNET/Thirteen
Source: RM Associates

Harold Lloyd: The Third Genius

Lloyd ranks alongside Chaplin and Keaton as the third genius of silent film comedy. A skilled actor and a cinematic innovator, he made nearly 200 films, was the first to exploit terrifying situations for their comic effect and developed the remarkable stunt techniques that became his trademark. Excerpts from: *High and Dizzy* (1920), *Never Weaken* (1922), *Safety Last* (1923), *Girl Shy* (1923) and *Speedy* (1928). Lindsay Anderson narrates. (November 15 and 22, 1989; 120 min.—2 x 60 min.)

Produced and directed by: Kevin Brownlow, David Gill
Executive producers: Suzanne Lloyd Hayes, Susan Lacy
A production of Thames Television, WNET/Thirteen and the Harold Lloyd Estate
Contact: Thames Television International (rights holder)

Milos Forman: Portrait

Among the works of the Czechoslovakian-born filmmaker are *One Flew Over the Cuckoo's Nest*, *Ragtime*, *Hair* and *Amadeus*. Forman discusses his life and career, shares his thoughts on directing, acting, music and politics. He is seen at work on the film *Valmont*, setting up shots, working with actors and juggling the details of a large production. (December 20, 1989; 60 min.)

Director: Vojtech Jasny
Producer: Yoram Mandel
Coproducer: Paolo Pagnoni
Executive producers: Susan Lacy, Pamela Hausman
A production of YM Productions, Pagnoni Films and WNET/Thirteen

SEASON FIVE, 1990

Preston Sturges: The Rise and Fall of an American Dreamer

The meteoric rise and fall of a great Hollywood innovator. As producer, screenwriter and director, Sturges made the classic "screwball" comedies of the 1930s: *The Great McGinty, The Lady Eve, Sullivan's Travels, The Palm Beach Story* and *The Miracle of Morgan's Creek*. Footage from many of Sturges's landmark films and recollections from his widow, Sandy Sturges, and from Eddie Bracken, Edwin Gillette, Betty Hutton, Joel McCrea, Frances Ramsden, Cesar Romero, Andrew Sarris and Rudy Vallee. (July 2, 1990; 60 min.)

Director, producer: Kenneth Bowser
Coproducer: Caroline Baron
Writer: Todd McCarthy
Executive producers: Susan Lacy, Marilyn Haft
Awards: Emmy Award: Outstanding Informational Programming
A Barking Dog production with WNET/Thirteen
Source: Universal Pictures

John Cassavetes

Over three decades, Cassavetes pushed the limits of independent filmmaking in such movies as *Shadows, Faces, A Woman Under the Influence, Husbands* and *The Killing of a Chinese Bookie*. This film was made in the weeks following Cassavetes's death, and it includes interviews with the directors Peter Bogdanovich and Martin Scorsese and two of Cassavetes's closest collaborators, Ben Gazzara and Peter Falk. The second half of the program is Tristram Powell's 1970 documentary *The Mak-ing of Husbands*, showing the methods Cassavetes used to create films of great realism and impact. (July 9, 1990; 60 min.)

Director: Debbie Geller
Producers: Alan Lewens, Jo Lustig
A production of Jo Lustig, Ltd., and BBC Television's Arena series
Source: VPI

Martin Scorsese Directs

The film goes on location to the set, editing room and mixing studio of Scorsese's *Good Fellas* to show the director in action. Complementing this are clips from Scorsese's own films and from the films that have influenced him. Interviews with: Michael Ballhaus, Jay Cocks, Robert De Niro, Barbara Hershey, Harvey Keitel, Mardik Martin, Joe Pesci, Nicholas Pileggi, Robbie Robertson and Thelma Schoonmaker. Also, conversations with Scorsese's parents and Father Francis Principe, his boyhood priest and a major influence on his life. (July 16, 1990; 60 min.)

Directed and produced by: Joel Sucher, Steven Fischler
Executive producer: Susan Lacy
A production of Pacific Street Film Projects and WNET/Thirteen
Source: RM Associates

You're the Top: The Cole Porter Story

Some of the most clever, funny and romantic songs ever written were Cole Porter's: *Night and Day, I Get a Kick out of You, Begin the Beguine, My Heart Belongs to Daddy, Let's Fall in Love* and many others. Such musicals as *Anything Goes, Red, Hot and Blue* and *Kiss Me Kate* are classics. His life and legacy are the subject of this film: outwardly, a sophisticated bon vivant and international partygoer, Porter was relentlessly dedicated to his profession. Reminiscences by Cyd Charisse, Alfred Drake, Douglas Fairbanks, Jr., Kitty Carlisle Hart, Bob Hope, Jean Howard, Garson Kanin, Gene Kelly, Patricia Morrison and others. Bobby Short hosts the film. (July 23, 1990; 60 min.)

Director, writer: Allan Albert
Producer: Kirk D'Amico
Executive producer: Susan Lacy
A production of VPI, Channel Four/ Britain and WNET/Thirteen
Source: VPI

Edward R. Murrow: This Reporter

The pioneering journalist is the subject of this two-part film profile. In World War II, Murrow's radio reports from London during the Blitzkreig, from the cockpits of Allied bombers and from Buchenwald after its liberation brought him national fame. In the 1950s, he confronted Senator Joseph McCarthy's Red Menace rhetoric. Well-known for the television series *See It Now* and *Face to Face*, Murrow broke with CBS in 1961 over his unyielding standards of journalism. He was director of the U.S. Information Agency until his death in 1965. (July 30 and August 6, 1990; 120 min.—2 x 60 min.)

Director, producer: Susan Steinberg
Writer: Ed Apfel
Executive producer: Susan Lacy
Awards: Emmy Award: Outstanding Informational Special
A production of WNET/Thirteen
Source: CBS Broadcast International (home video)

John Hammond: From Bessie Smith to Bruce Springsteen

Talent scout, record producer, impresario, jazz critic, civil rights activist, Hammond was one of the most influential forces in popular music in this century. In the 1930s and 1940s he promoted and produced Bessie Smith, Billie Holiday, Count Basie, Teddy Wilson, Charlie Christian, Freddie Green, Lionel Hampton and Helen Humes and was instrumental in breaking down racial barriers in the music industry. In the 1960s and 1970s, he helped develop the careers of Bob Dylan, Aretha Franklin, Bruce Springsteen, and many others. (August 20, 1990; 60 min.)

Director: Hart Perry
Writer: Gary Giddins
Executive producers: Susan Lacy, Jerry Durkin, Debbie Newman
Awards: 1991 Peabody Award
A production of CBS Music Video Enterprises and AMERICAN MASTERS
Source: Sony Music Video Enterprises (home video)

Sanford Meisner: The Theatre's Best Kept Secret

For over half a century, Meisner trained some of the most skilled performers of stage and screen. A founding member of The Group Theatre in the 1930s, he dedicated himself to teaching following its dissolution in 1941. Meisner's celebrated students appear in the film, including Robert Duvall, Peter Falk, Tony Randall, Gregory Peck, Mary Steenburgen, Jon Voight, Joanne Woodward, David Mamet, Bob Fosse, Elia Kazan and Sydney Pollack. (August 27, 1990; 60 min.)

Director: Nick Doob
Producer: Kent Paul
Executive producer: Sydney Pollack
Source: Columbia Pictures Television

John Cage: I Have Nothing to Say and I Am Saying It

The controversial composer has intrigued, outraged and challenged audiences and fellow composers with his philosophy of being open to all of nature and all experience, unimpaired by the filters of conventional taste and personal bias. He rejected harmony as the basis of composition early in his career, accepting all sounds as possible sources of music. Cage's application of this principle is demonstrated in pieces such as *Branches, Inlets, Water Music* and *4 minutes, 33 seconds.* (September 17, 1990; 60 min.)

Director, coproducer: Allan Miller
Producer, writer: Vivian Perlis
Executive producer: Susan Lacy
A production of the Music Project for Television, WNET/Thirteen and Lola Films
Source: RM Associates

DOCUMENTARY SPECIALS

Acting: Lee Strasberg and the Actors' Studio

Strasberg's acting school was in an old church in New York City's Hell's Kitchen; there the talents of such actors as Jane Fonda, Ellen Burstyn, Ben Gazzara, Robert De Niro, Diane Ladd, Al Pacino and Patricia Neal were nurtured. The film follows Strasberg's career, from his early days with the Yiddish Theatre, to his founding and involvement in The Group Theatre, to the creation of the Actors' Studio. Interviews with: Harold Clurman, Cheryl Crawford, Celeste Holm, Shelley Winters, Anne Jackson, Eli Wallach, Sylvia Miles, Paul Newman, Rod Steiger, Carroll O'Connor, Burgess Meredith, Elia Kazan. (Date of release: 1982; 110 min.)

Director: Herbert Kline
Festivals: Cannes Film Festival

Alfred Stieglitz, Photographer

Stieglitz's photographs and the reminiscences of those who knew him well define his importance in the history of photography as well as his role in promoting photography as an art form in the early 20th century. Interviews with: Ansel Adams, Mary Steichen Calderone, Harold Clurman, Aaron Copland, Arnold Newman, Isamu Noguchi. (Date of release: 1982; 30 min.)

Directors: Paul Falkenberg, Hans Namuth
Source: Museum of Modern Art

Ansel Adams, Photographer

The first definitive film on Adams's life and work. Seventy-nine years old when this film was made, he returns to many of his most famous locales, in Yosemite and elsewhere. Conversations with Beaumont Newhall and Georgia O'Keeffe; Adams and O'Keeffe reminisce about their 51-year friendship and discourse on the evolution of photography as an art form over the course of Adams's career. (May 13, 1981; 60 min.)

Director: John Huszar
Producers: Andrea Gray, John Huszar
A production of FilmAmerica
Presented on PBS by KQED/San Francisco
Source: FilmAmerica; Pacific Arts (home video)

Antonia: Portrait of a Woman

At 28, Antonia Brico was the first woman to conduct the Berlin Philharmonic. By the 1930s, her reputation as an orchestral conductor had been established. Yet as a woman, her career was hindered. The film depicts Brico's passion for music and the frustrations and discrimination she experienced. She talks about her friendships with Albert Schweitzer, Jean Sibelius and Sir Adrian Boult. Judy Collins, the folksinger and a student of Brico, conducts the interviews. *Antonia* was nominated for an Academy Award in 1975.(April 20, 1976; 60 min.)

Directors: Judy Collins, Jill Godmilow
Awards: Emily Award
A Rocky Mountain production
Presented on PBS by WNET/Thirteen
Source: Phoenix Films (educational)

The Art of Gerald Gooch

The San Francisco Bay-area artist Gooch's paintings, graphic works and sculpture, which draw on subjects from everyday life, are reviewed. Many of his works depict successive stages of an action, lending themselves to animation. (Date of release: 1977; 16 min.)

Director, producer: Seth Hill
A production of Creative Dimensions, Inc.

The Beat Generation—An American Dream

A portrait of the group of writers and painters who gathered in New York, San Francisco and other large cities to rebel against 1950s America. Rare archival footage and interviews with: Jack Kerouac, Neal Cassady, Thelonious Monk, Amiri Baraka, William Burroughs, Carolyn Cassady, Diane DiPrima, Lawrence Ferlinghetti, Allen Ginsberg, Jan Kerouac, Anne Waldman, Abbie Hoffman and Timothy Leary. Archival footage of everyday life in the 1950s depicts the mainstream culture against which the "Beats" reacted. Music by David Amram. Steve Allen narrates. (Date of release: 1986; 90 min.)

Director, producer: Janet Forman
A Renaissance Motion Pictures Release
Source: Samuel Goldwyn Company

Before the Nickelodeon

Edwin S. Porter was a prolific innovator during the early years of the motion picture. In thirteen years, 1896 to 1909, Porter progressed from projectionist to editor to film director to has-been, as movies evolved from novelty loops for peep-show viewing through rudimentary newsreel reenactments of current events to short fictional narratives. Porter's western, *The Great Train Robbery* (1902), defined what was to become Hollywood's most popular genre, and remained the country's favorite film until *Birth of a Nation* (1915), directed by D.W. Griffiths, who as an actor, was given his first movie break by Porter. The 88-year-old silent-screen star, Blanche Sweet, narrates. (Date of release: 1982; 60 min.)

Director, producer: Charles Musser
Executive producer: Stephen Brier
Writers: Warren D. Leight, Charles Musser
A Film For Thought presentation; A New York-Hollywood Feature Film production
Source: Devillier and Donegan Enterprises

Bukowski Reads Bukowski

A performance documentary on the controversial writer and poet, featuring Charles Bukowski at home in Los Angeles and at a reading in San Francisco. As he drives through city streets, stops off at the Post Office and the race track and visits local haunts, he analyses his love-hate relationship with Los Angeles. (October 16, 1975; 30 min.)

Director: Taylor Hackford
A production of KCET/Los Angeles

... But Then She's Betty Carter

A cinematic portrait of the jazz vocalist Betty Carter—her genius, her paradoxical attitude toward fame, her dedication to personal expression. From her early days with Charlie Parker's quintet in the 1940s, to national tours with Lionel Hampton and Ray Charles, to her solo career, Carter has fulfilled her own criteria for success, which included establishing her own recording company and raising two sons as a single parent. (Date of release: 1980; 55 min.)

Director, producer: Michelle Parkerson
Source: Women Make Movies (educational)

Clementine Hunter

This 1974 film focuses on the 98-year-old black memory painter from Natchitoches, Louisiana, whose paintings depict the scenes she knew as a child: cotton, fruit and pecan picking, hauling cotton, women washing, weddings, birthday parties, revival meetings, fish fries and religious scenes. Her paintings are in libraries throughout Louisiana.

Director: Madeline Anderson

A Composer's Notes: Philip Glass and the Making of Akhnaten

The preparation of Philip Glass's opera *Akhnaten*, from the early discussions with collaborators to the 1984 European and American premieres, including comments from musicians and directors who worked with Glass. The finale of *Akhnaten* is presented, received with the boos and applause of the opening-night audience. (Date of release: 1985; 90 min.)

Director, producer: Michael Blackwood
Source: Michael Blackwood Productions, Video Artists International

Colin McPhee and the Lure of Asian Music

The Canadian-born composer was lured to Bali after World War I by a gramophone recording of Balinese music. He wrote three books on Balinese life and music and composed in the Balinese style for western instruments. Includes footage by McPhee of Balinese village life, music and dance. Featured in the film are: John Cage, Aaron Copland, Lou Harrison, Steve Reich, Dennis Russell Davies, the Dreamtiger Ensemble of London, the gamelan orchestras, Angklung of Sayan and Semar Pegulingan of Teges. (Date of release: September, 1985; 60 min.)

Director: Michael Blackwood
Source: Michael Blackwood Productions

Conversations with Willard Van Dyke

A portrait of the distinguished and outspoken documentary filmmaker, photographer and curator with excerpts from many of Van Dyke's films; conversations with his colleagues Ralph Steiner, Joris Ivens and Donald Richie; and footage of Edward Weston, Van Dyke's close friend and mentor. As director of the Department of Film at the Museum of Modern Art, Van Dyke transformed its Film Library into a major curatorial department in the 1960s, a significant step in establishing film as an art. (Date of release: 1981; 60 min.)

Director, producer: Amalie R. Rothschild
Writers: Julie Sloane, Amalie R. Rothschild
Source: New Day Films, Museum of Modern Art

Czeslaw Milosz: The Poet Remembers

The life and works of the poet, essayist and novelist Czeslaw Milosz, who won the 1980 Nobel Prize for Literature and who has lived in exile from his native Lithuania for more than three decades, most recently in California. The poet is presented as a voice of hope in an age darkened by war and destruction, as part of the Poland's literary underground during World War II and later when his poetry became an inspiration for Poland's Solidarity movement. His writings speak for a generation that has experienced worldwide cataclysm and the rise and fall of nations. Interviews with: Susan Sontag, Joseph Brodsky, Robert Hass, Zbigniew Brzezinski, Michael Kaufman. (April 27, 1990; 60 min.)

Director: Jan Nemec
Producers: Blair Gershkow, Lynn O'Donnell
Executive producers: gayle k. yamada, Louise Lo
A production of KQED/San Francisco

Dear Mark

A highly personal view of the sculptor Mark di Suvero, as one of his huge iron and steel sculptures is erected in Paris, accompanied by a Gene Autry soundtrack and interjections of Roman busts and medieval armor. (Date of release: 1980; 15 min.)

Director: Danny Lyon
Source: Bleak Beauty Films

Diego Rivera: I Paint What I See

This film biography documents the painter's career from his early cubism to his monumental murals in Mexico and the United States. Rivera, a colorful and controversial artist, is seen in home movies and at work in archival footage. The narration draws from the writings of Rivera and his wife, the painter Frida Kahlo. The film reports on the controversy surrounding Rivera's politically inspired works, his tempestuous relationship with Kahlo and his influence on 20th-century art. (Date of release: 1990; 60 min.)

Director: Mary Lance
Producers: Mary Lance, Eric Breitbart
Additional funding: National Endowment for the Humanities
Source: Direct Cinema

George Crumb: Voice of the Whale

A portrait of the Pulitzer Prize-winning American composer who discusses the connections between his life and art. Includes performances of the rural gospel music that has influenced Crumb and his composition, *Voice of the Whale*, by the Penn Contemporary Players conducted by Richard Wernick. (June 6, 1978; 60 min.)

Director: Robert Mugge
Source: Rhapsody Films, Direct Cinema

George Stevens: A Filmmaker's Journey

The life and career of the great Hollywood director chronicled by his son. We go behind the scenes of many of the films for which Stevens is best known: *Alice Adams, Vivacious Lady, Swingtime, Shane, The Greatest Story Ever Told, Giant,* and *The Diary of Anne Frank.* Film clips from them are seen as is Stevens's remarkable World War II color footage. Interviews with: Warren Beatty, Frank Capra, Douglas Fairbanks, Jr., Katharine Hepburn, John Huston, Rouben Mamoullian, Joseph Mankiewicz, Joel McCrea, Alan Pakula, Max von Sydow.

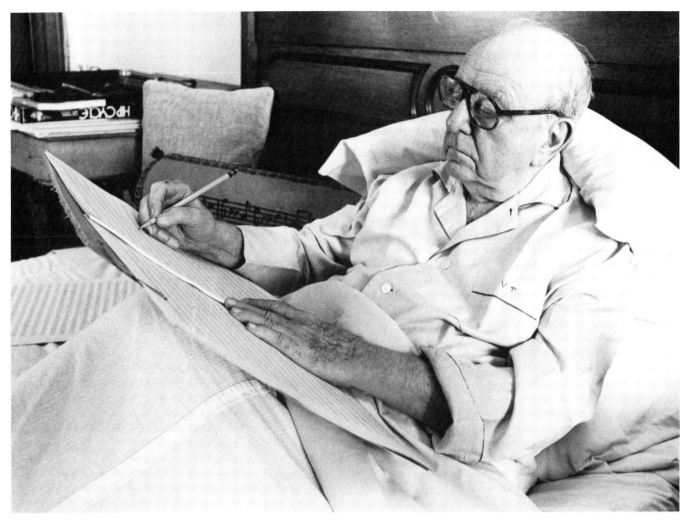

A scene from Virgil Thomson, Composer, *whose preferred method of composing was to write in bed. Photo by John Huszar.*

Director, producer, writer: George Stevens, Jr.
A production of the Creative Film Center and the Cultural Council Foundation
Source: Castle Hill

The Girl with the Incredible Feeling: Elizabeth Swados

A film about the composer and director, who works in a variety of styles and contexts. Swados, who has composed for Peter Brook's International Center for Theatre Creation, the New York Experimental Theatre Company and for La MaMa Theatre, is seen conducting her works. (December 31, 1978; 60 min.)

Director, producer: Linda Feferman
Source: Phoenix Films

A Good Dissonance Like a Man

A dramatized portrait of the iconoclastic composer, Charles Ives, based on reminiscences and on interviews with friends and relatives. Ives's major influences—the New England countryside, his college days, family life and the insurance business—his musical roots and their evolution into the complex tonalities of his work are woven together with narration taken from Ives's *Memos.* Ives's music was poorly received, and in one scene he admonishes a listener, "When you hear music like this why don't you sit up and take it like a man!" *Principal cast:* John Bottoms, Richard Ramos, Sandra Kingsbury, Louis Zorich, Louis Turenne, Joshua Hamilton, Bob McIlwain. (October 11, 1977; 60 min.)

Director, producer: Theodor Timreck
Created in conjunction with the Oral History Program of the Yale School of Music under the direction of Vivian Perlis
1977 Peabody Award for Broadcast Excellence
Source: HomeVision

Gottschalk: A Musical Portrait

The New Orleans-born composer Louis Moreau Gottschalk (1829 - 1869) is a little-known American composer of the first importance. The film offers a selection of the formats in which Gottschalk wrote, from symphonic interpretations based on African and Caribbean rhythms, to American folk themes, all composed within the romantic-classical tradition. The New Orleans Symphony conducted by Philippe Entremont with Moses Hogan as guest pianist perform three major works: *Grande Tarentelle for Piano and Orchestra*, *A Night in the Tropics*, *Symphony no. 1* and *Marche Solennelle for Orchestra and Band*. On-camera commentary by the musicologist and historian Robert Offergeld. (March 2, 1988; 60 min.)

Director, producer: John Huszar
A production of FilmAmerica
Source: FilmAmerica

How the Myth Was Made

Robert Flaherty was the pioneering documentary filmmaker whose *Man of Aran* (1934) provoked George Stoney, himself a pioneer of the social documentary film, to return to the island of Aran, where his father was born. The film shows how Flaherty adjusted locations and customs to fulfill his romantic vision. Islanders who participated in the original film heatedly argue the "myth" versus the truth in Flaherty's portrayal of them 40 years before. (Date of release: 1978; 60 min.)

Directed and produced by: George C. Stoney, James Brown
Source: Texture Films, Museum of Modern Art

In Motion: Amiri Baraka

From his early days as a poet in Greenwich Village to his current literary and political activities, Amiri Baraka, formerly LeRoi Jones, is shown to be an artist marked by a singular commitment to social justice. Scenes from several of Baraka's plays, including *The Dutchman*, are included. Allen Ginsberg, A.B. Spellman and Joel Oppenheimer provide insight into Baraka as a poet; Ted Wilson and Askia M. Toure discuss his political activism in Harlem. (Date of release: 1985; 60 min.)

Director: St. Clair Bourne
Source: Facets Video

Jackelope

A film about contemporary artists in Texas. Three artists, George Green, James Surls and Robert Wade, are profiled as they create their works and discuss their survival as artists, the special character their surroundings impart to their work and their attempt to evade the classification of "regional artists." Four other artists, Mike McNamara, Letitia Eldridge, Mel Casas and John Alexander, are also seen in interviews and at art events. Caught somewhere between two worlds, none is so different from the jackelope, an animal of southwestern lore, half jackrabbit and half antelope, said to sing at night in a voice that sounds almost human. (Date of release: 1976; 60 min.)

Director: Ken Harrison
Source: KERA Public Communications

John Jacob Niles

Made a few years before his death, the film captures the man who became one of the better known folk interpreters of our time. His talents undiminished by

age, Niles shares his love of music and comments on his life, as he collected and performed the traditional music of the Appalachian mountains. (Date of release: 1978; 32 min.)

Directors: Bill Richardson, Mimi Pickering, Ben Zickafoose
Source: Appalshop

Lee Krasner: The Long View

A study of the abstract expressionist painter Lee Krasner by Barbara Rose, the art historian and critic. The film discusses Krasner's life and work, her apprenticeship with Hans Hoffmann and her marriage to Jackson Pollock. Comments by William Lieberman, John Myers, Kenneth, Marcia Tucker.

(Date of release: 1978; 30 min.)

Director, producer: Barbara Rose
Source: American Federation of the Arts

Mama's Pushcart: Ellen Stewart and 25 Years of La MaMa E.T.C.

A portrait of the founder of New York City's La MaMa Experimental Theatre Club (E.T.C.), who has been a leader in avant-garde theater for 25 years. Interviews with notable artists associated with La MaMa: Peter Brook, Harvey Fierstein, Elizabeth Swados, Wilford Leach, Tom O'Horgan. (Date of release: 1988; 60 min.)

Director, producer: Demetria Royals
Executive producer: Louise Diamond
A production of Rebekah Films
Source: Women Make Movies (educational)

Martha Clarke/Light and Dark

A portrait of the choreographer and dancer, one of the first female members of the dance company Pilobolus, whose works draw from diverse sources: modern dance, mime, the clown's repertoire, painting and treat such themes as loneliness and loss, the nature of performance, what it means to be a woman and an animate being. The film traces the gradual evolution of an original work by Clarke, from its initial concept to premiere performance, shortly after she left Pilobolus. (Date of release: 1980; 60 min.)

Director: Joyce Chopra
Source: Phoenix Films

Maurice Sendak and All the Wild Things

The film examines how the scenic designer, author and writer and illustrator of children's books approaches his work, exploring Sendak's extraordinary ability to recreate particular moments of childhood. (Release date: 1985; 60 min.)

Director, producer, writer: Herbert Danska
Executive producers: Herbert Danska, Morton Schindel
An Emerald City production with Weston Woods Productions
Source: Weston Woods Studio

Memories of Eubie

A tribute to Eubie Blake, the ragtime and Broadway composer and performer. Blake's contribution to music and the advancment of black musicians is recounted in historical materials, interviews and performances. A number of his songs are performed: *Hot Feet*, sung and danced by Gregory Hines; *Daddy*, sung by Lynnie Godfrey; *You Got to Git the Gittin While the Gittin's Good*, sung and danced by Maurice Hines; *Memories of You, It's All Your Fault* and *Love Will Find a Way* performed by Alberta Hunter. Blake joins Hunter on some numbers, and also plays piano. Billy Taylor is musical director. (January 13, 1980; 60 min.)

Director: Allan Miller
Producers: Allan Miller, Vivian Perlis
Executive producer: Ruth Leon
Source: Ruth Leon Productions

Painting the Town: The Illusionistic Murals of Richard Haas

A documentary based on the life and work of Richard Haas, the architectural muralist whose *trompe l'oeil* paintings have enhanced the appearance of buildings across America. One of the first to apply the technique to the American urban environment, Haas has created more than 77 monumental murals on both interior and exterior walls in dozens of American cities. (Date of release: December, 1989; 60 min.)

Director, producer: Amalie Rothschild
Writer: Julie Sloane
A production of Anomaly Films
Source: Direct Cinema

Setting the Record Straight

Papa John Creach, the consummate violinist and master of myriad styles, is a classically trained violinist and a veteran of the West Coast jazz circuit. Creach became widely known performing with rock groups such as Jefferson Airplane and Hot Tuna, though he considers this the least challenging aspect of his career. Through interviews, rehearsals and major concert performances, the documentary allows the 70-year-old Creach to retrace his long and versatile career, "setting the record straight," so the public may know him for the master violinist that he is. (Date of release: 1987; 60 min.)

Director, producer: Stevenson J. Palfi
Executive producer: Julien Sorel
A production of Mississippi Educational Television and the Contemporary Arts Center
Source: Stephenson Productions

The Shadow Catcher

A study of the life and work of Edward S. Curtis, who spent forty years, 1890 to 1930, documenting every aspect of the lives of Native American he believed were doomed to extinction, recording some 10,000 songs, taking 40,000 photographs and thousands of feet of 35mm film as well as transcribing tales of origin and the customs of everyday life. Includes Curtis's rare footage of the Navajo Yebechai ceremony in 1906, his initiation into the Snake fraternity of the Hopi in 1912 and the reconstruction of the masked dancers of the Kwakiutl of the northwest coast. Donald Sutherland narrates the film. (July 2, 1975; 90 min.)

Director, producer: Teri McLuhan
A production of South Carolina ETV

Signals Through the Flames

A portrait of the work and goals of The Living Theatre became the defining force in experimental theater in the United States. Rare performance footage from 13 of the Living Theater's productions, including *The Connection, The Brig, Paradise Now, Prometheus* and *Antigone*. (Date of release: 1984; 100 min.)

Directors: Sheldon Rochlin, Maxine Harris, Rachel McPherson
Source: Mystic Fire Video

Straight, No Chaser: Thelonious Monk

A pivotal figure in the evolution of be-bop in the 1940s and a prolific composer, Thelonious Monk stopped performing in the mid-1970s and lived in total seclusion until his death in 1982. Monk and his work are seen in previously unreleased performance and interview footage shot by Christian and Michael Blackwood in the late 1960s. Excerpts of more than 25 of Monk's compositions, including 'Round Midnight, Ask Me Now and Ruby My Dear. (Date of release: 1989; 90 min.)

Director: Charlotte Zwerin
Producer: Bruce Ricker
Executive producer: Clint Eastwood
Source: Warner Home Video

Style Wars

A journey through New York's "hip hop" subculture of the early 1980s— the cradle of graffiti, break-dancing and rap music. The film's youthful graffiti writers—Skeme, Kase II, Seen, Dondi, Shy 147, Noc and Iz the Wiz— risk arrest and injury to send their names around on the trains. The phenomenon of "bombing" (decorating) trains is considered a vernacular art form by some and a recalcitrant problem by others. Public officials, transportation authorities and others voice their frustration with graffiti's spread, while art dealers attempt to appropriate it. The film also explores the break dancing craze, following the rise of Crazy Legs and Frosty Freeze, among others. (January 18, 1984; 60 min.)

Director: Tony Silver
Producers: Henry Chalfant, Tony Silver
Source: New Day Films

Thomas Hart Benton's "The Sources of Country Music"

Toward the end of his life, Benton received a commission from the Country Music Hall of Fame in Nashville, Tennessee, to produce a mural on country music. The film chronicles the mural from its inception to its completion shortly before Benton's death in January, 1975, at age 85. Benton's love of country music, his lifelong interest in the history of the United States and its people and his ability to capture in his art the essence of rural America are reflected in the film and in the painting itself. (May 27, 1977; 30 min.)

Directed, produced and written by:
John Altman, Mary Nelson
A Pentacle Production in association with the Mid-America Arts Alliance

Virgil Thomson, Composer

First broadcast on Thomson's 84th birthday, the film features many friends, including Gertrude Stein and John Houseman, as well as scenes from his stage works, notably the premiere performance of the opera *Four Saints in Three Acts* (the first of two written with Stein) and the ballet, *Filling Station*, danced by members of the San Francisco Ballet. Other works excerpted on the program are the operas *The Mother of Us All* and *Lord Byron, Symphony on a Hymn Tune* and the film score *Louisiana Story*. An update of the film, Virgil Thomson at 90 aired on PBS in 1986. (November 24, 1980; 60 min.)

Director: John Huszar
A production of FilmAmerica and WNET/Thirteen
Source: FilmAmerica

Chapter 9:
SPECIAL SERIES

*Langston Hughes. Photo by Clarence Jefferson,
courtesy the Milton Meltzer Collection.*

AMERICA BY DESIGN

VOICES AND VISIONS

WORD INTO IMAGE

THE PAINTER'S WORLD

WOMEN IN ART

MEDIA PROBES

AMERICA BY DESIGN

To convey its scale and depth, architecture, like dance, needs to have its spaces "re-built" and made legible on the television screen. This pioneering series, with the teacher and historian, Spiro Kostof, ranges the built environment of the North American continent using five subjects as its vehicle: the house, the workplace, streets and highways, public places and monuments, and the land itself. In each, history, social context and economic imperatives have been matched by design imagination and ingenuity. These five elements inflect our behavior during our everyday transactions. A companion volume, *America by Design* by Spiro Kostof, was published by Oxford University Press in 1987.

Executive producer: Charles Guggenheim
Director, producer: Werner Schumann
Writers: Spiro Kostof, Werner Schumann
Professional advisors: Henry Millon, Sanford Anderson, Lois A. Craig, Everett L. Fly, Dolores Hayden, John Brinckerhoff Jackson, Kevin Lynch, Charles W. Moore, Rai Y. Okamoto, Michael J. Pittas
Additional funders include: Haworth, Inc., American Institute of Architects, Corporation for Public Broadcasting, Andrew W. Mellon Foundation, Public Broadcasting Service
A production of Guggenheim Productions and WTTW/Chicago
Source: PBS Video

The House

The evolution of the American house and the social, economic and political forces that shaped it. The detached house, seen as the central symbol of the American dream, is followed in the structures of colonial Williamsburg, Jefferson's Monticello, the row house, the Hearst castle at San Simeon and the modern suburban house and mobile home. (September 28, 1987; 60 min.)

The Workplace

The development of mills, factories and office towers symbolizes the success of American enterprise. The effects of industrialization and modern building technologies are shown in historical context. The program begins with the rural homestead and the southern plantation; it goes on to trace the impact of industrialization in factories such as River Rouge in Dearborn, Michigan; the company town of Pullman, Illinois, and Louis Sullivan's Chicago skyscrapers, and it concludes with a study of modern efforts to make the office and factory humane environments. (October 5, 1987; 60 min.)

The Street

The relationship between our transportation network—streets and roads—and the character of American cities and towns is demonstrated. Among the many classic examples shown are Pierre L'Enfant's avenues of Washington, D.C., which radiate from a central mall; James Oglethorpe's grid system of parks and streets for Savannah, Georgia; and the City Beautiful movement (spearheaded by the Chicago architect and entrepreneur Daniel H. Burnham) which brought order to American cities— from Springfield, Massachusetts, to San Francisco, California. (October 12, 1987; 60 min.)

Public Places and Monuments

The nation's public life is enhanced by a "ceremonial realm" in which design reveals the values of the people who commissioned and built monuments, churches, libraries, parks and civic centers. Kostof traces the incipient stages of the development of an American public realm from the New England common and courthouse square, to grandiose public buildings adorned in classical European styles. Ultimately, Kostof contends, a unique expression of values held in common reaches fruition in the statehouse and the urban park, pioneered by Frederick Law Olmsted's Central Park for New York City. (October 19, 1987; 60 min.)

The Shape of the Land

How more than 300 years of occupation has redesigned the landscape, with the clearing of forests, the draining of marshlands, the damming of rivers. The program reexamines the national mandate to tame the frontiers, beginning in the grid laid down in Congress's Land Ordinance of 1785. Aerial photography shows the persistence of these initial boundaries on today's landscape. The program also investigates the role of engineering in shaping the landscape, from the earliest bridges to massive hydroelectric generators. Accompanying the will to exploit the land is a strong tradition of concern to preserve its integrity, visible in the system of national and state parks. (October 26, 1987; 60 min.)

The Vietnam Veterans Memorial in Washington, D.C., a scene from Public Places and Monuments *on the series* AMERICA BY DESIGN. *Photo by Grace Guggenheim.*

VOICES AND VISIONS

"Poetry on television" was an uncontested contradiction in terms until the producer Lawrence Pitkethly found a way to convey a small-audience art through the mass medium. Combining documentary, narrative and experimental film techniques, the 13-part series gives primary emphasis to the poetry itself, often isolating on the screen the Word in its primal glory. As it moves from Whitman, who would have relished the audience television delivers, to such masters of confessional poetry as Lowell and Plath, the series also appeals to the ear as poems are spoken as well as seen. The films also comprise a college-level course and two companion volumes were published: an anthology, *Modern American Poets: Their Voices and Visions*, edited by Robert DiYanni (Random House, 1987), and a collection of critical essays, *Voices and Visions: The Poet in America*, edited by Helen Vendler (Vintage Books, 1987).

Executive producer: Lawrence Pitkethly
Senior producers: Jill Janows, Robert Chapman
Major funders include: Annenberg/CPB Project, National Endowment for the Humanities, with additional funding from Arthur Vining Davis Foundations, Ford Foundation
A production of New York Center for Visual History
Presented on PBS by South Carolina ETV
Closed captioned by the National Captioning Institute
Source: Intellimation

Robert Frost

Through his lyric poems and dramatic narratives, Frost asserts that nature is the clearest window into the human personality. Includes interviews with the poet conducted over 15 years as well as dramatized versions of some poems. (January 26, 1988; 60 min.)

Director: Peter Hammer
Senior producer: Lois Cuniff
Producer: Robert Chapman
Writer: Margot Feldman
Literary advisor: Richard Poirier

Ezra Pound: American Odyssey

Pound, the most controversial modern American poet, is seen in his journeys across Europe to Venice, to the south of France and then to London, where he set up a one-man literary center from 1908 to 1918 and became a leader in the modernist movement. Relatives, friends and critics discuss Pound's obsession with economic and political ideas while in Italy during World War II. (February 2, 1988; 60 min.)

Director, producer, writer: Lawrence Pitkethly
Literary advisor: James Laughlin

Langston Hughes: The Dreamkeeper

On-location footage from Senegal, France, Kansas and Harlem helps chronicle Hughes's work and life. Performances of his lyrics reveal their inspiration in the music he loved— jazz, the blues and gospel. Contemporary writers explore Hughes's influence on their work. (February 9, 1988; 60 min.)

Director: St. Clair Bourne
Producer: Robert Chapman
Writer: Leslie Lee
Literary advisor: Arnold Rampersad

Walt Whitman

Whitman was the first major poet to create a truly American vision and style. Readings of his poems convey their exuberance, poignancy and sheer power. The program reveals the eclectic influences on Whitman's poetry, including Emerson, the King James Bible, opera and political oratory. (February 16, 1988; 60 min.)

Director: Jack Smithie
Producer, writer: Lawrence Pitkethly
Literary advisor: Justin Kaplan

Hart Crane

The powerful images of contemporary machinery and the Brooklyn Bridge illustrate Crane's preoccupation with technology and its human impact. His optimistic belief that history and autobiography can be unified within a myth of America emerges through dramatizations of his life in the Caribbean, New York and Ohio. (February 23, 1988; 60 min.)

Director: Lawrence Pitkethly
Producer: Lois Cunniff
Writers: Derek Walcott, Margot Feldman
Literary advisor: Derek Walcott

William Carlos Williams

"No ideas but in things" was the aesthetic dictum of the New Jersey poet-physician whose work established a distinctly American kind of poem. Presentations of Williams's work demonstrate his innovative use of common objects and everyday experience as topics for poems as well as his formal experiments with the cadences of American speech. Also shown are the connections between Williams's poetry and the visual arts. (March 1, 1988; 60 min.)

Director: Richard P. Rogers
Producer, writer: Jill Janows
Literary advisor: Marjorie Perloff

Emily Dickinson

Dramatic recreations evoke the domestic context in which Dickinson wrote her metaphysical poetry. Along with rich New England landscapes, this backdrop illuminates Dickinson's epigrammatic genius. Though a recluse, the range of experience expressed in her poetry remains one of the most remarkable feats of the imagination. (March 8, 1988; 60 min.)

Director: Veronica Young
Producer: Jill Janows
Writer: Judith Thurman
Literary advisor: Richard Sewall

Marianne Moore: In Her Own Words

Poets and critics praise and explain the "wild decorum" of Moore's unique style. Presentations of her work show its use of idiosyncratic poetic forms and her penchant for incorporating quotations. Special emphasis is given to Moore's extraordinary powers of observation, whether of animals or artifacts, places or paintings. (March 15, 1988; 60 min.)

Director: Jeffrey Schon
Producers: David Schmerler, Robert Chapman
Writer: Vickie Karp
Literary advisor: Grace Schulman

T.S. Eliot

Footage from St. Louis, Boston, London and France helps trace Eliot's rise to eminence as the most influential poet of his generation. The film follows Eliot's career from the bold originality of *Prufrock* to the meditative inquiry of *Four Quartets*. (March 22, 1988; 60 min.)

Director, writer: Lawrence Pitkethly
Producers: Sasha Alpert, Lawrence Pitkethly
Literary advisor: Frank Kermode

Wallace Stevens: Man Made Out of Words

Footage of the Hartford, Connecticut, of Stevens's era sets the stage for the dual life he pursued as a successful insurance executive and poet. Several works reveal his sense of imagination not as an escape from reality, but as a journey to a new reality—a new order for modern man. (March 29, 1988; 60 min.)

Director: Richard P. Rogers
Producer: Jill Janows
Writer: Robert Seidman
Literary advisor: Helen Vendler

Elizabeth Bishop: One Art

The film explores Bishop's preoccupation with perception and the boundaries of consciousness, and it makes use of exotic documentary footage to heighten the magical realism of her poetry. Brazilian and North American images and artifacts convey Bishop's acute visual sense and idiosyncratic attention to poetic detail. (April 5, 1988; 60 min.)

Director, producer, writer: Jill Janows
Literary advisor: David Kalstone

Robert Lowell: A Mania for Phrases

Scenes from Italy, Amsterdam, Tennessee, Maine, Boston and New York illuminate the work of the historian-poet Lowell. Interviews discussing Lowell's use of autobiography as subject matter for poetry are interspersed with scenes of the poet in his apartment, on anti-war protest marches and tramping around Boston. (April 12, 1988; 60 min.)

Director: Peter Hammer
Producers: David Schmerler, Robert Chapman
Writer: Lawrence Pitkethly
Literary advisor: Herbert Leibowitz

Sylvia Plath

Archival footage of 1950s pop culture depicts the era of American society in which Plath reached maturity. The places she lived and wrote, Massachusetts, New York, Smith College, London and the Devon countryside, are used to illuminate her poetry. The complex relationship between Plath's troubled life, death and her brilliant work is discussed. (April 19, 1988; 60 min.)

Director: Lawrence Pitkethly
Producers: Sasha Alpert, Lawrence Pitkethly
Writer: Susan Yankowitz
Literary advisor: Frances McCullough

WORD INTO IMAGE:

WRITERS ON SCREENWRITING

The hazardous art and craft of the screenwriter is one of the least appreciated components in the group activity that results in a feature film. The screenplay, however, is the indispensable foundation on which the movie is built. Six distinguished screenwriters discuss how they adapt novels and plays and develop original ideas into screenplays, of which words are only one aspect, as the writer indicates silences, camera angles and editing through cuts and fades. The script's transformations through several versions are traced, and the relationship of the screenplay to the finished film, a link often invisible or underrated in the public eye, is made clear. The films examine each screenwriter's motivations and the obstacles they surmount to realize their goals. Film clips illustrate the results of the writer's—and the film's—odyssey.

Executive producer: Terry Sanders
Directed and produced by: Terry Sanders, Freida Lee Mock
Additional funders include: Public Broadcasting System
A production of the American Film Foundation in association with KOCE-TV/ Huntington Beach and the California Institute of the Arts
Source: American Film Foundation

William Goldman

This master of suspense has written such films as *All the President's Men, Butch Cassidy and the Sundance Kid* and *A Bridge Too Far*. Insisting on the importance of the screenwriter, Goldman challenges the notion that film is the director's medium. He considers the essence of the screenplay not dialogue or random character but the structure that carries the film as a whole. (October 10, 1982; 30 min.)

Paul Mazursky

With credits such as *Bob and Carol and Ted and Alice* (with Larry Tucker), *An Unmarried Woman, Blume in Love* and *Harry and Tonto* (with Josh Greenfeld), Mazursky has been widely recognized for his ability to elicit memorable characterizations from actors in his writing and directing. (October 17, 1982; 30 min.)

Eleanor Perry

One of a number of articulate women screenwriters, Perry wrote the screenplays for *Diary of a Mad Housewife, David and Lisa, Ladybug, Ladybug* and *Last Summer*. Her work addresses serious contemporary themes, and she is best known for dealing with the subjects of human disintegration and mental illness. (October 24, 1982; 30 min.)

Neil Simon

A fine line separates humor and tragedy. Simon, the immensely successful and prolific writer of comedy for stage and screen, plies his craft at the edges of this boundary. He believes that the best humor arises from the careful observation of credible, recognizable characters. His best-known works include *The Odd Couple, The Goodbye Girl, The Sunshine Boys, Chapter Two, Plaza Suite, The Out-of-Towners* and *Barefoot in the Park*. (October 31, 1982; 30 min.)

Carl Foreman

Internationally known as a filmmaker, screenwriting is basic to his art. His screenplays center on one major theme: the struggle of the individual against a hostile environment. Foreman speaks openly about Hollywood in the 1950s when he was blacklisted as an uncooperative witness before the House Un-American Activities Committee. Among his best-known films are *High Noon* and *Home of the Brave*. (November 7, 1982; 30 min.)

Robert Towne

In screenplays such as *Chinatown, Shampoo, Personal Best* and *The Last Detail*, Towne believes "You must ask [of a character] what it is he or she is *really* afraid of. It's my best way of getting into character." According to Towne, the writer has more control over his art than the director. "When I write," he says, "the only limits are my imagination and my ability to do it." (November 14, 1982; 30 min.)

THE PAINTER'S WORLD

Six half-hour programs explore the art of painting from the Renaissance to the present, and the changing themes, conventions and institutions that affect the practice of western painting. How art and artists function in society over the centuries is also explored.

Executive producer: Judith Wechsler
Additional funders include: National Endowment for the Humanities, Arthur Vining Davis Foundations, George Gund Foundation
A production of WGBH/Boston, Channel Four/Great Britain and Judith Wechsler, Inc.
Source: Coronet/MTI (educational)

Painting and the Public

Examines the shift from the private art collections of the Renaissance to today's public museums and the commerce in art at a Sotheby's auction and behind the scenes at some of the world's great museums. Also explored are how value accrues to works of art and whether art can be judged aesthetically while it is treated as a commodity. Interviewed are Leo Castelli, dealer; Dominique de Menil, collector, and Avigdor Arikha, artist. (October 18, 1989; 30 min.)

Director, writer: Judith Wechsler
Producer: Linda Zuck

The Training of Painters

What does a painter need to know? How much of painting is inherent talent and how much can be learned? The techniques of instruction, styles and changing values are examined. Film footage from a 1951 class given by Joseph Albers at Yale illustrates the Bauhaus belief that only craft, not art, can be taught. Visits to the Royal Academy of Art in London and the Ecole des Beaux Arts in France show young artists practicing the techniques that obtained 300 years ago. (October 20, 1989; 30 min.)

Director: Judith Wechsler
Producers: Mike Dibb, Penny Forster

The Artist and the Nude

The nude, perhaps the most persistent theme in the visual arts, is a subject whose complexity has challenged artists for centuries. The film looks at the changing role of the nude in art, evolving notions of beauty, the making and breaking of traditions and the shift in images of the human figure from prominent men to sensuous women. (October 27, 1989; 30 min.)

Director, producer: Judith Wechsler

Portraits

Changing conventions have influenced modern portraiture and the invention of photography has challenged portraitists to reassess their art. The invention of photography in the mid-19th century forced artists to consider what painting could express that photographs could not. Discussing and illustrating the inherent differences of these approaches are the painters Philip Pearlstein and Yolanda Sonnabend and the photographers Joel Meyerowitz and Jo Spence. (November 3, 1989; 30 min.)

Producer, director: Judith Wechsler
Writers: Judith Wechsler, Linda Nochlin

The Arrested Moment

"Movement is life," says David Hockney, demonstrating his approach to extending time through his art. The evocation of movement has long been a high measure of a painter's skill, centuries before the photograph. Michelangelo, Rembrandt, Picasso and Pollock all depict moments that express change through time and space within the canvas. Strategies change, but today's artists face the same problems as their predecessors. (November 10, 1989; 30 min.)

Director, producer, writer: Judith Wechsler

Abstraction

Abstract art has dominated 20th-century art. Rejecting artistic conventions handed down since the Renaissance, abstract painters have struggled for the acceptance from a public hesitant to assimilate this new language of art. The film traces the development of abstract art through the works of major innovators: Paul Cezanne, Piet Mondrian and Vassily Kandinsky; Jackson Pollock and Frank Stella. (November 17, 1989; 30 min.)

Director, producer: Judith Wechsler
Writers: Judith Wechsler, Henri Zerner

WOMEN IN ART

WOMEN IN ART explores the lives and work of American women artists. In each of six films, one outstanding woman artist is portrayed; the seventh film, *Anonymous Was a Woman*, relates how many American women in the 18th and 19th centuries expressed their creativity in the needlework and decorative crafts that adorned their homes. All seven films were telecast in 1979 as part of a larger series entitled *The Originals*. WOMEN IN ART served as inspiration for a book entitled *Originals: American Women Artists*, by Eleanor Munro (Simon & Schuster, 1979).

Executive producer: Perry Miller Adato
Additional funders include: Corporation for Public Broadcasting
A production of WNET/Thirteen

Georgia O'Keeffe

Based on interviews in her New Mexico home, the film provides a rare glimpse of the painter's life. O'Keeffe discusses her art and the New Mexico landscape that inspired her; photographs by Ansel Adams, Alfred Steiglitz and Edward Steichen illustrate her career and personal history. First broadcast on the artist's 90th birthday in November, 1977. (March 9, 1978; 60 min.)

Director, producer: Perry Miller Adato
Source: Films, Inc. (educational);
HomeVision (home video)

Mary Cassatt: Impressionist from Philadelphia

Mary Cassatt (1845 - 1926) settled in Paris in the 1870s where she was a colleague of the French impressionists. Yet Cassatt always considered herself an American. "When you write about my work. . . make sure to say I'm American, plain and simply." The film traces Cassatt's career as an artist, the influence of Pissarro and Degas, and her own compulsion to embrace innovation. "Acceptance on someone else's terms," she stated, "is worse than rejection." French and American scholars discuss Cassatt's contribution and recount the difficulties she faced as a woman and an artist in the late 19th century. (February 2, 1978; 30 min.)

Director, producer: Perry Miller Adato
Source: Films, Inc. (educational);
HomeVision (home video)

Nevelson in Process

Louise Nevelson, born in 1899 in Russia, created her monumental sculptures in wood and in steel. The film opens with the dedication of an environment for New York City's Chapel of the Good Shepherd and concludes with the dedication of her colossal sculpture for San Francisco's Embarcadero. Throughout, the artist reflects on her life and her art. (February 9, 1978; 30 min.)

Directed and produced by: Susan Fanshel, Jill Godmilow
Source: Films, Inc. (educational);
HomeVision (home video)

Spirit Catcher: The Art of Betye Saar

Prowling swap meets and flea markets, Betye Saar gathers the materials for her collages, assemblages and altars. Saar explains that these found objects, the photos, mementos and miscellany, all carry overtones of absent people, the spirits her works capture. She discusses the progression of her work from graphic art, to printmaking to assemblage, and touches on being black and being an artist, in her view "the best of both worlds." (February 16, 1978; 30 min.)

Director, producer: Suzanne Bauman

Alice Neel: Collector of Souls

According to the artist, "Art is essential to living, no matter how uncomfortable it makes [people]." Neel dislikes being referred to as a portraitist; her works go deeper than the surface of the images of the people she paints, incorporating insight and originality in a genre more often tailored to the sitter's self-image rather than the painter's perception and self-expression. The film follows Neel as she creates a work, recounts the progression of her career since the 1930s and concludes with her induction into the American Academy of Arts and Sciences in the late 1970s. (February 23, 1978; 30 min.)

Director, producer: Nancy Baer

Anonymous Was a Woman

The story of American women in the 18th and 19th century and the art they created as part of their duties of running a household and raising families: quilts, needlework, watercolors, embroidery and other crafts. The film celebrates the anonymous woman's will to clarify and beatify the ordinary world. A book of the same title by Mirra Bank was published by St. Martin's Press in 1979. (March 2, 1978; 30 min.)

Director, producer: Mirra Bank

Frankenthaler: Toward a New Climate

Helen Frankenthaler traces her 30-year career from the 1950s. She discusses abstract expressionism and its influence on her and works on her large-scale canvases, which she describes as reflecting an abstract climate, "not nature per se, but a feeling of order and therefore of nature—order out of chaos. . .,the same battle nature is always fighting." (March 9, 1978; 30 min.)

Director, producer: Perry Miller Adato

The sculptor Louise Nevelson at the 1983 Spoleto Festival USA. Photo by William Struhs.

MEDIA PROBES

By educating viewers and listeners to decode the assumptions implicit in much popular entertainment, the audience's critical abilities are enhanced. Broadcast in 1982, MEDIA PROBES is one of the earliest attempts to teach literacy in media through the medium of television itself. An educational guide for use with the series was produced by Prime Time School Television, a nonprofit foundation.

Producers: Kit Laybourne, Mickey Lemle, Marty Ostrow, Alan Goldberg
Additional funders: Corporation for Public Broadcasting, Ford Foundation, Rockefeller Foundation, Alfred P. Sloan Foundation, public television stations
A production of WQED/Pittsburgh

Photography

Examines the work and ideas of five people who make their livelihoods behind the camera: the photo-essayist, Bruce Davidson; the Pulitzer-Prize winning photographer, David Kennerly; the *New York Daily News* photojournalist, Mary DiBiase; a commercial photographer, Michael O'Neill, and a wedding photographer, Gil Amaral. Cheryl Tiegs is host. (April 21, 1982; 30 min.)

Soap Operas

A behind-the-scenes view of the production process that yields the daily "soap," here ABC's *All My Children*. The host, Ruth Warrick, tracks the evolution of one dramatic scene. Pete Lemay, a writer for *Another World* and *Search for Tomorrow*, discusses the rigors of writing for this genre and speculates about the impact of soap operas on culture. (April 28, 1982; 30 min.)

TV News

Examines the construction of the TV news package: interviews with "news consultant" Frank Magid in Marion, Iowa; a close-up of a news show in Phoenix, Arizona, which uses a jet helicopter to expand its live coverage; the task facing a third-place CBS station in Los Angeles trying win in that market's ratings war. Hosted by John Cameron Swayze, television's first national anchorman. (May 5, 1982; 30 min.)

Language

Language, the medium of everyday discourse, is examined as one of the mass media. Its impact on nearly every aspect of our culture comes across: in a rehearsal and performance with the National Theater of the Deaf; in the influence of the women's movement on recent editions of the Barnhart Dictionary; in a seminar with a leading authority on abusive language and in an animated *Doonesbury* comic strip. The host, Victor Borge, adds his own special linguistic humor. (May 12, 1982; 30 min.)

Political Spots

The techniques used by political image makers are sampled through political spots from across the country, representing all parties and many levels of government. Two media consultants, Bob Squier and Bob Goodman, share their views on the subject; some renowned negative "attack spots" are examined. The host is Mark Shields, the political columnist for the *Washington Post*. (May 19, 1982; 30 min.)

Design

Every object in the man-made environment not only serves a function, but carries a message. The fashion designer Bill Blass takes viewers behind the scenes at the showing of one of his collections; the graphic designer and illustrator Milton Glaser and the product designers Morison and Michael Cousins are interviewed; the designer Herb Lubalin narrates an animated sequence depicting the evolution of the PBS logo. (May 26, 1982; 30 min.)

Soundaround

The man-made sound environment unfolds as viewers meet the president of Muzak, Inc., whose analytic and stimulus-programming practices are contrasted with the experimental music of the Obie Award-winning composer Elizabeth Swados. The writer Tony Kahn hosts the program. (June 2, 1982; 30 min.)

The Future

An examination of society's growing interface with communications technologies: interactive computers, cable television and video discs, among others. The program explores the effects of these new media forms on the way we live, work and play. Peter Schwarz, futurist, hosts the program. (June 9, 1982; 30 min.)

Chapter 10:

MEDIA ART

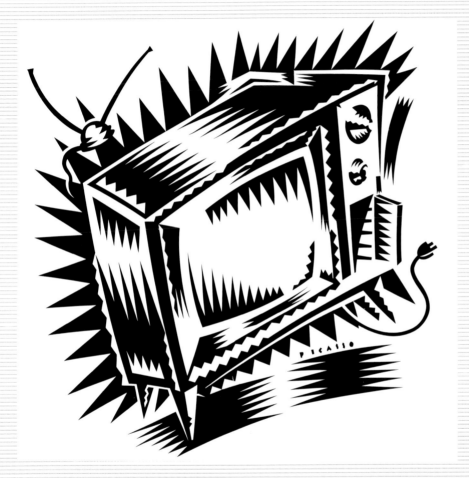

ALIVE FROM OFF CENTER

NEW TELEVISION

P.O.V.

THE INDEPENDENTS

NON-FICTION TELEVISION

MEDIA SPECIALS

A graphic emblem from ALIVE FROM OFF CENTER, whose print and video graphics have received numerous awards.

ALIVE FROM OFF CENTER

In summer of 1985, the avant-garde made its first concerted attack on the exclusive precincts of public television's prime-time. Individual programs, no matter how brilliant, gain sporadic access unless they are formatted into a series with its own distinct profile. Recognizing this, Melinda Ward, the series' founding producer, established a vigorous liaison with individual media artists in dance-video, performance and video art, organizing a frozen constellation of separate films and videos into aggressive themes, and beginning the commissioning of programs nationally and internationally that became the series' defining signature.

ALIVE FROM OFF CENTER pioneered the notion that advanced video art belonged not in the confines of gallery and museum, but on the air as part of the broadcast landscape. There, unprotected by the special pleading intrinsic to institutional exhibition, it has acquainted a vastly extended audience with the dazzling spatial rhetoric and technological virtuosity of advanced video art. MTV and television commercials have already donated their idea of process through epigrammatic compression and inventive contrast to several generations of television watchers. ALIVE's two major achievements are to force television to examine its own processes with a comparable energy while opening up imaginative vistas in word and image unavailable to any other medium. The younger audience the series brought to public television frequently had to search for it in marginal time slots in several schedules. Despite this, each program, on average, attracted 1.5 million viewers. In contrast to television's usual prose, the series articulates in a new electronic language an urgent, demanding poetry.

Executive producers: Melinda Ward (seasons 1 - 3), John Schott (seasons 4 - 6), Alyce Dissette (season 7)
Producers: Tom Adair (season 1), John Schott (seasons 2 - 3), John Ligon (seasons 4 - 7)
Acquisitions and new productions: Neil V. Sieling (seasons 5 - 7)
Additional funders include: AT&T Foundation, Corporation for Public Broadcasting, Ford Foundation, John D. and Catherine T. MacArthur Foundation, Northwest Area Foundation, Rockefeller Foundation
A production of ALIVE FROM OFF CENTER and Twin Cities Public Television (KTCA/St. Paul-Minneapolis)

SEASON ONE, 1985

A production of KTCA/St. Paul-Minneapolis and the Walker Art Center

Host: Susan Stamberg

Short Video Artworks

Ear to the Ground, by John Sanborn and Kit Fitzgerald, follows the percussionist David Van Tieghem through the streets of Manhattan. In *Discreet Charm of the Diplomacy* by Zbigniew Rybczynski a parade of animals crashes a White House reception. In *Ringside*, by Michael Schwartz, the dancer Elizabeth Streb performs on a circular platform set on a slant. *Sharkey's Day*, by Laurie Anderson, uses computer graphics styled as a video game. Among several short pieces by William Wegman is *Singing Stomach*. *Sankai Juku* is the Japanese Butoh dance group whose disturbing yet mystical performance style probes the Japanese national identity. (July 1, 1985; 30 min.)

Video Dance

Maasai: Pages from the Book of Rain, by Gary Hurst, is a symbolic tale about freedom in tribal and urban life by England's black dance group, Maasai. *Parafango*, made for French television, is a collaboration between the video artist Charles Atlas, the choreographer Karole Armitage and the composer David Linton. It mixes fantasy and reality in plots and sub-plots revolving around Armitage's relationship with four men. (July 8, 1985; 30 min.)

Smothering Dreams

A powerful autobiographical work by Dan Reeves that creates memorable images of combat through the eyes of a Vietnam veteran. Dedicated to American soldiers who died in a Vietnam ambush on January 20, 1969, *Smothering Dreams* incorporates clips from government archives, reenacted combat scenes and childhood memories. The soundtrack by John Hilton is composed of spoken words, music and electronically synthesized sound. (July 15, 1985; 30 min.)

Awards: Emmy Award: Best Documentary
Source: ALIVE FROM OFF CENTER

Comedy on Video

The Day Before, by Zbigniew Rybczynski, shows a Soviet cosmonaut deliriously enjoying his vodka. In *Deodorant Commercial*, William Wegman applies a skewed perspective to the world of television commercials. *Man Ray, Man Ray* (also by Wegman) though ostensibly about the artist, Man Ray, turns out to be about Wegman's dog, Man Ray. *Thirty-Second Spots*, by Joan Logue, use the visual language of commercials to advertise artists. *Made for TV*, by Ann Magnuson and Tom Rubnitz, captures the multitude of characters seen on a TV screen—from faith-healing evangelists to MTV-style rock queens. (July 22, 1985; 30 min.)

Source: ALIVE FROM OFF CENTER

Tongues

A monologue written by Sam Shepard and directed by Shirley Clarke, *Tongues* tells a man's dreams, stories and recollections in a cycle of poems performed by Joseph Chaikin. It incorporates experimental techniques and innovative use of language: Clarke uses a different directorial style for each monologue and meshes the reading of the poetry with a syncopated jazz percussion score. Produced by the Women's Interart Center. An interview between Clarke and the host, Susan Stamberg, follows the video. (July 29, 1985; 30 min.)

Summer Dances

Five short dance videos excerpted from longer pieces. *Window Dance* (from *George's House* choreographed by Dan Wagoner) evokes memories of a West Virginia childhood. Directed by David Atwood. *August 27, Coney Island*, an excerpt from *From an Island Summer* by Karole Armitage and Charles Atlas, celebrates Latin street dance in New York City. *Dance in Front of the Church* (from *Secret of the Waterfall* by Douglas Dunn and Charles Atlas), is based on a text by the poet Anne Waldman. Also shown are *City Hall Plaza* from *District One* by Rudy Perez and *Street Dances* from *You Little Wild Heart* by Marta Renzi. (August 5, 1985; 30 min.)

Source: WGBH/Boston

Dear ALIVE FROM OFF CENTER:

Congratulations on ALIVE FROM OFF CENTER, in my mind the finest, most exhilarating half-hour on television.

Thanks—and keep up the good work!

D.R.A., Beaverton, Ore.

A Personal History of the American Theater

The performance artist and actor Spalding Gray reconstructs his experiences in the contemporary theater in an original work directed by Skip Blumberg. Gray's idiosyncratic anecdotes impart glimpses of plays, directors, colleagues, theaters, audiences and the media. *A Personal History of the American Theater* was taped in Minneapolis in June, 1985. (August 12, 1985; 30 min.)

Source: ALIVE FROM OFF CENTER (1985 - 2001)

Artists' Music Videos

Dancing Man by Mitchell Kriegman features Bill Irwin and the disco song *Shake your Groove Thing*. *The Women's Group*, by David Cunningham of the Flying Lizards, is an ironic interpretation of the song *And Then He Kissed Me*. *Lake Placid 80*, by Nam June Paik, is a look at the 1980 Winter Olympics set to Mitch Ryder's *Devil With a Blue Dress/ Good Golly Miss Molly*. In *Record Players* by Christian Marclay, 20 "human record players" scratch, hit, shake, slap, wobble, rattle and break phonograph records. *Act III*, by John Sanborn, is an abstract tale told through computer graphics and video imagery, with music by Philip Glass. The program concludes with an early version of *Once in a Lifetime* by David Byrne and the Talking Heads. (August 19, 1985; 30 min.)

SEASON TWO, 1986

Host: Susan Stamberg

Animation, Dance and Comedy

Luminare by John Sanborn and Dean Winkler is a dazzling display of video pyrotechnics that explores man's interaction with technology. Commissioned for Expo '86 in Vancouver. *Jump* by Charles Atlas presents a dance cabaret with choreography by Phillipe DeCoufle and music by The Residents. Originally produced for French television. *These are the Rules* by Doug Hall and *The Sounds of Defiance* by Teddy Dibble are video/performance works with satire and social commentary. (June 30, 1986; 30 min.)

Source: ALIVE FROM OFF CENTER

Sister Suzie Cinema

A screen adaptation of Lee Breuer's original stage production. Directed by John Sanborn, *Sister Suzie Cinema* is a high-energy opera about adolescent love and romantic movies of the 1940s and 1950s. Composer Bob Telson created the 1950s-style musical score. The work features 14 Karat Soul, an *a cappella* doo-wop group and actor Ben Halley, Jr. Produced by the Women's Interart Center for ALIVE FROM OFF CENTER. (July 7, 1986; 30 min.)

Source: ALIVE FROM OFF CENTER

Fire, Light, Sticks/ Rotary Action

Fire, Light, Sticks spotlights the juggler and "new vaudevillian" Michael Moschen, best known for his "circus-artworks." Here he performs with crystal balls, glowing rods and shooting flames. Directed by Skip Blumberg; music by David Van Tieghem. Produced in association with the Brooklyn Academy of Music.

Rotary Action features the choreographers Bill T. Jones and Arnie Zane performing in their distinctive, vigorous style. Directed by Geoff Dunlop. (July 14, 1986; 30 min.)

Source, Rotary Action only: WGBH/Boston

Computer Animation

Two international productions use computer animation technology for dramatic psychological effects. *Hyster Pulsatu*, by the Dutch artist and composer Jaap Drupsteen, is an apocalyptic musical fantasy in which travelers journey through a computer-animated landscape. *Mt. Fuji*, by Ko Nakajima, is an electronic ode to Japan's most celebrated mountain, as it is made to float and twist through space to reflect the different seasons of the year. (July 21, 1986; 30 min.)

The World of Photography

William Wegman and the performance artist Michael Smith spoof "how-to" shows and self-improvement courses. The two artists pose as a world-weary photography teacher and an innocent student bumbling through a series of adventures and misadventures. Produced in association with the CAT Fund. (July 28, 1986; 30 min.)

Source: ALIVE FROM OFF CENTER

Video Theater and Dance

Four dancers perform in *Visual Shuffle*. Each deals with a different "video space" and special effect. *Fractured Variations* presents a series of athletic stunts performed by three dancers. Directed by John Sanborn and Mary Perillo; music by Bill Buchen and Scott Johnson; choreography by Charles Moulton. *Rude Raid*, produced for French television, recalls the primitive rites of manhood as ancient myth meets popular culture in a sophisticated electronic dance the-

ater. Directed by Mark Caro; choreographed by Regine Chopinot. (August 4, 1986; 30 min.)

Three Choreographers

Accumulation with Talking plus Water Motor, directed by Jonathan Demme, is a virtuosic dance in which the choreographer Trisha Brown tells three stories and simultaneously performs two dances. *Nine-Person Precision Ball Passing*, directed by Skip Blumberg, is an athletic work by the former Merce Cunningham dancer, Charles Moulton. Moulton's choreography explores the potential of movement design through dance and athletic forms, with an emphasis on rhythmic structure and lyricism. *Caught*, by David Parsons, uses strobe lighting to create the illusion of dancing on air. Directed by Roberto Romano; music by Robert Fripp. (August 11, 1986; 30 min.)

Source: ALIVE FROM OFF CENTER

Young Video Artists

Works by young artists that comment on contemporary social values and a media-saturated culture. Five comedy sketches by Teddy Dibble are presented, including *The Sound of Music*, *A Scar-y Story*, and *What a Difference a Day Makes*. *Vault*, by Bruce and Norman Yonemoto, reworks soap operas in a love story about a woman pole vaulter/ concert cellist and a cowboy/ abstract expressionist painter. *Perfect Leader*, by Max Almy, is a musical satire on political image-making. *Hippie to Yuppie*, by Benjamin Bergery, is a video poem made from computer-generated graffiti in which the values of the 1960s become the trivia of the 1980s. (August 18, 1986; 30 min.)

Source: ALIVE FROM OFF CENTER

In As Seen On TV, *the performance artist, clown and "new vaudevillian," Bill Irwin, finds himself trapped inside a TV set, first with members of Sesame Street and later with Beatriz Rodriguez, a ballerina with The Joffrey Ballet. Photo by Paula Court.*

SEASON THREE, 1987

Host: Laurie Anderson

As Seen on TV

Bill Irwin in an homage to the great silent film comedians. Irwin himself has been acclaimed as a "new vaudevillian" for his performances as actor, dancer and clown. In *As Seen on TV*, he becomes imprisoned in the manic world of television, stumbling through a series of familiar television programming genres: a music video, a cultural program with The Joffrey Ballet and *Sesame Street* with Bert and Ernie. Directed by Charles Atlas; choreography by William Whitener and Diane Martel. (July 13, 1987; 30 min.)

Source: ALIVE FROM OFF CENTER (until 1995)

Street of Crocodiles

Timothy and Stephen Quay's animated puppet drama *Street of Crocodiles* is based on stories written by Bruno Schulz during the Nazi occupation of Poland. The film takes a surreal journey through miniature cityscapes populated by porcelain-faced dolls, into the darker reaches of our collective psyche. Produced by Keith Griffiths; puppet design by Olivier Gillon; music composed by Leszek Jankowski. (July 20, 1987; 30 min.)

Source: ALIVE FROM OFF CENTER

Steps

Zbigniew Rybczynski merges social satire and wit with state-of-the-art video technology in *Steps*, taking off in

Choreography by David Gordon

Three works by David Gordon. In *Dorothy and Eileen*, directed by Ed Steinberg, two women dance while confiding stories about their mothers. *Close-up*, also directed by Steinberg, features Gordon and Valda Setterfield (husband and wife) in a work that evokes the dynamics of the couple relationship. *Panel* is a discussion of Gordon's work and its meaning by ten characters—all played by Gordon himself. (August 25, 1986; 30 min.)

Source: ALIVE FROM OFF CENTER

What You Mean "We"?

The first extended work created for broadcast television by the composer and performance artist Laurie Anderson. In *What You Mean "We"?* Anderson uses computer animation, storytelling, folk, pop and new music to explore such issues as the nature of individuality, creativity, progress and fear of technology. Anderson performs alongside video-generated "clones" of herself. (September 1, 1986; 30 min.)

Source: WGBH/Boston, Video Data Bank

an unexpected direction from the famous Odessa Steps sequence in Sergei Eisenstein's *Battleship Potemkin*. Combining old film footage with new video images, Rybczynski causes a busload of American tourists to show up at the Odessa Steps as the Cossacks are about to fire on their victims. Music composed by Michael Urbaniak. (July 27, 1987; 30 min.)

Source: ALIVE FROM OFF CENTER

Metabolism/Geography

Two collaborative works by the choreographer Molissa Fenley and the video artists John Sanborn and Mary Perillo. *Metabolism* is a non-stop dance that focuses on the inner workings of the body in motion and in transit. Music by David Van Tieghem. *Geography*, filmed on location in the Painted Desert of New Mexico, pins the body of the dancer against a strange and harsh southwest landscape. Soundtrack by James Newton. (August 3, 1987; 30 min.)

Source: ALIVE FROM OFF CENTER

Funhouse

An adaptation of Eric Bogosian's 1985 off-Broadway solo show in which he paints a bleak landscape of contemporary society. In *Funhouse*, Bogosian portrays the haves and have-nots, the disadvantaged and those who prey upon others. He segues smoothly from the telephone salesman pitching life insurance, to a down-and-out wino, to a sadistic spaced-out killer, to an agent good-naturedly leading a seminar on the techniques of torture. Directed by Howard Silver. (August 10, 1987; 30 min.)

Source: ALIVE FROM OFF CENTER

Operation X

A series of four comic vignettes by the performance/video artists Teddy Dibble and Mitchell Kriegman. In *The Time Traveler*, a character has solved time travel, but only in short hops of five or ten minutes. *Try Not to Worry* is a troubled doctor's ironic effort to comfort his patient. In *Where Am I?*, a surprised character keeps waking up in a new location. *Out of Sync* is the frustrating story of a man whose world falls out of sync. (August 17, 1987; 30 min.)

Source: ALIVE FROM OFF CENTER

The Flood

A video opera directed by Jaap Drupsteen and based on the 1961 work by Igor Stravinsky. Derived principally from the book of *Genesis* and the York and Chester miracle plays, *The Flood* blends electronic theater and Stravinsky's lyric retelling of the story of creation. Elsa Lancaster and Sebastian Cabot are featured; narrated by Laurence Harvey; music by the Columbia Symphony Orchestra and Chorus. (August 24, 1987; 30 min.)

Source: National Video Corporation

Five Dances on Video

Airdance and *Landings*, two dances by Elizabeth Streb, use risk-oriented situations to express the artist's concern with extending the physical boundaries of performance. Michael Clark and company perform two dances from *Hail the New Puritan* that combine dance, music, costumes and brash ideas characteristic of his "post-punk" choreography. Directed by Charles Atlas. *Daytime Moon*, a work of Butoh (a Japanese modern dance) by the choreographer Min Tanaka, is a stylized vision of evolution and creation. Directed by Sandy Smolan; soundtrack by Libby Larson. (August 31, 1987; 30 min.)

Ellis Island

Meredith Monk's and Bob Rosen's *Ellis Island* evokes the experience of the sixteen million people who came through Ellis Island, the "Isle of Tears," from 1892 to 1927. Abandoned since 1954, Monk populates the ruins with men in black suits and hats and women in dark 19th-century dresses and shawls, recreating a world through sound and image that poignantly recalls our immigrant beginnings. (September 7, 1987; 30 min.)

Source: ALIVE FROM OFF CENTER

Calabash/Sticks/ Aquamirabilis

In *Women of the Calabash*, directed by Skip Blumberg, an all-female percussion and vocal ensemble combine ideas and sounds from old and new worlds to create an exotic melody. *Sticks on the Move*, by Pooh Kaye and Elisabeth Ross, employs stop-action photography to create the illusion of large wooden posts moving, sliding and marching along city streets as dancers move among them. Gene Menger's musical score in *Aquamirabilis* sensually enhances the languid images of underwater dancing. Created by the choreographer Dee McCandless. (September 14, 1987; 30 min.)

Source: ALIVE FROM OFF CENTER

SEASON FOUR, 1988

Hosts: Ann Magnuson, William Wegman

Bite and Smile/Aria

A satire on advertising by Broadcast Arts, *Bite and Smile* takes a behind-the-scenes look at a fantasy-land advertising production house as desks fly and potatoes talk. Directed by Stephen Oakes. Julian Temple's segment of the feature film *Aria*, a multi-part work in which ten filmmakers interpret oper-

Dear ALIVE FROM OFF CENTER:

I saw a program on Wisconsin Public Television a few months ago called Between Two Hands *from* Dancing Hands. *I thought it was great, and thought it would be a great basis to develop a lesson around. (I am an elementary school teacher.) How may I get a copy of this program? I simply must have it.*

Sincerely,

T.F., Madison, Wis.

atic arias, is set to the score of Verdi's *Rigoletto*. Filmed at the Madonna Inn in San Luis Obispo, California. (July 11, 1988; 30 min.)

Alter Image

Five selections from *Alter Image*, a production of Britain's Channel Four. *Love Me Gangster*, written by Malcolm Bennett and Aidan Hughes, spoofs the gangster movie. *Rory McLeod* shows the rapper and harmonica player performing one of his urban ballads in lesser-known parts of London. *Dustbin Dance*, set to music by Pookie Snackenberger and choreographed by Micha Bergese, depicts a gang rumble in an underground garage. *Laurie Booth in Camera* spotlights the choreographer as a solitary figure in a stark room. The choreographer Michael Clark performs the title role in *The Shivering Man* by Angela Conway. (July 18, 1988; 30 min.)

Source: ALIVE FROM OFF CENTER

Men Die Sooner/Endance

Men Die Sooner is a one-man performance by Tom Cayler as Everyman, worried as to why men die earlier than women. Cayler brings a comic urgency to current theories of male biochemistry and psychosocial behavior. Directed by Niles Siegel. Filmed live at Henry Street Settlement in New York

City. In *Endance*, the former choreographer Timothy Buckley articulates the reasons why he withdrew from a career in the institutionalized dance world. Directed by John Sanborn; music by "Blue" Gene Tyranny. (July 25, 1988; 30 min.)

Source: ALIVE FROM OFF CENTER

The World Within Us/ Commitment

The World Within Us by Terry Flaxton explores the thoughts and memories of a dying man. Narrated by Jonathan Pryce; starring Llewellyn Rees. *Commitment: Two Portraits*, by Blondell Cummings, is a television adaptation of two dance/performance works examining woman's role as nurturer and the female black American experience. *Nun*, an excerpt from the stage performance *The Art of War*, is a collaboration between Cummings and the writer Jessica Hagedorn examining the barriers of race, sex and nationality. (August 1, 1988; 30 min.)

Source: ALIVE FROM OFF CENTER

The Kitchen Presents

Three experimental videos coproduced by The Kitchen, Ex Nihilo and ALIVE FROM OFF CENTER. All are collaborations between American and French video artists. *Godard*, by the French director Robert Cahen and the American composer John Zorn, evokes the spirit of the filmmaker Jean-Luc Godard in contemporary New York and in Switzerland, Godard's childhood home. *The Fourth Dimension* by Zbigniew Rybczynski visualizes four pictorial dimensions electronically from multiple points of observation. *Sotto Voce* by the French director Jean-Louis Le Tacon and the New York choreographer/dancer Stephen Petronio is a layered series of movements based on the gestures and images of celebrated singers and public figures. (August 8, 1988; 30 min.)

Source: The Kitchen

In a Garden/ Three Sisters Who Are Not Sisters

The Dutch video artist Jaap Drupsteen's post-modern version of two Gertrude Stein plays, *In a Garden* and *Three Sisters Who Are Not Sisters*, evokes the world of Stein's poetry through song and recitation, stylized performance and computer-generated theater. The two plays, atypical of Stein's opus, were written for and originally performed by the children of a small village. They mix fairy tale images with the frightening elements of a child's world. Music by Fay Lovesky. (August 15, 1988; 30 min.)

Source: RM Associates

Two Dance Companies from Canada

Jericho, performed by Montreal Danse, is a black-and-white performance about the consequences of betrayal choreographed by Daniel Levelle. *Tell*, by Montreal Danse, is a work for four male dancers that ranges from comedy to drama, choreographed by Paul-Andre Fortier. La La La Human Steps, a company founded in 1980 by the choreographer Edouard Lock, performs *Human Sex Duo No. 1*. The pas de deux is set in a deserted ballroom that ends up underwater. Also an excerpt from *Exhibition*, a collaboration between the director Bernar Hebert and the choreographer Daniele Desnoyers. (August 22, 1988; 30 min.)

Source, Exhibition only: Antenna

Dancing Hands

Nine works by choreographers and dancers that use only hand and arm gestures. Each piece is performed by its creator: *Finger Tapping* by Harold Nicholas; *Ballet Hand Isolations* by Robert LaFosse; *Joe and Blanche* by Blondell Cummings and Keith Terry; *Hip Hop Hands* by Steve "Wiggles" Clemente and Gilbert "Shalimar"

Kennedy; *Cassie's Dream*, an interpretation by Wendy Perron of a text by Sophie Healy; *X-Ray* by Wendy Perron and Lisa Bush; *Prevailing Conditions (Handshake Sequence)* by Ellen Fisher; *Between Two Hands* by Sally Hess; and *Body Music for Hands* by Keith Terry. Directed by Skip Blumberg. (August 29, 1988; 30 min.)

Source: ALIVE FROM OFF CENTER

SEASON FIVE, 1989

Ile Aiye (The House of Life)

In *Ile Aiye (The House of Life)* David Byrne examines *Candomble*, the all-consuming religion, music and way of life of Bahia, the northeastern province of Brazil. The film shows this culture in a more realistic light than the devil-worshipping, spell-casting image often portrayed. (June 30, 1989; 60 min.)

Source: ALIVE FROM OFF CENTER

Tribute to Georges Melies

A video homage to one of the founding masters of fantasy and special effects in cinema. Melies, a successful magician, began investigating film as a medium of trickery in 1896. Through inventive optical effects and elaborate sets and props, he discovered how to make objects and people appear, disappear and grow larger and smaller. While best known for his fantastic tales, Melies also produced witty advertising films and re-stagings of actual events. Shown are several of Melies's original pieces and three creative responses to his legacy: Philippe Gautier's *The Seven Deadly Sins*, Aline Isserman's *The Slap of Beate Klarsfeld* and Pierre Etaix's *The Artist's Dream*. (July 6, 1989; 30 min.)

Source: ALIVE FROM OFF CENTER

Dance/Video Collaborations

Untitled, directed by John Sanborn and Mary Perillo, is a tribute by Bill T. Jones to his long-time partner, Arnie Zane, who recently died from AIDS. Jones includes Zane's voice on recordings, animates still images of him dancing, then recreates some of Zane's unique steps. *Arms*, directed by Isabelle Hayeur for Agent Orange, is an exploration of power relationships between men and women featuring the choreographer Susan Marshall and Arthur Armijo. Ishmael Houston-Jones's *Relatives* (directed by Julie Dash) focuses on the family and one's ambivalence toward it. In one segment, Houston-Jones dances while his mother, Pauline Jones, delivers an improvised monologue. (July 13, 1989; 30 min.)

Source: ALIVE FROM OFF CENTER

The Way Things Go

In *The Way Things Go*, the Swiss artists Peter Fischli and David Weiss harness air, water, fire, chemical reagents and simple machines to enact a chain of events that becomes an endlessly inventive meditation on cause and effect generating continuous process. (July 20, 1989; 30 min.)

Source: First Run/Icarus Films

Codex

The French director and choreographer Philippe DeCoufle creates a mysterious document from an unexplored ancient culture in *Codex*. In this "beautifully graphic poem, filled with non sequiturs," a lanky young man reads nonsense syllables with blustering sincerity while sand pours on his head and two dancers move in precise symmetry—one frequently upside-down. These evocative moments are introduced by titles in an unfamiliar script, and the music ranges from Arabic to Asian to Fats Domino to opera and yodeling. (July 27, 1989; 30 min.)

Source: Ellipse

Mountain View

A short story about love and reunion, essentially told without words, *Mountain View* is directed by John Sayles and choreographed by Marta Renzi. Through choreography, popular and folk music, the relationships among a dozen people who happen to stop at a country tavern are developed. The people include newlyweds on their honeymoon, mother and son, old and young, close friends and estranged friends, travelers, young lovers and long-time lovers. The group also meets the next day at a picnic. *Principal cast:* Jane Alexander, Jace Alexander, Marta Renzi & Dancers. (August 3, 1989; 30 min.)

Source: ALIVE FROM OFF CENTER

Multicultural Dance

Raoul Trujillo's *Shaman's Journey* draws upon the rites of the shamans, the spiritual visionaries of many Native American tribal peoples. Trujillo, a member of the Genizaro tribe, draws from his background in Native American dance and as a member of the Alwin Nikolais Dance Theater. Directed by Susan Rynard for Agent

Orange. The New York-based troupe *DanceBrazil*, led by Jelon Vieira, presents three dance pieces, including a *capoeira* work, a dance with roots in the Brazilian martial arts and the slave trade. Directed by Bernar Hebert for Agent Orange. *Undertow*, directed by James Byrne, features the dancers Eiko and Koma, who appear to dance and float weightlessly. Music for *Undertow* is by Ushio Torikai. (August 10, 1989; 30 min.)

Source: Alive From Off Center

American Animators

My Dinner with the Devil Snake, by Jim Blashfield, combines several types of animation with live-action photography, visualizing a West African folk tale told by a sculptor from Mali. George Griffin's *Koko*, set to the music of Charlie Parker, scatters images from the 1940s and 1950s amid scraps of colored paper to evoke the improvisational excitement of bebop. Sally Cruikshank's *Face like a Frog* captures the jazzy spirit of 1930s studio cartoons and the sounds of Eastern European Klezmer music. Jane Aaron's *This Time Around* offers a new way to see the world—a kinetic view of a backyard landscape from a whirling house. Music composed by Donald Fagen. (August 17, 1989; 30 min.)

Source, This Time Around only: Museum of Modern Art

Book of Days

A highly unusual depiction of medieval village life by the director, composer and choreographer Meredith Monk, *Book of Days* explores the parallels and contrasts between the present and the Middle Ages—eras of uncertainty, spiritual apocalypse and upheaval. The film moves back and forth from a 14th-century Jewish community to scenes of contemporary life, emphasizing the constants of human nature.

The performance is enacted by Monk's frequent collaborators, collectively known as The House. (August 30, 1989; 60 min.)

Source: Ken Stutz Company

From San Francisco: Dancing on the Edge

Works by four Bay Area artists: Rinde Eckert, Margaret Jenkins, Joe Goode and Ellen Bromberg. *Shorebirds Atlantic*, a multidisciplinary piece by Eckert and Jenkins directed by Gino Tanasescu, deals with isolation, chance acquaintance and death. In Goode's *29 Effeminate Gestures*, directed by Tim Boxell, the central figure probes the symbolic limbo of his own thoughts. Bromberg's *The Black Dress* (also directed by Tanasescu) is inspired by a 1950s portrait of a woman in six poses. Six characters, each wearing the same black dress, perform a dance that deals with restraint, uniformity and escape. (August 31, 1989; 30 min.)

Source: Alive From Off Center

SEASON SIX, 1990

The Lyon Opera Ballet's Cinderella

Maguy Marin's version of the classic fairy tale *Cendrillon (Cinderella)* performed by the Lyon Opera Ballet takes place in a dark yet charming world peopled by benign and fearsome figures. The dancers appear dressed as dolls and wearing surrealistic masks, while candy canes, wooden horses, rag dolls and wind-up cars spring to life. Set to music by Sergei Prokofiev and a soundtrack of electronic sounds and human noises. Directed by Mans Reutersward. (June 1, 1990; 90 min.)

Source: HomeVision

Postcards

Mark Rappaport's drama, *Postcards*, tells the story of the slow unraveling of a relationship, conveying the innuendoes and failed attempts at communication through a series of postcards that function as cinematic backdrops. Dialogue is limited to familiar one-liners from the postcard vocabulary like "Wish you were here" and "Don't do anything I wouldn't do." *Principal cast*: Ron Vawter, Dorothy Cantwell. (July 5, 1990; 30 min.)

Source: Alive From Off Center

Kumu Hula: Keepers of a Culture

Robert Mugge and Victoria Holt Takamine's film *Kumu Hula: Keepers of a Culture* is a record of Hawaii's current performers and teachers of traditional hula, a dance form that goes back 1,500 years. *Kumu hula* are the islands' hula masters. Each leads a *halau*, or school of dancers, and recreates the ancient rhythms of the hula tradition or its modern variants, adapting the dance to nearly any kind of music. (July 12, 1990; 30 min.)

Source: Alive From Off Center; Rhapsody Films (home video)

House of Tres/It Doesn't Wait

House of Tres, directed by Diane Martel and Jeff Preiss, celebrates the underground/pop phenomenon, "house" dancing, an expressive form born in New York City neighborhoods. Often displayed in competitions, house ranges from martial-arts movements and "hip-hop" gymnastics to the elegant "voguing" derived from fashion runways and modern dance. *It Doesn't Wait*, choreographed by Doug Elkins and directed by Mark Obenhaus, takes place on New York City streets. The dancers, drawing on the look and rhythms of popular dance forms, emerge and disappear while cars, pedestrians and passersby who happen along the street become part of the work. (July 19, 1990; 30 min.)

Music Transfer

Five short works by film and video artists interpreting traditional ethnic music in contemporary video styles. The five works are *Kniespiel (Kneeplay)* by Claus Blume of West Germany; *Hammer* by the American, Matt Mahurin; *Dhikr* by Dalibor Martinis and Sanja Ivekovic of Yugoslavia; *Living Eastern European Animals* by Andreas Wahorn of Hungary and *O Pastor (The Shepherd)* by Licinio Azevedo of Mozambique. (July 26, 1990; 30 min.)

Source: Antenna

Dance of Darkness

Edin and Ethel Velez's *Dance of Darkness* is a video homage to several of the most important Butoh practitioners, including Kazuo Ohno, the late Tatsumi Hijikata and the troupes Dai Rakuda Kan, Byakko Sha and Hakutoboh. Butoh, roughly translated as "dance of darkness," is the powerful and mystical performance style that probes the Japanese national identity. (August 2, 1990; 30 min.)

Source: ALIVE FROM OFF CENTER

Words on Fire

Six story tellers interpret the word "fire" showing the many ways in which a story can be told. Christopher Durang creates a mini-sitcom on the woes of inactivity; Fred Curchak is seen in a one-man Shakespearean performance; Rinde Eckert recites two 17th-century French love poems; Jo Carson relates intimate tales of Appalachian life; Todd Alcott offers a spontaneous diatribe on living in the "heat" of urban life; and Robert Joy reads a text by Jack Finney in which time stands still as a fire starts. Directed by John Sanborn and Skip Blumberg. (August 9, 1990; 30 min.)

Source: ALIVE FROM OFF CENTER

The Myth of Modern Dance

A personalized history of the dance by the dancer Douglas Dunn, directed by Charles Atlas. *The Myth of Modern Dance* is inspired in part by Dunn's solo concert piece, *Haole*; the several segments visit diverse centuries—prehistory and the birth of humanity, the Renaissance, the 1960s. Each segment represents either a period of dance history or an abstract concept of cultural change. (August 16, 1990; 30 min.)

Source: Alive From Off Center

Video Dance

Three dance narratives from the United States, France and Canada. *Mass*, by the choreographer Elizabeth Streb and the video artist Mary Lucier, is about the survival of an artist's vision in an urban environment. Music by Earl Howard. *La Chambre*, by the French company L'Esquisse of Le Havre, is a melancholy vision inspired by the writings of Marguerite Duras. Choreographed by Joelle Bouvier and Regis Obadia.

Tango Tango, choreographed by Lila Greene and directed by Francois Girard, is a stylized mystery with surreal overtones, set by a remote hilltop pool. (August 30, 1990; 30 min.)

Source: La Chambre: INA; Tango Tango: Agent Orange

Road

An adaptation of Jim Cartwright's stage play directed by Alan Clarke, *Road* portrays life in the downtrodden industrial north of England through four young people who try to escape their lives for a night. In spite of their desperate economic straits and psychological distress, *Road* offers a glimmer of hope that they can rise above the harsh realities of Thatcher-era England. *Principal cast:* Jane Horrocks, Mossie Smith, Neil Dudgeon, William Armstrong. (September 13, 1990; 60 min.)

Source: Lionheart Television

The Butoh dancer Byakko-sha appears in Dance of Darkness. *Photo by Ethel Velez.*

NEW TELEVISION

Beginning in 1987 as a modest, half-hour broadcast in Boston and New York City late in the evening, New Television proved a claim long insisted on by video artists but viewed skeptically by most television professionals: that video art, broadcast without explanation or intervention, would gather to itself a passionate audience, and that that audience would not be insignificant in size. The series achieved national distribution in 1990, its fourth season. By removing this youngest of the arts from the monitor in the gallery to the television screen in the home, the series allows each work to appeal directly to the viewer. In its disavowal of television orthodoxies, its frequent use of language on the screen, its pursuit of elusive content, and its ingenious development of an individual "voice," video art is the poetry of the media "published" on the air.

Executive producers: Susan Dowling, Lois Bianchi
Additional funders include: Rockefeller Foundation, New York State Council on the Arts, Massachusetts Council on the Arts and Humanities
A production of WGBH/Boston and WNET/Thirteen

SEASON FOUR, 1990

Put Blood in the Music

Put Blood in the Music, by Charles Atlas, is a documentary on the collaboration and competition among rock musicians in New York City. The piece presents the varied cultures and musical styles of emerging composer-musicians. Its pace reflects the frenetic quality of the music and of the city. Also presented are *Coney Island* and *Manhattan*, both excerpts of *From an Island Summer*. Directed by Charles Atlas with movement sequences by Karole Armitage. (April 1, 1990; 90 min.)

Source: Put Blood in the Music: Windmill Lane Productions

Sun, Moon & Feather

A hybrid musical comedy and documentary, *Sun Moon & Feather* traces the life and times of three Native American sisters growing up in Brooklyn during the 1930s and 1940s, combining song and dance re-enactments of family and tribal stories with home movies taken over a 30-year period to create a unique sense of time and

place. Produced by Bob Rosen and Jane Zipp in collaboration with Spiderwoman Theater. (April 8, 1990; 30 min.)

Source: Metropolitan Arts

Changing Steps

Elliot Caplan combines two versions of Merce Cunningham's 1973 work, *Changing Steps*: black-and-white footage filmed in the studio in 1974 and a new version of the work shot at Sundance Institute in 1989. The carefully framed and edited mix of old and new creates the illusion of unbound bodies in abandoned motion. The score is *Cartridge Music* by John Cage. (April 15, 1990; 30 min.)

Source: Cunningham Dance Foundation

Cultural Identity

Coffee Coloured Children, by Ngozi Onwurah, examines the struggle of mixed-race children for self-definition and pride and explores how cultural pressures define one's self-image. *Virginia Dare's Vision*, by Sarah Drury, combines electronic, computer-generated music with imagery referring to the life of Virginia Dare, the first European child born in America. Silvana Afram's *Darkness of My Language II* is a video-poem on colonialism revealing how it defines personal identities and perpetuates cultural ignorance. (April 22, 1990; 30 min.)

Source: Children and Darkness: Women Make Movies; Virginia Dare: The Kitchen

Desire, Inc.

Lynn Hershman's *Desire, Inc.*, explores loneliness, the creation of a persona and the medium of television, which stimulates desire through deceptive and alluring messages. Hershman placed personal ads on cable television inviting viewers to respond via an 800 number, then interviewed respondents about their own desires and aspirations. (April 29, 1990; 30 min.)

Belladonna/The Dogs

Belladonna, by Beth B and Ida Applebroog, combines readings of various texts and testimonies, figurative drawing and processed images in a disturbing program about child victimization. *The Dogs*, by Burt Barr, is set on a bright summer's day at the seashore, as the nervous, beer-drinking protagonist and a panting dog transform the benign scene into a landscape of fear, longing and Ballantine ale cans. (May 6, 1990; 30 min.)

The Houses That Are Left

Shelly Silver mixes narrative with documentary sequences in *The Houses That Are Left* to describe the search for meaning that engages the generation coming of age in the 1990s. The title refers to a statement by Gustave Flaubert suggesting that what is most telling about a historical period is not what it creates but what it tears down or loses. Silver explores whether the freedoms available to this generation

have paralyzed it, leaving it without boundaries and without achievable goals. (May 13, 1990; 30 min.)

Source: Video Data Bank

Radio Inside/Funeral

Radio Inside, by Jeffrey Bell, concerns a young man in a love triangle involving his brother and his brother's girlfriend. His reaction is to turn to Jesus by calling him on a pay phone. Music from various radio stations, from gospel to rock and roll, helps recreate the struggle between faith and flesh. *Funeral*, by Marina Zurkow, is an elegy to the elusive memories of family, recalled through dreamlike glimpses, while examining the nature of grieving through a structure that parallels the process of remembering. (May 20, 1990; 30 min.)

Animation, Dance and Video

La Femme a la Cafetiere, by Robert Wilson, introduces movement into the paintings of Cezanne as Suzushi Hanayagi, a Kabuki dancer, performs the role of la femme. *Hall's Crossing*, by Dennis Darmek, is a crossroads in the American West where tour buses collide with nature, and scenic vistas and cultural myths overlap. *Neo Geo: An American Purchase*, by the Australian artist Peter Callas, is a hand-drawn, animated video portrait of the contemporary American cultural landscape. Callas layers images of national stereotypes with nightmare images to unveil the dark side of American cultural memory. (May 27, 1990; 30 min.)

Source: La Femme: INA; Neo Geo: Electronic Arts Intermix

Hoppla!

In Wolfgang Kolb's video-dance *Hoppla!* four women dance in unison, without special effects, leaving the movement and the music to speak for themselves. Choreography by Anne

Teresa de Keersmaeker; music by Bartok. (June 3, 1990; 30 min.)

Source: AO Productions

Total Rain

In Richard Foreman's *Total Rain*, Foreman and his alter ego, played by Ron Vawter, act out his own aesthetic, social and moral dilemmas as he travels from America to Paris and back. As he interacts with his alter ego, he reveals some of the neurotic tendencies entrenched in contemporary American society. (June 10, 1990; 30 min.)

Video Short Stories and Poetry

Carmen, by Ann Sargent Wooster, reinterprets Bizet's opera in New York City's lower East Side as a romance between a rock-and-roll singer and a record producer. Carmen is played by Emily XYZ, who also composed the original score. In *Lies and Humiliations*, by Eder Santos, an elderly woman's material possessions evoke memories of a lifetime shared. *Les Anges Rebelles*, by Marie Binet, uses special effects to depict the creative process of the French artist Jacques Brissot as he creates a collage, *La Chute des Poubelles*, inspired by Breughel's painting, *La Chute des Anges Rebelles*. (June 17, 1990; 30 min.)

Source: Lies: Electronic Arts Intermix; Les Anges: INA

Spitting Glass

In *Spitting Glass*, Ed Bowes expands the conventions of television drama to explore the shifting psychological landscape of a young doctoral candidate struggling for recognition. Through a series of dramas, confrontations and dramatically rich interior monologues, the story presents the personal setbacks she experiences in her drive to succeed in the competitive hierarchy of academia. (June 24, 1990; 60 min.)

P.O.V.

Offering Academy Award-winning documentaries, pungent personal commentary and original subjects, P.O.V. brings to public television the work of several generations of independent media artists. The series functions like a magazine, with an executive editor (David M. Davis), an editor-in-chief (Marc N. Weiss) and an editorial board made up of staff members from the four sponsoring stations in Los Angeles, South Carolina, Boston, and New York, and distinguished independent artists. The board reviews media art works submitted for "publication," i.e., broadcast, and makes its recommendations to the editor-in-chief. Since many independent works are of unequal length, the series "packages" them into one- to two-hour programs with consistent themes. Audiences for the series have ranged from 2,830,000 for *American Tongues/Acting Our Age* (season 1) to 4 million viewers for *Metamorphosis* (season 3). P.O.V. (the title is taken from the screenwriter's direction to the camera: point of view) establishes on broadcast the independent media artist's voice—aggressive, often humorous, sometimes idiosyncratic, wary of cant, always true to its material. Programs range widely across geographic, ethnic and artistic boundaries, from cowboy poets to a debutante ball, from the problems of two disadvantaged women in India to the heroic Argentine mothers of the "disappeared," from a murder in Detroit to three runaway girls—subjects clarified and transformed by the film- and videomaker's art.

Executive director: David M. Davis
Executive producer: Marc N. Weiss
A production of the American Documentary, a consortium of the public television stations KCET/Los Angeles, South Carolina ETV, WGBH/Boston and WNET/New York
Major funders include: John D. and Catherine T. MacArthur Foundation, Corporation for Public Broadcasting, Harris Foundation, Benton Foundation, public television stations

SEASON ONE, 1988

American Tongues/ Acting Our Age

American Tongues uses the prism of language to reveal our attitudes toward each other. From Boston Brahmins to black Louisiana teenagers, from Texas cowboys to New York professionals, the film elicits perceptive, shocking and always telling comments on American English in all its diversity.

Directors: Louis Alvarez, Andrew Kolker
Awards: Peabody Award
Additional funding: National Endowment for the Humanities
Source: New Day Films

"There's nobody that's not going to get old—unless they die," says Enola Maxwell at the beginning of *Acting Our Age*. Six women aged 65 to 75, offer new perspectives on aging, body image, sexuality, family life and death. (July 5, 1988; 95 min.)

Director: Michal Aviad
Source: Direct Cinema

Fire from the Mountain

Based on the autobiography of the Nicaraguan author Omar Cabezas, the film follows his political evolution from student activist, to guerilla, to an official in the Sandinista government. Nominated for an Emmy Award in 1988. (July 12, 1988; 60 min.)

Director: Deborah Shaffer
Source: First Run/Icarus Films

Pearl, right, overcomes her own fears and helps her son, Philly, prepare to live on his own in Best Boy, *the Academy Award-winning chronicle of Philly's road to independence.*

Dear Mr. Ira Wohl, c/o P.O.V.:

I have just had an experience that I find almost impossible to relate coherently or even in proper perspective.

Last night I watched Best Boy.

Mr. Wohl, what a film, what a story.

I laughed, I cried, but most of all, I felt good when the film ended.

Your film is truly remarkable.

What a wonderful tribute to Philly, Pearl, Max and Fran.

I must tell you I have not experienced such an emotional high since I visited the Wailing Wall. Best Boy has been on my mind this entire day and I am sure for many days to come.

I plan on watching Best Boy *this evening with my wife.*

I wish I could put on paper a more eloquent expression of my feelings, but I guess, simply put, Best Boy *is the* best *film I have ever seen.*

Much luck in your future films.

G.I.K., Kansas City, Mo.

Armageddon's Door/ Living with AIDS

In *Knocking on Armageddon's Door*, half comedy, half horror story, several spokesmen for America's survivalist movement reveal the way they think, play and prepare for the next world war.

*Directors: Torv Carlsen, John Magnus
Source: Producer Services Group*

Living with AIDS shows a community providing compassionate care for a courageous 22-year-old victim of the disease. (July 19, 1988; 60 min.)

*Director: Tina Di Feliciantonio
Awards: Emmy Award: Special Classification for News and Documentary Achievement
Source: Carle Medical Communications*

Rate It "X"

A candid view of men's feelings toward women by two feminist filmmakers who traverse the landscape of American sexism, interviewing corporate executives, a funeral parlor director, purveyors of pornography and Santa Claus. (July 26, 1988; 60 min.)

*Directors: Lucy Winer, Paula de Koenigsberg
Source: Interama; International Video Entertainment (home video)*

Las Madres: The Mothers of Plaza de Mayo

In the late 1970s, thousands of men, women and children were abducted by the right-wing military government in Argentina. While most of the population was terrorized by these actions, a small group of mothers of the "disappeared" staged weekly demonstrations to demand that their children be released and the kidnappers brought to justice. This is the dramatic story of their courageous struggle, which ultimately helped topple the dictatorship. Nominated for Academy and Emmy awards. (August 2, 1988; 60 min.)

*Directors: Susana Munoz, Lourdes Portillo
Source: Direct Cinema*

The Good Fight

Five years before the United States entered World War II, 3,200 young Americans went to Europe to fight fascism in the Spanish Civil War, risking their lives defending a democratically elected government. Fifty years later, the survivors recount the story of those years and tell how it affected their subsequent lives. Studs Terkel narrates the film. (August 9, 1988; 90 min.)

*Directors: Noel Buckner, Mary Dore, Sam Sills
Additional funding: National Endowment for the Humanities
Source: First Run/Icarus Films*

Metropolitan Avenue

We are introduced to a lively Brooklyn neighborhood facing problems caused by racial tensions and cuts in municipal services. A group of traditional homemakers from varied ethnic backgrounds rises to the challenge and leads the effort to save their community. Nominated for an Emmy Award in 1988. (August 16, 1988; 60 min.)

Director: Christine Noschese
Additional funding: National Endowment for the Humanities
Source: New Day Films

Louie Bluie

A lively portrait of 76-year-old Howard "Louie Bluie" Armstrong, musician, artist, raconteur and rogue. The leader of the last black string band in America, he demonstrates the influence of string band music on blues, jazz, country, gospel, ragtime, western swing and rock and roll. (August 23, 1988; 60 min.)

Director: Terry Zwigoff
Additional funding: National Endowment for the Humanities
Source: Corinth Films; Pacific Arts Video (home video)

Gates of Heaven

A film ostensibly about pet cemeteries and their owners, but as the story grows much more complicated and bizarre, it hints at larger issues—love, immortality, failure and the elusiveness of the American Dream. (August 30, 1988; 90 min.)

Director: Errol Morris
Festivals screenings: Cannes, New York and Berlin Film Festivals
Source: New Yorker Films; RCA/Columbia Home Video

Best Boy

The Academy-award winning documentary about Philly Wohl, a 53-year-old retarded man, follows his preparation for the time when his aging parents will no longer be able to care for him. The film examines the bonds between Philly, his father Max and his mother Pearl, who speaks of the son who never left home as her "best boy." (September 6, 1988; 120 min.)

Director: Ira Wohl
Awards: Academy Award: Best Feature Documentary
Source: International Film Exchange; Today Home Entertainment (home video)

SEASON TWO, 1989

Who Killed Vincent Chin?

On a hot summer night in Detroit in 1982, Ronald Ebens, an autoworker, killed a young Chinese-American engineer with a baseball bat. Ebens confessed to the killing but never spent a day in jail. Some called the killing an accident; others, a racially motivated murder. The film probes the implications of the murder for the families of those involved and for the American justice system. Nominated for an Academy award. (July 16, 1989; 90 min.)

Directors: Christine Choy, Renee Tajima
Awards: Peabody Award
Source: Film News Foundation

Wise Guys!/ Coming Out

In *Wise Guys!* a stamp dealer from Los Angeles, a former school teacher from Miami, a born-again Christian from Las Vegas and a whiz-kid law student compete in the *Jeopardy!* "$100,000 Tournament of Champions." We see the tricks of staging, the contestants' hopes and anxieties and an inkling of the meaning, beyond the prize money, victory holds for the players.

Director: David Hartwell
Source: School of Cinema-Television, University of Southern California Film Distribution Center

Coming Out is a ritual of upper-class society, the debutante ball. We see Miss Mary Stuart Montague Price, founder and chairman of the Debutante Cotillion in Washington, D.C., command an army of florists, dressmakers and much-sought-after military escorts. This new generation of debs is different from previous ones—they come out to make business and networking contacts as well as to meet potential suitors. (July 23, 1989; 60 min.)

Director: Ted Reed
Producer: Susan Bell
Source: Counterproductions

The Family Album

Watching this film is like leafing through a long-lost box of family photos. Enchanting, humorous and sometimes eerie, the film, created over several decades, blends home movies and audio tapes gathered from flea markets and garage sales into a composite lifetime of the American family. (July 30, 1989; 60 min.)

Director: Alan Berliner
Source: Filmmakers' Library

Dark Circle

A documentation of the link between nuclear power and the production of nuclear weapons, and the threat both pose to public health. When first released in 1982, the film was denounced by officials and shunned by broadcasters. Since then, the safety issues raised have become today's headlines. (August 6, 1989; 90 min.)

Directors: Christopher Beaver, Judy Irving, Ruth Landy
Awards: Emmy Award: Outstanding News and Documentary Individual Achievement
Source: New Yorker Films; The Video Project (home video)

Jack Levine: Feast of Pure Reason

An unconventional portrait of one of America's leading social realist painters doing what he does best: skewering corrupt politicians, raging over social injustices and satirizing the petty foibles of humankind. The film also covers Levine's time with the Works Progress Administration, his reminiscences on art and baseball with art historian Milton Brown and a retrospective of his paintings. (August 13, 1989; 60 min.)

Director: David Sutherland
Additional funding: National Endowment for the Humanities
Source: David Sutherland Productions; HomeVision (home video)

Whatever Happened to Zworl Quern?/ No Applause, Just Throw Money

Zworl Quern was a stage name adopted by Janet Wolfe, whose brief, bizarre acting career included being sawed in half by Orson Welles. In *Whatever Happened to Zworl Quern?* everyone in Janet's life—including Eartha Kitt, Shelley Winters and her ex-husband—has a story to tell about this irrepressible woman who has traveled the world in search of adventure, art and love.

Director: Deborah Matlovsky
Source: Zworl Quern Productions

On the streets and subways of New York, 101 itinerant performers whirl firesticks, mimic passersby, imitate Stevie Wonder, tap dance and perform classical music. *No Applause, Just Throw Money* celebrates joyful encounters on New York City streets. (August 20, 1989; 60 min.)

Director: Karen Goodman
Awards: Emmy Award: Outstanding Individual Achievement in Film Editing
Source: Direct Cinema

Partisans of Vilna

The untold story of a handful of Jewish youths who organized an underground resistance against the Nazis in the ghetto of Vilnius, Lithuania ("Vilna" in Russian) and later in the surrounding woods. Interspersed with archival footage from 1939 to 1944 are 40 interviews in Hebrew, Yiddish and English with former partisans in Israel, New York City, Montreal and Vilnius. (August 27, 1989; 120 min.)

Director: Josh Waletzky
Producer: Aviva Kempner
Additional funding: National Endowment for the Humanities
Source: The Ciesla Foundation

The Fighting Ministers

Moved by the growing desperation of thousands of laid-off steel workers, a group of ministers in Pittsburgh confronts the city's government and corporate establishment. Their passionate and unorthodox actions led to controversy and profound soul-searching, rejection by the church and imprisonment. (September 3, 1989; 60 min.)

Directors: Bill Jersey, Richard Wormser
Source: California Newsreel

Cowboy Poets/ Binge/ Doug and Mike

Three short films on the search for identity in a changing world. *Cowboy Poets*, by Kim Shelton, shows how

three contemporary cowboy poets (Waddie Mitchell, Slim Kite and Wally McRae) keep tradition alive. To that end, they have even appeared on the *Johnny Carson Show*. *Binge*, by Lynn Hershman, is an intimate narrative about her efforts to control her weight. *Doug and Mike, Mike and Doug*, by Cindy Kleine, probes the inner and outer lives of identical twins Doug and Mike Starn, whose collaborative painting and photographic work has been acclaimed in the art world. (September 17, 1989; 80 min.)

Source: Cowboy Poets: Direct Cinema; Binge: Picture Start

Lost Angeles

A look at the lives and struggles of a group of homeless people who have been moved into an "urban campground" in Los Angeles. The complicated realities of life on the streets are graphically and unsentimentally portrayed. (September 24, 1989; 60 min.)

Director: Tom Seidman
Source: Extension Media, University of California

Girltalk

The juvenile courts are after three runaway girls with histories of abuse and neglect: Pinky, a Puerto Rican girl who refuses to go to school; Mars, on the streets since age 13, who now works as a stripper, and Martha, product of a dozen foster homes, who is now a teenage mother. The film follows each girl's life on the streets, elicits the reasons they fled oppressive homes and speculates on whether they can escape the cycle of abuse in their own adult lives. (November 20, 1989; 90 min.)

Director: Kate Davis
Source: Filmmakers' Library

SEASON THREE, 1990

Through the Wire

In 1986, three women convicted of politically motivated offenses were transferred to a secret high-security prison in Lexington, Kentucky, where for nearly two years they were kept in constantly lit, near-isolation, watched 24 hours a day and strip-searched routinely. The film investigates the secret unit in which they were confined. Narrated by Susan Sarandon. (June 26, 1990; 90 min.)

Director: Nina Rosenblum
Source: Fox/Lorber Associates

Metamorphosis: Man into Woman

Gary, a successful 39-year-old animation artist and a devout Christian, is pursuing a lifelong dream—to become a woman. For three years Gary prepares physically and emotionally for sex reassignment surgery. The film raises key, sometimes humorous questions about gender. (July 3, 1990; 60 min.)

Director: Lisa Leeman
Producer: Claudia Hoover
Source: Filmmakers' Library

On Ice/Larry Wright

Cryonics—the freezing of human beings after death for possible future revival—is the subject of this off-beat film by two science-buffs-turned-filmmakers. With commentary from Timothy Leary, a theologian and skeptical scientists, *On Ice* is alternately deadpan and dead serious.

Directors: Grover Babcock, Andrew Takeuchi
Source: Manic Films

With a subway platform as his stage and a plastic can as his instrument, 14-year-old *Larry Wright*, a self-taught drummer with astonishing talent, is part of a tribute to Harlem youth and the rich culture of the urban streets. (July 10, 1990; 60 min.)

Directors: Ari Marcopoulos, Maja Zrnic
Source: First Run/Icarus Films

Letter to the Next Generation

Are college students today apathetic and self-centered? Twenty years after National Guardsmen opened fire on student anti-war demonstrators at Kent State University, Jim Klein, a former radical, visits the campus. With young patrons of a local tanning salon, activists-turned-professors and an ROTC captain, Klein discusses the social forces changing college campuses and the entire country in the 1990s. (July 17, 1990; 90 min.)

Director: Jim Klein
Source: Heartland Productions

Salesman

The Maysles brothers' *cinema-verite* classic from the early 1960s follows four door-to-door Bible salesmen as they are sent from one town to the next. Alternately encouraged to be missionaries and to be entrepreneurs, the four men doggedly travel from sales convention, to hotel room, to remote parishes around the country. (July 24, 1990; 90 min.)

Directors: Albert and David Maysles, Charlotte Zwerin
Source: Maysles Films

Police Chiefs

Three big-city police chiefs reveal sharply differing philosophies of law enforcement. From Daryl Gates, who introduced SWAT to Los Angeles, to Anthony Bouza, who ruffled feathers in Minneapolis, to Lee Brown, who recently left Houston for New York, these top cops' ideas about the causes and cures of crime are as varied as their personalities. (July 31; 1990; 60 min.)

Directors: Alan and Susan Raymond
Source: Video Verite Library

Kamala and Raji

The complexities of everyday life in India unfold as two poor women try to improve their lot. Their resourcefulness, aspirations and capacity for joy break the stereotype of Indian women as voiceless figures leading desolate lives of poverty. The two women join an organization of street vendors and laborers; as a result, the husbands and wholesalers of Ahmedabad may never be the same. (August 7, 1990; 60 min.)

Director: Michael Camerini
Source: University of Wisconsin, South Asian Studies

Golub/Days of Waiting

Golub is a portrait of the socially committed painter Leon Golub, whose massive canvases are often about torture and brutality and how they are conveyed by the media.

Directors: Jerry Blumenthal, Gordon Quinn
Source: New Day Films

Estelle Peck Ishigo accompanied her Japanese-American husband into an internment camp during World War II, one of the few Caucasians to do so. *Days of Waiting* vividly recreates from Ishigo's own memoirs, photos and paintings the shattering relocation experience from an "outsider's" perspective. (August 14, 1990; 90 min.)

Director: Steven Okazaki
Awards: Academy Award: Best Short Documentary
Source: Mouchette Films

On stage on the sidewalk, 14 year-old Larry Wright astonishes passersby with his inspired percussion. Photo by Ari Marcopoulos.

Going Up/Green Streets

In *Going Up*, the creation of a skyscraper becomes an exhilarating visual experience when compressed by time-lapse photography. Hardhat banter and construction-worker choreography are set to a score by 15 new music composers in an urban ballet 40 stories above New York harbor.

Director: Gary Pollard
Source: Filmmakers' Library

If a tree can grow in Brooklyn, can an eggplant flourish in the Bronx? *Green Streets* charts the spontaneous emergence of community gardens in New York City and shows how they have nourished neighborhood pride, racial tolerance and a sense of hope for hundreds of enthusiastic gardeners in the urban jungle. (August 21, 1990; 70 min.)

Director: Maria De Luca
Source: De Luca Films

Motel

Behind the faded signs of three motels in the American Southwest lie entire worlds of passion, loyalty and adventure. The film explores the people who make up this American subculture. (August 28, 1990; 90 min.)

Director: Christian Blackwood
Source: Christian Blackwood Productions

Teatro!/Ossian

Teatro! is the story of a grassroots theater company in Honduras founded by a Jesuit priest from St. Louis, Missouri, as the company takes to the road to enlighten and inspire villagers in the impoverished countryside.

Directors: Ed Burke, Pam Yates, Ruth Shapiro
Source: Burke/Shapiro Productions

Ossian: American Boy, Tibetan Monk

is the story of Ossian Maclise, born in Massachusetts, who has lived in a Tibetan Buddhist monastery since the age of four. At age seven, his monastic order recognized Ossian as a *tulku*—a reincarnation of a high Tibetan lama. *Ossian* offers a fascinating glimpse into the life of a young man in whom Eastern and Western cultures merge. (September 4, 1990; 90 min.)

Director: Thomas Anderson
Source: Mystic Fire Video

People Power

After years of witnessing first-hand the horrors of guerilla war, the Israeli-born filmmaker Ilan Ziv traveled to Chile, the Philippines and the West Bank to explore the development of "people power" and to reexamine his own long-held belief that violence is a necessary evil in the overthrow of oppressive governments. Set against a background of the predominantly nonviolent transformation of Eastern Europe, the film examines and evaluates nonviolence as an effective strategy for political change. (September 11, 1990; 60 min.)

Producer, director: Ilan Ziv
Source: Icarus/Tamouz Films International

THE INDEPENDENTS

In 1980, aware that cable television opened opportunities for "narrow-casting" artworks by independents which had difficulty finding their audience, the Endowment sought an appropriate cable outlet. Negotiations with The Learning Channel, then a subsidiary of the Appalachian Community Service Network, led in 1984 to THE INDEPENDENTS' first series, DIS/PATCHES, assembled around the theme of fusing video and America's diverse artforms, and curated by Gerald O'Grady of Media Study, Buffalo, N.Y. The future of the series was assured when the interest of the late William Kirby of the John D. and Catherine T. MacArthur Foundation was engaged by Virgil Grillo of the Rocky Mountain Film Center. Strong and sustained support from MacArthur carried the program through the nine series listed here and later ones as well; each, following an open call for artworks, was assembled by a curator from a media art center.

Without MacArthur's continued support, the series would have been aborted. Kirby's passionate understanding of independent media artists made him particularly sensitive to the view of America projected by their collective vision. With work drawn from every part of the country, exploring generational conflicts, the family, problems of youth and age, neighborhoods, minorities, and often showing the individual insisting on decent and humane solutions in difficult situations, the nine series offer a picture of the country radically different from that available on sit-coms and soap operas. The hundreds of media artists who contribute to these series do so from an angle of vision that renovates their subjects. Each series is hosted by distinguished interlocutors known for their sympathy to the art of the independent maker. The Learning Channel is now available to 15 million homes.

Executive producer: Robert Shuman
Producer: Chiz Schultz
Director: John Desmond
Awards: 1987 ACE Award: Best Documentary Series
Additional funders: The John D. and Catherine T. MacArthur Foundation
A production of The Learning Channel (TLC) for the American Community Service Network (ACSN)

DIS/PATCHES, FALL, 1984

DIS/PATCHES presents 42 independent works—dispatches—that report on all the arts from every region of the country, creatively interpreting jazz, dance, storytelling, handicrafts, new and experimental music and other forms. The series draws attention to the individual artist's vision, present in forms as disparate as handicraft and video works. The noted independent filmmaker Robert Young hosts the series.

Curator: Gerald O'Grady
A production of ACSN, TLC and Chiz Schultz, Inc.

Sound Patterns

A selection of experimental sound works. In *Dreamer that Remains*, by Stephen Pouliot, the maverick American composer Harry Partch recollects his life as a hobo, his youth, the Depression, and performs his music on the 72-string cithara, glass bells cut from bottles and other instruments of his own making. *Hydrogen Seas* by David P. Crews integrates images inspired by the transformation of matter into energy with an experimental music track. *Oblique Strategist Too* by Edin Velez is a portrait of the composer Brian Eno. *Ear to the Ground* by John Sanborn and Kit Fitzgerald presents the percussionist David Van Tieghem drumming up street sounds in early morning in New York City. (October 14, 1984; 60 min.)

Source: Dreamer That Remains: New Dimensions Media; Hydrogen Seas: Austin Cable Vision; Ear to the Ground: Sanborn, Perillo and Company

The Fantastic Four—Delores Brown, DeShone Adams, Robin Oakes and Adrienne "Nicky" Adams—appear in Skip Blumberg's Pick Up Your Feet: The Double Dutch Show. Photo by Peter Aaron/ESTO.

Land Forms

Three views of landscape and architecture. *Ohio to Giverny: Memory of Light* by Mary Lucier journeys through space and time—from the Ohio landscape where her visual imagination was formed to Monet's Giverny in France. *Prairie School Architecture* by Mark Stanley profiles the school founded by Louis Sullivan and developed by Frank Lloyd Wright. *Arches* by Dan Reeves presents images of naturally sculpted rock formations. (October 21, 1984; 60 min.)

Source: Arches: Port Washington Public Library

TV Tactics

A collection of commentaries on television's role in modern life. *Why I Got Into TV and Other Stories* by

Ilene Segalove is a series of short stories in which television is cast as a character in Segalove's personal history. *Teletapes* by Peter D'Agostino looks at television and everyday life in three parts: tricks, games and puzzles. *Made for TV* by Tom Rubnitz and Ann Magnuson spoofs television programming by flipping through TV channels, starring characters created and portrayed by Magnuson. (October 28, 1984; 60 min.)

Teletapes: Museum of Modern Art

Choreographic Contrasts

Independent media artists bring the patterns and figures of dance into the video dimension. *Capoeira of Brazil* by Warrington Hudlin records the ritual dance, *capoeira*, born of the slave rebellion in Brazil. *Coast Zone*

by Charles Atlas and Elliot Caplan is a video interpretation of a performance by the Merce Cunningham troupe in a New York City church. In *Seascape*, by Mary Daval and Art Nomura, dancers pretending to be sunbathers perform in boxes that grow, shrink and float across the screen. *Piper at the Gates of Dawn* by Ken Rowe and Elaine Gardner presents dance, video and performance in symbiosis. (November 4, 1984; 60 min.)

Source: Choreographic Contrasts: Cunningham Dance Foundation

Street Scenes

Three open-air performances in urban environments. *Emergency Exit* by JoAnne Kelly is a monologue about a woman trying to escape routine. *Pick up Your Feet: The Double Dutch Show* by Skip Blumberg is a delightful work about young virtuosi skipping rope. *Street Poets* by Freeman Crocker and Maureen Crocker uses video techniques to enhance performances by street poets. (November 11, 1984; 60 min.)

Source: Emergency Exit: Video Free America; Pick up Your Feet: Museum of Modern Art; Street Poets: Stone River Multi-Media Productions

Videocraft

Four video art works. *Sunstone* by Ed Emshwiller is based on computer graphics animation. *Ancient of Days* by Bill Viola progresses from a structured perceptual exercise to rich tableaux of light, color and movement (exerpted from *Vegetable Memory*). *Electronic Masks* by Barbara Sykes uses interactive video environments and electronic image generation. *Information Withheld* by Juan Downey is a cross-cultural story of science and symbols in the graphic and visual arts. *The Day of the Dead* by Ernest Gusella applies the format of the music video to a thematic history of Mexico (excerpted from *What Under the Sun?*). (November 18, 1984; 60 min.)

Source: Sunstone: Museum of Modern Art; Ancient of Days: Museum of Modern Art; Information Withheld: Castelli Sonnabend Films & Tapes

Music Modes

Three distinct types of progressive jazz. *The Art Ensemble of Chicago* by Terrence Stegner and Mainframe, Inc., presents a progressive jazz form that marries the avant-garde with bebop and African music. *Elvin Jones: Different Drummer* by Edward Gray profiles the jazz drummer who is perhaps best known as a member of John Coltrane's quartet in the late 1960s. Jones's polyrhythmic style, rooted in African choral drum rituals, revolutionized jazz drumming. *Transnotations* by Sally Shapiro and Suzanne Mutchnik is an expressionistic video poem about the saxophonist Frank Foster. (November 25, 1984; 60 min.)

Source: Different Drummer: Rhapsody Films

City Beats

Abstract interpretations of urban life: *Urban Episodes* by Steina Vasulka records life at a big-city intersection. *Organism* by Hilary Harris sees the body as a metaphor for the city. *Castro Street* by Bruce Baillie marries color images of one side of an industrial street with black and white images of the other side. In *Boccioni's Bike* Skip Battaglia interprets the futurist work in animated felt-tip pen and pencil drawings. *Bridges-Go-Round* by Shirley Clarke captures man-made spaces with lightning-like movement. (December 2, 1984; 60 min.)

Source: Organism: Phoenix Films; Castro Street, Bridges-Go-Round: Museum of Modern Art

American Indian Images

Three artists look at the Native American experience. *Video Girl and Video Song for Navajo Sky* by Shigeko Kubota unites old rites with new technologies to express the heritage of Native Americans and women. *The Shadow Catcher* by Teri McLuhan is a documentary about Edward S. Curtis's massive record of Native American life created between 1890 and 1930—an unmatched feat of anthropology that included audio recordings of some 10,000 songs, 40,000 photographs and thousands of feet of 35mm film. Narrated by Donald Sutherland. *Hopiit-81* by Victor Masayesva, Jr. depicts the changing seasons and lifestyles in a Hopi village. (December 9, 1984; 60 min.)

Source: Hopiit-81: Intermedia Arts

Storytelling

Turtle Tooth by Helen Caswell depicts moments of creation and change in a rural family over two years. *American Grizzly: Frederick Manfred* by Michael Hazard and Jim Mulligan profiles the Minnesota novelist Frederick Manfred, whose works captured the 19th-century American west and the middle American character. In *Diary of a Travel Across an Imaginary Continent* by Joan Guerin the landscape and a journey from coast to coast become a metaphor for intimacy and discovery. (December 16, 1984; 60 min.)

Culture in Motion

Three works on community and folk art forms: *Anatomy of a Mural* by Rick Goldsmith follows the making of a collaborative mural at the Mission Cultural Center in San Francisco. *Stilt Dancers of Long Bow Village* by Richard Gordon and Carma Hinton journeys into the folklore and tradition of stilt dancing in a village in China. *When the Strings Come Together* by Dennis Darmek presents children's kites in flight and in history at a festival of the air. (December 23, 1984; 60 min.)

Source: Stilt Dancers: Long Bow Group

Handwork

Four works develop the idea of craft and show how traditional art forms and the modern media are vehicles of distinctly personal expression. *Floater* by Jane Veeder is created through real-time computer animation with a synthesized soundtrack. *Excavations* by Shalom Gorewitz makes a statement about Israel's past and future. *Handcarved* by Herb E. Smith and Elizabeth Barret, of Appalshop, profiles Chester Cornett, a master chairmaker and innovative designer. *Crystal* by Maggi Payne is a video poem created through microscopy. (December 30, 1984; 60 min.)

Source: Handcarved: Appalshop

AGENDA, WINTER - SPRING, 1985

Independent film and video artists often take controversial or delicate issues as their subjects. Often, it is precisely this determination to uncover truths that keeps them independents. AGENDA consists of eight documentaries that examine social and environmental issues in different regions of the United States. These works often indicate how communities have come to grips with problems that others around the nation share. The series was nominated for an ACE Award in 1985. The author and television commentator Edwin Newman hosts.

Curator: Gerald O'Grady
A production of ACSN, TLC and Chiz Schultz, Inc.

The Secret Agent

A documentary on the effects of Agent Orange, the herbicide sprayed by the United States to clear jungles and crops in Vietnam and believed to cause afflictions ranging from virulent skin conditions to infertility and birth defects. Dioxin, a carcinogenic substance believed to be a by-product of Agent Orange, is identified as the cause of the afflictions, and the film speculates about the risks posed by the wide use in the past of compounds similar to Agent Orange on lawns, rangelands and crops. Veterans who were exposed to the herbicide, their family members, government and corporate spokespersons and scientists are interviewed. (60 min.)

Director: Jacki Ochs
Source: Green Mountain Post Films

To Love, Honor and Obey

The film probes the social, psychological and cultural factors contributing to violence against women in the home. A complex web of dependence and exploitation is pictured: battered women discuss the situations they lived through and escaped from; men who have admitted to beating their wives discuss their behavior and the reasons they see for it; children who have grown up in such homes discuss their painful experiences. Researchers, social workers and concerned individuals describe efforts to stem the tide of abuse and offer insight into why most domestic abuse goes unreported and why so many in homes plagued by violence remain with their abusers. (60 min.)

Directors: Christine Choy, Marlene Dann (60 min.)
Source: Third World Newsreel

Stopping History

Practically every generation has fought wars or engaged in violent conflict, a fact that might imply that human nature is aggressive and violent. The film follows activists preparing to demonstrate against nuclear arms proliferation at a nuclear weapons research facility, asking them how they deal with this historical evidence and the seeming futility of attempts to end war—is this tantamount to stopping history? It explores the conflicts surrounding disarmament, the moral dilemmas posed by the threat of nuclear war and the hesitation of people inside and outside the peace movement to confront these issues. (60 min.)

Director: Peter Adair
Source: Adair and Armstrong

The Four Corners: A National Sacrifice Area?

The film reports on the hidden costs of U.S. energy exploration and extraction processes, examining the consequences of uranium and coal mining and the development of synthetic fuels in the Four Corners, where the southwestern states of Utah, Arizona, Colorado and New Mexico meet. The film argues that this region's culture and natural beauty are being sacrificed to satisfy the energy requirements of our industrialized society, jeopardizing the integrity of national parks and traditional Native American lands. (60 min.)

Directors: Christopher McLeod, Glenn Switkes, Randy Hayes

Presumed Innocent

The film investigates the grievances of men incarcerated at New York's Rikers Island House of Detention. Although they have not yet faced trial, these men are detained because they cannot afford bail and are subjected to overcrowding and substandard hygiene. The film raises doubts about the guarantee of basic rights proffered by the U.S. criminal justice system, as these men appear victimized by their socioeconomic status. (60 min.)

Directors: Stefan Moore, Claude Beller
Awards: Emmy Award
A production of the TVG Documentary Arts Project
Source: The Cinema Guild

In Our Own Backyard

In 1978, toxic waste contamination was found in a residential area of Love Canal near Niagara Falls. A partial removal of the endangered inhabitants followed this initial discovery, and the remaining residents organized a battle to win a federally mandated total evacuation. The events of the two-year struggle are recounted from the points of view of the families, their advisors and the government officials involved in the negotiations. (60 min.)

Director: Lynn Corcoran
Source: Bullfrog Films

Poletown Lives!

In July, 1980, the city of Detroit and General Motors announced plans to build a new Cadillac plant. Using a new "quick take" law, some 465 acres were to be cleared within eight months. The plans called for eviction of 3,500 people and demolition of a neighborhood called Poletown, targeting 1,500 homes, 144 business, 16 churches, a

school and a hospital for destruction. The film chronicles the events, from community meetings, to protests and arrests, to the arrival of the wrecking ball. (60 min.)

Director: George Corsetti
Source: Information Factory

The Last Pullman Car

The story of the closing of the Pullman Standard Passenger Carworks in Chicago, Illinois, in the early 1980s and of the three-year struggle by Pullman workers, represented by USWA Local 1834, against the modern Pullman conglomerate. Pullman rail passenger cars were an integral part of American railroads in their heyday and the company, which operated for 114 years, was an early model of company protection of workers. The film examines the issues of job protection, changes in the transportation industry and the weakening of the labor unions, and documents the economic dislocations and personal shocks wrought by the decline of America's heavy industry in the late 1970s and the 1980s. (60 min.)

Directors: Gordon Quinn, Jerry Blumenthal
Source: Kartemquin Films

ORDINARY PEOPLE— INDEPENDENT PORTRAITS, FALL, 1986

One time-honored theme of independent film and video is the revelation of the surprising and extraordinary amidst the seemingly unremarkable. The 33 biographical and autobiographical works in ORDINARY PEOPLE— INDEPENDENT PORTRAITS uncover a sense of depth, humor, freshness or emotion in the lives of individuals—a uniqueness that might be overlooked

but for the imagination and curiosity of an independent filmmaker. The feature filmmaker Paul Mazursky hosts.

Curator: Deirdre Boyle
A production of ACSN, TLC and Chiz Schultz, Inc.

Looking Back, Moving On

In *An Acquired Taste*, Ralph Arlyck gives a comic assessment of his life upon reaching 40 years of age. *Letter to My Uncle* by Deborah Lefkowitz portrays her uncle's painful struggle with death, combining evocative images with his own words recorded on audiotape. *Photo Album* by Enrique Oliver is a portrait of the director's Cuban-American family, which has one foot planted in Cuba and the other in their almost exclusively Cuban neighborhood in Boston. (October 12, 1986; 60 min.)

Source: An Acquired Taste: Timed Exposures; Photo Album: Flower Films

Women's Rites of Passage

Leaving Home by Ilana Bar-Din examines the effect on her family when her two younger sisters leave home to make it on their own. *The Uprooting* by Joanna Winship uses animation to show the wide range of emotions— from elation to despair—that she experienced during her separation and divorce from the man she had lived with for half of her life. *Daughters of Chaos* by Marjorie Keller weaves images of sexuality, marriage and motherhood into a tight fabric of female bonding, centered on her niece's wedding. (October 19, 1986; 60 min.)

Source: Leaving Home: Direct Cinema

Charleen

A portrait by Ross McElwee of *Charleen*, a South Carolina poet, mother, eccentric and unforgettable high school English teacher, who was later the star of his *Sherman's March*. We are introduced to a woman of rare honesty and insight, with a magnetic passion for life. (October 26, 1986; 60 min.)

Source: Icarus Films

City Folk

Sometimes I Run is James Blaine Dunlap's portrait of Stanley Maupin, a Dallas street flusher who cleans the sidewalks at night, who has a special brand of street philosophy. *T.Z.* by Robert Breer looks at the director's apartment overlooking the Tappan Zee Bridge and the hundreds of familiar items that lend a singular meaning to his life. *Not Just Garbage* by Julie Akeret profiles Mierle Ukeles, New York City's artist-in-residence at the sanitation department. (November 2, 1986; 60 min.)

Source: T.Z.: Museum of Modern Art

Frank: A Vietnam Vet is the story of one man's struggle to come to grips with the war and its aftermath.

The Psyche, Young and Old

Second Grade Dreams by Maxi Cohen enters the unconsciousness of second graders as they recount their nighttime adventures and fears. In *Frank: A Vietnam Vet*, by Frederick Simon and Vincent Canzoneri, a war veteran, Frank Barber, shares his vivid recollections of war and its aftermath. (November 9, 1986; 60 min.)

Source: Frank: A Vietnam Vet: Filmmakers' Library; Second Grade Dreams: Video Repitone, Ltd.

Women and Fate

Three stories of how women have dealt with the fortunes and misfortunes of life. In *Songs of Wool* by Cathey Edwards 91-year-old Vena Tipton creates brilliant and vibrant hooked rugs. *The Rug* by Maureen Selwood is the animated retelling of Edna O'Brien's story of hope and disappointment. *Where Did You Get That Woman?* by Loretta Smith is a portrait of Joan Williams, an aging black washroom attendant in a trendy Chicago disco. Williams reminisces about her past and gives her opinions of the "beautiful people" who patronize the disco. (November 16, 1986; 60 min.)

Source: Songs of Wool: Filmmakers' Library

Stitches and Stories

Sewing Woman by Arthur Dong is the story of a Chinese immigrant woman who came to America seeking a better life for her family. Nominated for an Academy Award. *Junebug Jabbo Jones* by Stevenson Palfi features the actor and playwright John O'Neal performing as Junebug, the legendary black storyteller. Nominated for an ACE Award. (November 23, 1986; 60 min.)

Source: Sewing Woman: Deep Focus Productions; Junebug: Stevenson Productions

First-Class Women

Metropolitan Avenue by Christine Noschese profiles a working-class neighborhood in Brooklyn not far from the one in which she grew up. Led by a handful of women, a community of Italian-Americans, Polish-Americans and African-Americans rallies to combat the decline of their neighborhood, fighting against city cutbacks that would have closed the police precinct and fire department, ultimately preserving the neighborhood and its character. (November 30, 1986; 60 min.)

Additional funding: National Endowment for the Humanities
Source: New Day Films

Tales of Survival

Possum Living, by Nancy Schreiber, is a documentary about a man and his daughter living outside Philadelphia who manage to get by comfortably on $2,000 a year, cleverly living off the leavings of the mainstream and growing as much as they can themselves. *From Harlem to Harvard*, by Marco Williams, David Lewis, Carole Markin and David Gifford, follows a black Harlem youth in his first year at Harvard University. The dream the young man had worked so long to achieve is not what he expected— though he makes the grades, he does not fit in. (December 7, 1986; 60 min.)

Four Portraits

George Griffin's *Head* is an unconventional self-portrait using photography, drawings and animation. *Boy with a Microphone* by William Stamets is an account of the director's infant nephew and his discovery of language. *Enthusiasm* by Gordon Ball chronicles the process of coping with the death of his mother. *The Stars Are Beautiful* by Stan Brakhage is a reverie intertwining daily life and the director's inventive explanations of the origins of the universe. (December 14, 1986; 60 min.)

Source: Boy with a Microphone: Rocky Mountain Film Center; The Stars Are Beautiful: Museum of Modern Art

Teenagers

Conversations with Phreddie by Paula Granger introduces us to an Atlanta punk rocker, Phreddie Vomit, and to his alienation, friends, hairstyles, poetry and the world in which he functions. *That's It, Forget It* by Branda Miller is a fast-paced parody of the music-video way of life. *Algebra and Other Menstrual Confusions* by Connie Coleman and Alan Powell recounts the skewed world brought on by the first teenage surge of hormones. *Trick or Drink* by Vanalyne Green is a first-person account of the alcoholism that plagued her family and the bulimia that afflicted her. (December 21, 1986; 60 min.)

Source: Trick or Drink: Women Make Movies; That's It, Forget It: Electronic Arts Intermix

The Pursuit of Happiness

A film by Julie Gustafson and John Reilly about three couples who share the common denominator of prison experience: a warden and his wife, a lifer and his girlfriend and a peace activist and her husband. *The Pursuit of Happiness* tells the stories of their struggles to do more than merely survive. (December 28, 1986; 60 min.)

Additional funding: National Endowment for the Humanities
Source: Global Village

DECLARATIONS OF INDEPENDENTS, SPRING, 1987

DECLARATIONS OF INDEPENDENTS captures the highlights of nearly half a century of innovative and creative film and video, showcasing classic examples of the cinematic forms independent producers developed: cultural, social and *cinema-verite* documentaries;

From Quasi at the Quackadero, *Sally Cruikshank's animated film from 1975.*

dreamscapes; video art and animation. From the surreal world of Maya Deren, a pioneer of avant-garde filmmaking in this country, to recent forays into alternative television, the series touches on the landmarks of independent and experimental film and video. The feature filmmaker Sydney Pollack hosts.
Curators: Melinda Ward, John Schott
A production of TLC and KTCA/St. Paul-Minneapolis

Ethnic Portraits

World Eskimo-Indian Olympics by Skip Blumberg takes us to an extraordinary athletic event in Alaska where competitors display their mastery of ancient tribal survival skills. *La Migra* by Louis Hock documents the struggle of illegal Mexican workers in San Diego to avoid falling into the hands of *la migra*, the dreaded border patrol. (April 5, 1987; 60 min.)

Cinema Verite

To the American independent film-maker, *cinema verite*, "film truth," is a story that tells itself on film or video as the filmmaker follows events with a camera, recording them as they un-fold. One such film is *The Chair*, by the pioneering artists Robert L. Drew, Richard Leacock, D.A. Pennebaker and Gregory Shuker, a 1960s black-and-white film that chronicles the last-minute attempts to save a man from the electric chair. The work is a col-laborative effort between network broadcasters and a group of indepen-dents. (April 12, 1987; 60 min.)

Source: Drew Associates

Social Conscience

Newsreel by Newsreel Collective (a network of "protest" filmmakers who recorded political events from their own perspectives) is a sampler of works documenting the turmoil of the 1960s. *Hiroshima/Nagasaki* by Erik Barnouw makes use of film footage shot by Akira Iwasaki, a Japanese cameraman, one week after the bomb-ing of Hiroshima and which had been impounded by the Department of Defense until 1968. *Witness to War*, by Deborah Shaffer and David Goodman, is the story of an Air Force Academy graduate whose journey of conscience turns him from a Vietnam pilot into a doctor behind rebel lines in El Salva-dor. (April 19, 1987; 60 min.)

Awards, Witness to War: Academy Award
Source: Newsreel: Third World Newsreel; Hiroshima/Nagasaki: Museum of Modern Art; Witness to War: First Run Features

Women in Social History

Union Maids, by Jim Klein, Julia Reichert and Miles Mogulescu, tells the story of three working-class women from Chicago and their memories of the labor movement of the 1930s and 1940s, in which women played pivotal roles. *Voices* by Joan Priestley is a short animated film in which the direc-tor reflects on the experiences of women. (April 26, 1987; 60 min.)

Source: Voices: Picture Start; Union Maids: Heartland Productions, New Day Films

Classic Experimental Films

The experimental techniques common to today's rock videos, commercials and feature films began as early as the 1940s, as avant-garde filmmakers used the space and time of film to create poetic, abstract works. *Meshes of the Afternoon* (1943) by Maya Deren and Alexander Hammid, *A Study in Chore-ography for Camera* (1945) by Maya Deren, and *Hymn to Her* (1974) and *Mothlight* (1963) by Stan Brakhage are all examples of how the leaders of this movement personalized the medium. *Mass for the Dakota Sioux* (1963 - 64) by Bruce Baillie is a lyrical poem of cultural despair. *Science Friction* (1959) by Stan VanDerBeek is an animated spoof on science and nuclear confrontation. (May 3, 1987; 60 min.)

Source, (all segments): American Federation of the Arts

Pushing the Limits

Daybreak Express (1953) by D.A. Pennebaker gives a fast-paced view of New York City stirring to life. *Notes on the Circus* (1966) by Jonas Mekas uses in-camera editing and speeded-up motion. *A Movie* (1958) by Bruce Conner is a brilliant collage of old movies and news footage that became a landmark in experimental film. *Loose Corner* (1986) by Anita Thacher gives free rein to optical effects. *Suspicious Circumstances* (1985) by James Blashfield tells a surrealist detective story through animation. (May 10, 1987; 60 min.)

Source: Daybreak Express: Pennebaker and Associates; Loose Corner: Museum of Modern Art; Suspicious Circumstances: Picture Start

The Art of Animation

Viewmaster (1976) by George Griffin and *Quasi at the Quackadero* (1975) by Sally Cruikshank are based on traditional drawing techniques. Four works experiment with clay and com-puters: *Frank Film* (1973) by Frank and Caroline Mouris, *Closed Mondays* (1974) by Will Vinton, *Remains to be Seen* (1983) by Jane Aaron and an excerpt from *Lines of Force* (1979) by Robert Snyder. *Film Exercise No. 4* (1943-45) by John and James Whitney, *69* (1968) by Robert Breer, and *Object Conversation* (excerpt, 1985) by Paul Glabicki raise animation to a provoca-tive art form. (May 17, 1987; 60 min.)

Source: Viewmaster, Quasi, Object Conversation: Picture Start; Frank Film: Direct Cinema; Closed Mondays, 69: American Federation of the Arts; Lines of Force: Video Data Bank

Classic Early Video

In the late 1960s, video came into its own as an artistic medium. Each of these works helped define the art form: *Transitions* (1973) by Peter Campus; *Summer Salt* (1982) by Steina Vasulka; *The Selling of New York* (1972) by Nam June Paik; *Scape Mates* (excerpt, 1972) by Ed Emshwiller; *Interpolations* (excerpt, 1979) by John Sanborn and Kit Fitzgerald; *Anthem* (1983) by Bill Viola; *Subatomic Babies* (1983) by Shalom Gorewitz and *Leaving the 20th Century* (1982) by Max Almy. (May 24, 1987; 60 min.)

Source: Summer Salt: Video Data Bank; all others except Anthem:

Electronic Arts Intermix

Independent Broadcast Television

Four More Years (excerpt) is by the video-making collective Top Value Television. *The Pascones of Third Avenue* is a video by Downtown Community Television. *Thirty-Second Spots: TV Commercials for Artists* by Joan Logue are elegantly conceived commercials for artists. Two independently produced television shows, also the work of collectives, are *Probably the World's Smallest Television Station* (excerpt) by Media Bus and *Paper Tiger Television* (excerpt) by Paper Tiger Television. *Hello* by Allen Kaprow and *Black* by Aldo Tambellini are both excerpts from the WGBH/Boston television series, *The Medium is the Medium*. (May 31, 1987; 60 min.)

Source: Four More Years, Smallest Television Station, Hello, Black: Electronic Arts Intermix; Pascones: Downtown Community Television; Spots: The Kitchen; Paper Tiger: Video Data Bank

Performing Arts Video

JGLNG (pronounced "juggling") by Skip Blumberg and *The Best of Wegman* by William Wegman are examples of performances created for the video format. *Global Groove* (excerpt) by Nam June Paik employs sophisticated electronic image manipulation. *Blue Studio* (excerpt) by Charles Atlas and Merce Cunningham electronically superimposes images to present dance in a new electronic space. *O Superman* by Laurie Anderson and *Ellis Island* by Meredith Monk

and Bob Rosen each invents a highly original style of performance video. (June 7, 1987; 60 min.)

Source: Wegman, Global Groove, Blue Studio: Electronic Arts Intermix; O Superman: Canal Street Communications; Ellis Island: Greenwich Film Associates

Life at the Margin

In the 1980s, independent films gave voice to disenfranchised communities. In two works by minority filmmakers, people tell the stories of their own cultures from the inside. *Freckled Rice* by Stephen Ning is the story of a boy's struggles between two cultures. *Hair Piece: A Film for Nappyheaded People* by Ayoka Chenzira is an animated film about racial identity which combines humor and pointed social criticism. (June 14, 1987; 60 min.)

Source: Freckled Rice: Third World Newsreel; Hair Piece: Women Make Movies

Early Spike Lee

Joe's Bed-Stuy Barbershop: We Cut Heads, the first movie by the independent filmmaker Spike Lee, prior to his commercial successes, is a drama set in the Brooklyn neighborhood Lee calls home. Zachariah, a young barber, takes over a barbershop after his partner, Joe, is killed for crossing the local racketeers who operate a numbers game out of the shop. Zach sets out to try to run the shop as a legitimate business. (June 21, 1987; 60 min.)

Source: Forty Acres and a Mule Productions

LIKELY STORIES, FALL, 1987

Fiction distills and intensifies reality. LIKELY STORIES presents 35 works of fiction by independents. The films and videos relate original stories, literary works and folk tales through techniques ranging from traditional sets and scripted actors to video transformations of scenery and actors to electronic and animated imagery. They probe unusual and difficult themes—superstition, obsession, the media, mental illness—and they consider more traditional themes in new ways. Glenn Close, herself an independent filmmaker, hosts.
Curator: Janet Sternburg
A production of TLC in association with Fireside Entertainment Corporation

Beating Them at Their Own Game

Illusions by Julie Dash is the story of a black woman executive, Mignon Dupree (played by Lonette McKee), who passes for white in 1940s Hollywood and achieves the power to make the movies she wants. Nominated for an ACE Award for art direction. *Cinderella* by Ericka Beckman tells the classic fairy tale as a board game gone mad. Using sets, props and computer graphics, Beckman shows that the rules don't always apply in board games or in life. (October 4, 1987; 60 min.)

Harrison's Tales

Ken Harrison uses East Texas as the setting for two stories. In *Mr. Horse*, a drama with an unsettling conclusion, Harrison explores the widening gap between generations. In *Hannah and the Dog Ghost*, he weaves a tale of

Dear INDEPENDENTS*:*

Earlier this year I saw a phenomenal program, Hannah and the Dog Ghost, *by Ken Harrison on a local channel's* THE INDEPENDENTS— LIKELY STORIES. *I was deeply moved by this story and would like to show it, or know when it will be shown. My Sunday-school class would benefit from this on two levels— both as an expression of our Afro-American heritage, and also from a feminist point of view.*

Please send any information you have on this to me.

Sincerely,

P.J., Goleta, Calif.

---

courage and suspense about a young widow and her unexpected ally, the "dog ghost" who helps save her son from an evil "fiddleman." (October 11, 1987; 60 min.)

Source, both segments: Phoenix Films

New Fictions

Six short pieces play—and play havoc—with the media. Done in the style of a 1920s silent movie, Anne Flournoy's *Nadja Yet*, is about a housefly hopelessly in love with a beautiful woman. *Vault*, by Bruce and Norman Yonemoto, tells the love story of a pole vaulter/concert cellist and a cowboy/abstract expressionist painter. *The Discipline of DE* by Gus Van Sant (based on a William Burroughs story) parodies self-help books, films and pamphlets. *Rough Draft* by Neal Rauch reveals and revels in the anguish of the creative artist at work. *I an Actress* by George Kuchar concerns a director and actress in a rehearsal that grows sillier with each passing

moment. *Big as Life* by Anne Flournoy is set in the year 2002, where people's lives and actions are dictated by re-runs of films and videos. (October 18, 1987; 60 min.)

Source: Vault: Electronic Arts Intermix

About Women

A Jury of Her Peers, by Sally Heckel, is a film adaptation of Susan Glaspell's story about a 19th-century farm woman accused of murdering her husband. The short film stars Diane de Lorian and Dorothy Lancaster. *A Table for One*, by Doris Chase, stars the late Geraldine Page in one of her last performances, as she dines alone in an elegant restaurant. (October 25, 1987; 60 min.)

Source: A Table for One: Museum of Modern Art

Survival

Harold of Orange by Rick Weise and Film in the Cities tells what happens when the Indians meet the White Men—only the time is now, the battle-ground is a foundation boardroom and the weapons are wit and ingenuity. *Chernobyl West* by Mark Gilliland is the story of a National Guardsman on a reconnaissance mission to search for survivors of a hypothetical nuclear accident in upstate New York. *The Marriage Dinner* by Herman Lew is a story about a marriage of convenience between an illegal alien girl from El Salvador and an American of Latin descent. (November 1, 1987; 60 min.)

Source: Harold of Orange: Film in the Cities; The Marriage Dinner: Third World Newsreel

Mental Illness, Fire and Death

You Are Not I, produced by Sara Driver, takes the viewer into the mind of a woman suffering from a severe mental illness. The work is based on a

short story by Paul Bowles and is co-directed by Jim Jarmusch. *Master of Ceremonies*, an animated short by Christopher Sullivan, introduces Death as an arsonist and the mastermind of a fiery variety show. (November 8, 1987; 60 min.)

Stories of Uncertainty

The Ballplayer, produced by Chip Lord and based on a story by Garrison Keillor, brings the actor Richard Marcus face-to-face with the camera as a ballplayer who talks about life and loyalty. *More TV Stories*, by Ilene Segalove, is made up of six vignettes that show how television has crept into our souls and shaped our lives. *My Neighborhood* by Mitchell Kriegman is a guided tour of the director's neighborhood, where he knows everyone. But do they know him? (November 15, 1987; 60 min.)

Source: More TV Stories: The CAT Fund; My Neighborhood: Shadow Projects

Two Journeys

In *Night Work*, by James Blaine Dunlap, a 43-year-old man is on the run from the Nashville music scene and a failing marriage. As he rebuilds his life in Atlanta, he is faced with the question of whether he can really begin anew without resolving the past. *The Human Tube* is a surrealistic trek through a landscape of digital effects, found imagery, ancient stone carvings and penguins. From *Adelic Penguins* by Paul Garrin and Kit Fitzgerald. (November 22, 1987; 60 min.)

Source: Adelic Penguins: Electronic Arts Intermix

Tales of Suspense

In *No Place Like Home* Mary Filice's American Gothic tale, a young woman's daydream of escaping from her mundane farm life seems on the verge of coming true, only to take a dark and violent turn. *The Visit* by Leandro Katz is a film-noir mystery whose suspense is heightened by hysterical pace, menacing mood and labyrinthine settings. (November 29, 1990; 60 min.)

Problems, Problems

Tom Goes to the Bar by Dean Parisot takes us to Pete's Bar and Grill to listen to Tom Noonan trying to make sense of his topsy-turvy life, as he hangs upside-down. *Mr. Coffee and Mr. Fixit*, produced by Ray Munro and based on a short story by Raymond Carver, shows an ordinary man going about his morning routine all the while mumbling obsessively about betrayal. In *Ernie and Rose* by John Huckert, two Army buddies take care of each other in old age and are fearful of coping when one of them dies. *The Roar from Within* by Flip Johnson portrays our demons and fears as animated monsters racing through a watercolor-washed background. (December 6, 1987; 60 min.)

Source: Tom Goes to the Bar: Cinecom Entertainment Group; Ernie and Rose: Filmmakers' Library

Storytelling Magic

Masquerade, an animated short by Larry Jordan, uses colorful cut-out illustrations to tell the story of a duel after a masquerade party. *The Cruz Brothers and Mrs. Malloy* by Kathleen Collins is an adaptation of Henry Roth's novel that tells of an aging woman and the three Puerto Rican brothers she hires to prepare her home for one final grand ball—one that exists only in her mind but that brings magic into each of their lives. *The Legend* by Woody Vasulka (an excerpt from his work *The Art of Memory*) probes the possibilities of electronic narrative, as a man encounters a strange winged figure in a surreal landscape. (December 13, 1987; 60 min.)

Source: The Cruz Brothers: Mypheduh Films; The Art of Memory: Facets Video

Obsession

Ladykiller by Meredith Anthony and Donna Alstrand is the story of an icepick killer who stalks the streets of Manhattan and of the young woman who fears she may be the next victim. *Edge of Life* by Maxi Cohen concerns a video producer whose sole aim is to get her work on television, an obsession she uses as a crutch to escape more personal issues. *Savage Love*, produced and directed by Shirley Clarke, is a monologue written by Sam Shepard and Joseph Chaikin, and performed by Chaikin, laced with an anger and passion that only love can breed. (December 20, 1987; 60 min.)

Source: Edge of Life: Video Repitone, Ltd.; Savage Love: Women's Interart Center

Clarence and Angel

Clarence and Angel (1980) is Robert Gardner's wonderful story in which two New York City public school students play the lead roles of Clarence, a shy black child who can't read, and Angel, a lively Puerto Rican boy who can't stay out of trouble. The two spend most of their time in the hallway outside the classroom as punishment for misbehavior, and there, Angel begins to teach Clarence how to read. *Principal cast:* Darren Brown, Mark Cardova. (December 27, 1987; 60 min.)

Source: Movies Unlimited, Facets Video

IT'S ABOUT TIME, SPRING, 1988

Growing old in America—its rewards and problems—is the subject of the works on IT'S ABOUT TIME, a series celebrating aging. Many works introduce us to individuals who have found freedom, fulfillment and joy as they pass their fifties, sixties and on. Others examine aspects of aging that are seldom discussed openly with candor and directness—illness, poverty, loneliness and the loss of friends and family. The films help shatter myths and stereotypes created by society's fetish for youth. Celeste Holm, stage and screen actress, hosts.
Curators: Terry Lawler, Chris Straayer
A production of ACSN in association with TLC and Fireside Entertainment

Glory at 50, True Love at 80

Young at Heart, by Sue Marx and Pamela Conn, is a documentary about two octogenarians who fall in love and marry. *Silver and Gold*, by Lynn Mueller follows the careers of two older athletes: Marion Irvine, the oldest person to qualify for the Olympic track and field trials (at age 54); and Gail Roper, a competitor in the 1952 Olympics who came out of retirement to become the most accomplished Masters-level swimmer ever. The film was nominated for an Academy Award. *Back at Coney* by Paul Ziller goes back in time to capture the lingering memories of the Coney Island of years past. (April 24, 1988; 60 min.)

Awards, Young at Heart: Academy Award: Best Documentary Short Source: Young at Heart: Sue Marx Films; Back at Coney: Coe Film Associates

Food

Jerry's by Tony Palazzolo is about a manic, non-stop delicatessen owner. *Ruth Stout's Garden* by Arthur Mokin is a visit with a gardener who gives a lesson in how to grow vegetables effortlessly. *Chicken Soup* by Kenny Schneider making chicken soup, from the death of the unfortunate fowl to the serving of the soup—a process that turns into a hilarious ritual. *Table of Silence* by Annette Barbier studies the director's family at a meal and in so doing, notices details of the family's relationships. (May 1, 1988; 60 min.)

Source: Jerry's: Picture Start; Ruth Stout's Garden: Coe Film Associates; Chicken Soup: Carousel Film and Video

Follow Your Heart

In a Jazz Way by Louise Ghertler and Pamela Katz profiles Mura Dehn, the Russian-born dancer trained in the Isadora Duncan-style who fell hopelessly in love with jazz dancing in the 1930s. Dehn worked with several generations of black dancers and created the film, excerpted here, *The Spirit Moves: A History of Black Social Dance on Film.* In *My Man Bovanne*, by Bette Craig and C.R. Portz and based on the short story by Toni Cade Bambara, adult children disapprove when their mother, a single woman, gets a crush on a neighbor. *Principal cast:* Bill Cobbs, Theresa Merritt, Samm-Art Williams (May 8, 1988; 60 min.)

Source: In a Jazz Way: Filmmakers' Library; My Man Bovanne: Direct Cinema

Against the Grain

In *My Mother Married Wilbur Stump*, Skip Sweeney explores the effect of his widowed mother's remarriage on the family, as family members reveal their feelings about their new step-father, a piano-playing free spirit named Wilbur Stump. *Silent Pioneers*, a film by Pat Snyder, Lucy Winer, Harvey Marks and Paula de Koenigsberg, examines the problems older homosexuals faced in less tolerant times, and the problems associated with growing older, regardless of sexual preference. (May 15, 1988; 60 min.)

Source: Wilbur Stump: Video Free America; Silent Pioneers: Filmmakers' Library

Retirement

The Work I've Done by Ken Fink examines the dilemma of retirement. If you ask people who they *are*, they tell you what they *do*; so, who are you after you stop working? *All of Our Lives* by Laura Sky and Helene Klodawsky is about women who are alone and without the benefit of financial security in their older years. The film forces us to reconsider the undervalued task of child-rearing and to contemplate the inequities intrinsic to a society that places little value on "women's work." (May 22, 1988; 60 min.)

Source: The Work I've Done: Blue Ridge Mountain Films; All of Our Lives: National Film Board of Canada

Three Musicians

Sprout Wings and Fly by Les Blank profiles Tommy Jarrell, an old-time fiddler who turned to music to cope with retirement and the death of his wife. *Me and Stella* by Geri Ashur is about the country-blues musician Elizabeth Cotten and her guitar, nicknamed Stella. Cotten wrote the song *Freight Train* as a teenager, but didn't come into her own until retiring from working as a domestic. *Of Cannons and Bells* by Richard Sabatte captures the life of a veteran change-ringer. (May 29, 1988; 60 min.)

Source: Sprout Wings and Fly: Flower Films; Me and Stella: Phoenix Films; Of Cannons and Bells: Coe Film Associates

The Generations Meet

In *Peege*, by Randall Kleiser, a family visits their paternal grandmother who has been confined to a nursing home because of her failing memory and poor health. *Close Harmony* by Nigel Noble concerns a music teacher who brings together a group of youngsters and a senior citizens' chorus for a joint recital. The film follows the months of planning and rehearsals for the generation-spanning event. (June 5, 1988; 60 min.)

Awards: Close Harmony: 1982 Academy Award: Best Documentary Short
Source: Peege: Phoenix Films; Close Harmony: Devillier-Donegan Enterprises

Coping with Illness

I Know a Song by Brenda King is the story of the director's mother's struggle with Alzheimer's disease, and of the daughter's efforts to continue to communicate with her. *This Side is Good* by Stephen H. Barr is the story of 72-year-old Sidney Keller who, though paralyzed on one side after a severe stroke, is still able to perform volunteer work at a local hospital. *Not a Jealous Bone* by Cecilia Condit is a mini-opera about an 82-year-old woman who challenges society's obsession with youth. *Father Death Blues*, by Rose Lesniak of Manhattan Poetry Video, sets an Allen Ginsberg poem to music. (June 12, 1988; 60 min.)

Source: I Know a Song, This Side is Good: Filmmakers' Library; Father Death Blues: Video Data Bank

Difficult Decisions

My Mother, My Father by James Vanden Bosch documents the struggles of four Chicago-area families confronting the decisions that arise when a parent can no longer care for him- or herself. *The Street*, an animated work by Caroline Leaf based on a short story by Mordecai Richler, presents a child's perspective of the lingering illness and death of a grandparent. *Time Will Tell* by Holly Jacobs reveals the bonds of respect and affection that are forged when a group of teenagers who are required to perform community service are brought together with the residents of a retirement home. (June 19, 1988; 60 min.)

Source: The Street: Coe Film Associates; Time Will Tell: Filmmakers' Library

Distances within Families

Eulogy, by Meredith Wheeler and Joseph Kleinman, is an adaptation of James Richardson's stage play about the mixed emotions surrounding the death of a sibling who was insensitive and dishonest. John Randolph and Sarah Cunningham recreate their stage roles. *Sacred Hearts* by John Bonnano remembers the director's father and documents the ambivalence the family feels toward the husband and father they loved, but never quite knew. *Suburban Queen* by Mindy Faber is about a daughter's fervent wish that her mother—a hum-drum suburban housewife—was the strong, mythical woman of her dreams. (June 26, 1988; 60 min.)

Source: Eulogy: Terra Nova Films

Four Short Stories

Yudie by Mirra Bank tells the story of her vivacious and delightfully candid aunt Yudie, who took to the camera so well in Bank's film that she went on to land roles as an actress in movies. *Noon Song* by Helena Kolda combines a traditional Slovakian folk song with images of her husband as a personal expression of her sorrow over her husband's illness. *Cadillac Hotel* by James Forsher is the story of a small hotel in Venice, California, once a resident hotel for older people, and of the struggle by its manager and residents to keep the hotel going. *George and Rosemary* by the animator Eunice Macaulay is a love story between a shy bachelor and the "apple of his eye." Nominated for an Academy Award. (July 3, 1988; 60 min.)

Source: Cadillac Hotel: James Forsher Productions; George and Rosemary: Coe Film Associates

Built to Last, Built to Delight

Luther Metke at 94 by Steve Raymen introduces a poet and master builder of traditional log cabins. Nominated for an Academy Award in 1981. *Grandma's Bottle Village* by Allie Light and Irving Saraf profiles Tressa Prisbrey and the miniature village she created from bottles, pencils and found objects, attracting tourists and curiosity-seekers who pay her a small fee for a tour. (July 10, 1988; 60 min.)

Source: Luther Metke at 94: New Dimensions Media; Grandma's Bottle Village: Light-Saraf Films

Never Too Old

Happy Birthday, Mrs. Craig by Richard Kaplan is the story of 102-year-old Lulu Sadler Craig and her recollections: her father who swam the Missouri to join the Union Army and find freedom; her journey west in a wagon with her mother and father; the creation of the all-black settlement in Nicodemus, Kansas, and her 55 years as a school teacher. *Four Women Over 80* by Sandra Greenberg profiles four active and spirited women who deal with life after 80 the same way they dealt with it over 30—by living it fully. (July 17, 1988; 60 min.)

Source: Happy Birthday, Mrs. Craig: Filmmakers' Library; Four Women Over 80: Greenberg and O'Hearn Productions

SPIRIT OF PLACE, FALL, 1988

SPIRIT OF PLACE explores our relationship to the spiritual, cultural, psychological and geographical spaces in which we dwell. The 29 films and videos reflect America's regional and ethnic diversity, capture the uniqueness of the physical environment and portray social landscapes and the creation of a shared sense of community. They also focus on private places and an individual's personal, psychological or spiritual relationship to them. The journalist and author Ron Powers hosts.

Curators: John Schott, Helen DeMichiel
A production of ACSN in association with TLC and KTCA/St. Paul-Minneapolis

The Mirror of Language

Yeah You Rite!, a humorous documentary about New Orleans vernacular by Louis Alvarez and Andrew Kolker, explores how dialects and accents color people's perceptions of each other—the messages people deduce about social class and respectability from the way others talk, not from what they say. *Songs in Minto Life* by Curt Madison reveals how language defines the Minto, a traditional Alaskan people. The Minto have created songs reflecting every aspect of their lives, encompassing war, ritual and myth, and they now strive to educate their children in this tribal legacy. (October 23, 1988; 60 min.)

Source: Yeah You Rite!: Center for New American Media; Songs in Minto Life: One West Media

Ziveli

Ziveli by Les Blank captures the culture and spirit of Serbian-Americans, whose emigration to this country began in the mid-19th century. Concentrated in the Chicago area and in northern California, this ethnic group has preserved a unique, traditional way of life whose music, religion, food and dancing bind the generations and link them to Yugoslavia. The master musician and tamburitza player Adam Popovich performs. *Spots: New England Fishermen* (excerpts) by Joan Logue consists of brief and memorable video portraits of New England fishermen, a unique traditional breed of people. (October 30, 1988; 60 min.)

Additional funding (Ziveli): National Endowment for the Humanities
Source: Ziveli: Flower Films; Spots: The CAT Fund

The Sounds of Home

Going Up to Meet Him by Tom Davenport profiles the Landis family of North Carolina, who are bound to the land, the past and to each other by the gospel music they sing. *Victoria: Happy Come Home*, by D.A. Pennebaker, Chris Hegedus and David Dawkins, profiles Victoria Williams, a young musician who reflects the feeling, values and thinking of her native rural Lousiana in a musi-cal style that draws on blues, old-time country, folk tales and folk songs. (November 6, 1988; 60 min.)

Source: Victoria: Happy Come Home: Pennebaker and Associates

Down South

Writing in Water by Stephen Roszell, *Alabama Departure* by Peter Bundy and *L'Acadie* by Robert Russett challenge commonplace notions about the American South. *Hush, Hoggies, Hush*, by Bob Ferris and Judy Peiser and the Center for Southern Folklore, stars Tom Johnson, born in Yazoo County in 1898, and his praying pigs. (November 13, 1988; 60 min.)

Source: Hush, Hoggies, Hush: Picture Start

Without a Home

Inside Life Outside, by Scott Sinkler and Sachiko Hamada, documents the harrowing day-to-day life of a group of homeless people who build a makeshift community in the lower East Side of Manhattan. Each individual struggles to survive and to maintain dignity amid the traumas of homelessness and the fear of being "thrown out" or imprisoned for trespassing. The compassionate, unsentimental film gives a voice to individuals rarely seen as other than statistics, sensational headlines or civic nuisance or embarrassment. (November 20, 1988; 60 min.)

Source: New Day Films

Hometown

Tigertown by Daniel Sipe and David Rosenberg follows an Ohio town's high school football team, as the community struggles amid economic chaos. In *Backyard*, by Ross McElwee, the witty, ironic director revisits his hometown in South Carolina. (November 27, 1988; 60 min.)

Source: Tigertown: New Dimensions Media; Backyard: First Run Features

Dear INDEPENDENTS:

I am writing in regard to your fine independent films in your New to America series. I am particularly interested in attaining a copy of the program Chicano Park.

As a Spanish teacher, I am always looking for materials which positively portray the Hispanic-American. Even though we study the culture of all the Hispanic world, I feel that it is important to stress and give meaning to this important part of our own culture.

C.B., Bloomington, Ind.

The Land I

Silver Valley, by Michel Negroponte, Peggy Stern and Mark Erder, deals with the impact of a mine-closing on a small Idaho community. *Just Between Me and God* by Alexis Krasilovsky shows a couple's struggle to save their "piece of paradise" near Memphis. *And Now This . . .* by Kit Fitzgerald is a meditation on a Midwestern landscape. (December 4, 1988; 60 min.)

The Land II

Cowboy's Claim by Miranda Smith demonstrates how progress is changing the Florida rancher's way of life. *Fla. Me.* by Ted Lyman is a sensuous experimental film essay about the Florida landscape and the rugged coast of Maine (filmed in Sutton's Island, Maine, and Brookville, Florida). Excerpts from *Spots: New England Fishermen* by Joan Logue conclude the program. (December 11, 1988; 60 min.)

Out West

Southwestern Ballet by Dan Curry and Kim Loughlin and *Wyoming Passage* by Peter Bundy explore the cliches that color our image of the Great American West. *Greetings from Vacationland* by Mark Gilliland sends an ironic series of video postcards from holiday spots devastated by progress. (December 18, 1988; 60 min.)

Women's Places

In the Heart of Big Mountain by Sandra Sunrising Osawa tells of a Navajo matriarch whose family is being forced off their ancestral land. *Dorothy Molter: Living in the Boundary Waters*, by Wade Black and Judith Hadel, profiles a woman who lives happily in the Minnesota wilderness. (December 25, 1988; 60 min.)

Source: In the Heart of Big Mountain: Upstream Productions; Dorothy Molter: Jade Films

Place and Personal Change

Three works use personal symbols in the landscape as metaphors of life, love and memory. *Whisper, The Waves, The Wind* by Kathleen Laughlin records a performance art work by Suzanne Lacy in which 154 women aged 60 to 99 gather on the beach at La Jolla, California, and reflect on the nature of aging. In *The Man Who Couldn't See Far Enough*, Peter Rose explains that the act of looking at certain things defines who he is. Rose explores the Cross Bay Bridge in New York, one of his personal totems, with increasing daring and emotional intensity. Tim Zgraggen's *Requiem*, combines mundane images, symbols of death, the landscape, light and water in an elegy to a friend who died of AIDS. (January 1, 1989; 60 min.)

Source: The Man Who Couldn't. . . : Facets Video

Place and the Passage of Time

In *Ernie Andrews: Blues for Central Avenue* by Lois Shelton the popular jazz and blues singer tells of his life and career on Los Angeles's legendary Central Avenue in the 1930s, 40s and 50s, describing the clubs, now vanished, that nourished a generation of black talent. *Lost, Lost, Lost* (excerpts) by Jonas Mekas recalls his arrival in New York as a displaced person. *Time Squared* by Branda Miller is a video time capsule of New York City's Times Square. (January 8, 1989; 60 min.)

Source: Lost, Lost, Lost: Anthology Film Archives; Time Squared: The CAT Fund

Family Album

Alan Berliner's *Family Album* explores the sense of place—of identity, orientation and belonging—that family provides through a collection of home movies and audiotapes that follows the cycle of births, marriages and deaths over several decades. (January 15, 1989; 60 min.)

Source: Filmmakers' Library

NEW TO AMERICA, SPRING, 1989

NEW TO AMERICA reports on the experience of contemporary immigrants. The 25 films and videos show uprootings and transitions, cultural encounters and clashes, the search for identity and purpose, relationships between immigrants and their first-generation children and a host of other issues from the experience of new immigrants—how America changes them and how they are changing America. The actor Edward James Olmos hosts. Curators: Linda Blackaby, Tony Gittens
A production of ACSN in association with TLC and Fireside Entertainment

Blue Collar and Buddha

Blue Collar and Buddha by Taggart Siegel and Kati Johnston traces the experiences of a refugee Laotian community seeking a new life in the economically depressed factory town of Rockford, Illinois. These newcomers don't look, act, dress, think or worship like Americans, and the film demonstrates how easy it is for Americans to forget that their ancestors were once the latest arrivals in a strange land. Nominated for an ACE Award. (April 23, 1989; 60 min.)

Source: Filmmakers' Library

Music in the Melting Pot

A Bailar! The Journey of a Latin Dance Company by Catherine Calderon and Lloyd Goldfine tells of Eddie Torres's dream of creating a Latin Dance Troupe to preserve the mambo's unique combination of African, Cuban and American jazz rhythms. *The Lure and the Lore* by Ayoka Chenzira profiles the Jamaican performance artist Thomas Pinnock through interviews, dance and performance. Art Nomura's *Wok Like a Man* is a music video that suggests that acculturation to life in America is more like a quick stir-fry than a gradual melting. (April 30, 1989; 60 min.)

Source: A Bailar!: Cinema Guild

Chicano Park

Marilyn Mulford and Mario Barrera's *Chicano Park* tells the story of the efforts by the residents of San Diego's Barrio Logan to create a park for their families beneath a freeway. The giant footings supporting the freeway are covered with spectacular murals celebrating the rich culture of the barrio. (May 7, 1989; 60 min.)

Between Two Worlds

So Far from India by Mira Nair explores the emotional impact on an Indian family divided between the old and new worlds and the struggle to keep family bonds intact. *East Meets West* by Christine Lombard is a provocative work featuring a Chinese photographer who transports the viewer into a land where worlds collide. (May 14, 1989; 60 min.)

Additional funding (So Far from India): National Endowment for the Humanities
Source: So Far From India: Mirabai Films; East Meets West: Picture Start

Living in America

Gayla Jamison follows the ups and downs of Ybor City (now part of Tampa, Florida) and its mixture of Cuban, Spanish and Italian immigrants and their descendants in *Living in America: 100 Years of Ybor City.* The community grew up around a cigar factory in the 19th century and still retains a proud, multiethnic flavor despite hard times. (May 21, 1989; 60 min.)

Source: 100 Years of Ybor City: Filmmakers' Library

Reminiscences

Reminiscences of a Journey to Lithuania is Jonas Mekas's famous personal film diary. Part one of the diary is shown, shot by Mekas shortly after he immigrated to the United States—and excerpts from part two—the record of Mekas and his brother's return to Lithuania 25 years later. (May 28, 1989; 60 min.)

Source: Museum of Modern Art

Dear INDEPENDENTS*:*

Late last night, as I ferociously flipped through the cable channels, I paused at Channel 34—The Learning Channel, and for the next 45 minutes I was completely frozen to my chair.

It was a home movie of a man's journey back to Lithuania after two decades. What made it so very gripping was the fact that two years ago my parents and I visited Yugoslavia, my parents' first time back after emigrating to America 27 years ago, and my first time ever to the country of my heritage. I could so easily relate to the things the man in the movie said and felt.

Watching this movie brought back so many beautiful memories. I cried out of happiness, and out of sadness. . . . I am so grateful that I found this movie and this channel, even if it was by chance.

Thank you for this wonderful channel. And thank you for a most amazing film.

Very truly yours,

M.M.A., Waukegan, Ill.

Aliens

Carved in Silence is Felicia Lowe's story of Angel Island in San Francisco harbor where Chinese immigrants were detained pending admission to the United States. The film recalls the period from 1882 to 1943 when the Chinese Exclusion Act denied entry to the U.S. solely on the basis of race. *Both at Once* by Sylvie Carnot concerns a woman caught between two cultures, bombarded with endless questions upon her arrival in America. (June 4, 1989; 60 min.)

Source: Carved in Silence: Felicia Lowe Productions

Dear INDEPENDENTS:

I rarely watch TV, but happened in on the Sun Moon & Feather *portion of the program from* THE INDEPENDENTS—NEW TO AMERICA. *It was wild, crazy and wonderful! Can you tell me more about this program and details on the authors, actors or directors from* Sun Moon & Feather *and on your whole series on independent films. Can I get a copy? (I am a visual artist and my brother is a filmmaker.)*

K.D.R., Lexington, Ky.

P.S. One of the many things I loved about Sun Moon & Feather *was the* woman's *perspective!*

Italians

ItalianAmerican, produced by Saul Rubin and Elaine Attias and directed by Martin Scorsese as a student. Scorsese's mother and father relate their memories of their parents' experience as immigrants and of the evolution of their New York City neighborhood. *Washing Walls with Mrs. G* by Tony Buba profiles his 87-year-old grandmother, who at age 36 and with three small children, came to America from Italy. (June 11, 1989; 60 min.)

Source: Italianamerican: Museum of Modern Art

Political Refugees

Becoming American by Ken and Ivory Waterworth Levine chronicles the journey of a refugee family from Laos to Seattle, Washington, and a very different life. *Sanctuary: An Expression of Conscience* by Third World Newsreel introduces refugees and Americans involved in the sanctuary movement, which brings Central American refugees into the United States by whatever means, legal or illegal. *All Orientals Look the Same* by Valerie Soe is a short cutting rapidly through racial stereotypes. (June 18, 1989; 60 min.)

Source: Becoming American: New Day Films; Sanctuary: Third World Newsreel; All Orientals Look the Same: Women Make Movies

Out of Solidarity

Gaylen Ross's *Out of Solidarity: Three Polish Families in America* tells the story of three families who flee Poland out of fear of persecution because of their involvement in Solidarity. The documentary covers their first two years as exiles in America and their struggle to gain a foothold in a land whose promise always seems to be just a little out of reach. (June 25, 1989; 60 min.)

Source: Tapestry International

Origins and Identity

Vera Aronow's *To Uncle Alex* is a tribute to her uncle, the family patriarch, who emigrated from Russia in 1911 at age 15, on the occasion of his 90th birthday. In *Made in China*, Lisa Hsia, an American of Chinese ancestry, visits China. Though she speaks no Mandarin, she is mistaken for Chinese time and again, and she discovers, at age 22, what it is to be Chinese. *I Told You So* by Visual Communications is a portrait of Lawson Inado, a Californian of Japanese-American descent who by his own account thinks like a Chicano, and whose cross-cultural roots inspire his poetry. (July 2, 1989; 60 min.)

Source: Made in China: Filmmakers' Library; I Told You So: Third World Newsreel

Voyage of Dreams/Clouded Land

Voyage of Dreams by Raymond Cajuste and Collis Davis is about the despair (and the hope) that drive hundreds of Haitians to attempt to make it by boat to Florida every year. *Clouded Land* by Randy Croce chronicles the disputes over the ownership of the White Earth Reservation in Minnesota and their effect on three families. *El Milagro de las Tortillas* ("the tortilla miracle"), by Daniel Salazar, is an animated short produced with a class of fifth graders. (July 9, 1989; 60 min.)

Source: Voyage of Dreams: Cinema Guild; Clouded Land: Intermedia Arts Minnesota

Traditions, Alive and Well

The New Puritans: The Sikhs of Yuba City by Ritu Sarin and Tenzing Sonam is a documentary about a Sikh community in California which retains its age-old traditions and culture. *Sun, Moon & Feather* by Jane Zipp and Bob Rosen profiles three Native American women who have grown up in Brooklyn, the daughters of a Rappahannock mother and a Cuna father, with re-enactments of family and tribal stories told through dance and song, and with home movies from a 30-year period. (July 16, 1989; 60 min.)

Source: The New Puritans: Crosscurrent Media; Sun, Moon & Feather: Metropolitan Arts

DISTANT LIVES, SPRING, 1990

DISTANT LIVES travels the world beyond America's shores through the lens of the independent filmmaker. The series visits our closer neighbors: Mexico, Latin America and Haiti; distant countries of Asia: India, Nepal, Thailand and Bali; as well as Europe and Africa. Like letters and postcards from pen-pals abroad, these films and videos impart a sense of discovery and a depth of knowledge about the cultures and countries beyond our borders and across the seas. The actress

Linda Hunt hosts.
Curator: Helen DeMichiel
Executive producer: John Schott
A production of ACSN in association with TLC and KTCA/St. Paul-Minneapolis

Azul

Roland Legiardi-Laura travels to the embattled country of Nicaragua to explore its poetry, which has become the heart and soul of the nation. Five years in the making, *Azul* celebrates Nicaragua and the people who create poetry, from the soldier on the battlefield to the poet laureate. (April 22, 1990; 60 min.)

Rock and Rituals

USSR&R: Rock on a Red Horse, by Ken Thurlbeck, is an unofficial look at the Soviet Union's underground rock-and-roll scene, where the music criticizes both culture and politics. *Mode in France*, by William Klein, is a fictional documentary on haute couture that turns reality upside down. *Architecture of Rhythm*, by Fred Barney Taylor, captures West African and Caribbean rituals and street dance in a series of vignettes. (April 29, 1990; 60 min.)

Source: USSR&R: Rock on a Red Horse: Coe Film Associates

Bali

Learning to Dance in Bali, by Margaret Mead and Gregory Bateson, was produced by the noted anthropologists as part of their field work in the 1930s. *Kembali*, by Ideas in Motion, follows a gamelan orchestra from Berkeley, California, as they perform Balinese music before native audiences in Indonesia. (May 6, 1990; 60 min.)

Source: Learning to Dance in Bali: NYU Film and Video Library; Kembali: Ideas In Motion

Lyrical Images of Travel

Four lyrical works capture the imagery that often fades once a traveler returns home. *Valentin de las Sierras*, by Bruce Baillie, explores the textures, shapes and colors of the Mexican Sierras. *Venezia*, by Andrej Zdravic, is a whimsical study of the relationship between architecture and water. *In Paris Parks*, filmed in the 1950s by Shirley Clarke, celebrates the timeless rhythms of childhood. *Memories of the City*, by Peter Hutton, was created under the auspices of the Bela Balazs Studio in Budapest, Hungary. The film captures the pictorial grandeur of this classic European city. (May 13, 1990; 60 min.)

Source: Valentin, Paris Parks: Museum of Modern Art

Haiti

Two works by Jonathan Demme about post-Duvalier Haiti. *Haiti: Dreams of Democracy*, a collaboration between the British documentarian Jo Menell and Demme, combines interviews, political commentary, news footage and music. In *Konbit*, Demme uses the music video format to look at the economic inequities that beset Haiti and its people. (May 20, 1990; 60 min.)

Source: Haiti: Jane Balfour Films; Konbit: Clinica Estetico

Foreign Correspondents

Drought, by Bonnie Donohue, contrasts the effects of drought on South African blacks and South African whites in a powerful picture of economic disparity (an excerpt from *South Africa Tapes*). *Voyages*, by Susan Meiselas and Mark Karlin, travels to Nicaragua to probe the

journalist's ethical and professional dilemma when faced with the task of objectively covering news events that evoke strong moral and emotional responses. (May 27, 1990; 60 min.)

Source: Drought: X-Africa Productions; Voyages: Jane Balfour Films

Latino Visions

Two works examine the connection between art and politics in Latin America. *Plena is Work, Plena is Song*, by Susan Zeig and Pedro Rivera, is about a popular form of workers' music set to gentle Caribbean melodies. Shot in Puerto Rico and New York. *Ana Mendieta: Fuego de Tierra*, by Kate Horsfield, Nereyda Garcia-Ferraz and Branda Miller, is a biography of the late Cuban-born artist and filmmaker Ana Mendieta. (June 3, 1990; 60 min.)

Source: Ana Mendieta: Video Data Bank

Americans through Other Eyes

For Beautiful Human Life, by Louis Alvarez and Andrew Kolker, examines a popular Japanese institution, an American-themed "love hotel." In *Fake Fruit Factory*, by Chick Strand, female workers in a Mexican factory discuss money, romance and their American boss. *Juxta*, by Hiroko Yamazaki, explores the racial tensions that haunt two Japanese-American families of the 1950s. (June 10, 1990; 60 min.)

Source: For Beautiful Human Life: Center for New American Media; Juxta: Women Make Movies

Forest of Bliss

Robert Gardner's complex, subtle work about life along the Ganges River in Benares, India, *Forest of Bliss*, bypasses narration and other interpretive conventions, constructing a film from visual and sound elements that gradually evokes intimations of a universality transcending the plight of contemporary Indians. (June 17, 1990; 60 min.)

Source: Arthur Cantor Films

The Landscape—Physical, Cultural, Personal

Stones and Flies: Richard Long in the Sahara, by Philip Haas, follows a British artist as he creates sculptures from the empty volcanic moonscape of the desert. *Friendly Witness* is Warren Sonbert's personal expression of the diversity of culture and people the world over, crafted from the footage, recordings and still images of 20 years' worth of traveling. (June 24, 1990; 60 min.)

Cultural Clashes and Assumptions

Meaning of the Interval, by Edin Velez, is an experimental video that captures on ever-shifting grids the clash of cultures in contemporary Japan. Trinh Minh-ha's *Reassemblage* confronts the cultural assumptions and cinematic conventions of the traditional ethnographic documentary, continually undermining and recasting the interpretations of the West African women portrayed in the film. (July 1, 1990; 60 min.)

Source: Meaning of the Interval: Electronic Arts Intermix; Reassemblage: Women Make Movies

Origins of Struggles and Societies

Dreams from China, by Fred Marx, is a film journal of the director's time spent as a teacher in China. It foreshadows the uprisings at Tiananmen Square in 1989. In *After the Storm*, by Shalom Gorewitz, the director reworks the imagery of his travels in Morocco, Hawaii and New York State into a meditation on the roots of conflict. *Watunna*, by Stacey Steers, is an animated retelling of the creation myth of Venezuela's Orinoco Indians. *Flying Morning Glory*, by Skip Blumberg, captures the split-second precision involved in preparing Thai street cuisine. (July 8, 1990; 60 min.)

Tibetan Mystery

Destroyer of Illusion—The Secret World of a Tibetan Lama, by Richard Kohn, documents for the first time on film the ritual of Mani Rimdu, a ceremony performed annually by Tibetan Monks. Since 1959, the ritual has been performed in the Himalayas of Nepal, and it has been shrouded in mystery for centuries. Kohn, a Tibetan scholar, spent five years studying Mani Rimdu and translating the texts associated with it under the guidance of Trulshig Rinpoche, the Tibetan monk who presides over the ceremony. Richard Gere narrates. (July 15, 1990; 60 min.)

Source: Destroyer of Illusion: Gidney International

NON-FICTION TELEVISION

Concerned that the art of the documentary had virtually disappeared from public television and that outstanding documentarians were excluded from broadcast, the Ford Foundation (through the initiative of Fred Friendly and David Davis) and the Endowment (led by Nancy Hanks and Chloe Aaron) created the Independent Documentary Fund. When offered in open competition to public television stations and independent organizations, the reviewing panel selected the application of WNET/Thirteen, New York. Thus began an exhilarating six-year project, during which the late David Loxton as executive producer and his coordinating producer Katherine Kline introduced national audiences to documentaries by old and new masters on subjects as diverse as the resilience of a Washington State wheat farmer and the plight of emotionally disturbed children. The fund ensured the delivery of product by providing generous completion grants, thereby removing the onus of extended fundraising from the makers. The series, occasionally controversial, also introduced a careful review of facts, balance and presentation which did much to lessen chronic aggravations between station management and independent artists.

Executive producer: David Loxton
Coordinating producer: Katherine Kline
Additional funders include: Ford Foundation, Corporation for Public Broadcasting, Public Broadcasting Service
A production of the Television Laboratory at WNET/Thirteen

SEASON ONE, 1979

Paul Jacobs and the Nuclear Gang

The deadly effects of low-level nuclear radiation on people living in the vicinity of the early atomic experiments in the western United States immediately after World War II. The late Paul Jacobs, reporter and social activist, examines the U.S. stance on issues related to nuclear power, weapons and contamination. For 20 years Jacobs pursued the story of low-level radiation until he eventually succumbed to cancer himself, apparently the victim of prolonged contact with the deadly substances of which he wrote. (February 25, 1979; 60 min.)

Directed and written by: Jack Willis, Saul Landau
Producer: Jack Willis
Awards: Emmy Award: Outstanding Program Achievement
Source: New Time Films

Hamper McBee: Raw Mash

An intimate portrait of Hamper McBee, a moonshiner and one of the few remaining authentic hillbilly raconteurs and balladeers. Filmed in the hills of Tennessee, the documentary shows a unique breed of man—a Southern individualist with roots in the mountains trying to find his place in today's society. The film later aired on the series SOUTHBOUND. (April 6, 1979; 30 min.)

Producers: Blaine Dunlap, Sol Korine

La La, Making It in L.A.

An essay on the quest for stardom and status in music, movies and art. Some 55 aspiring entertainers speak directly to the audience about their lives, dreams and disappointments, offering advice to other aspiring performers. They discuss why they came to Los Angeles, their families' opinions, adopting stage names, supporting themselves, looking for work, the casting couch, their goals and their feelings about Los Angeles. (May 8, 1979; 60 min.)

Producers: Caroline and Frank Mouris
Source: Direct Cinema

Once a Daughter

The film focuses on four mothers and their daughters, interweaving footage of their relationships with scenes from dramas about the mother-daughter relationship. Its premise is that among all human relationships, the ties between mothers and their daughters are unique; they persist amidst and in spite of a lifetime of growth and change. (May 9, 1979; 60 min.)

Producer: Lynne Littman

Cat . . . A Woman Who Fought Back

Cathy "Cat" Davis was the first woman to become a licensed professional boxer in New York State. Davis, a speech major from Louisiana, went on to a professional career and became the world's Lightweight Women's Champion. The film includes interviews with prominent figures in boxing, including Muhammad Ali and Floyd Patterson, who discuss their attitudes toward women in the boxing arena. (May 16, 1979; 30 min.)

Director, producer: Jane Warrenbrand
Source: Films, Inc. (educational)

SEASON TWO, 1980

Deadly Force

This documentary about police accountability when force is used to subdue unarmed suspects focuses on the highly publicized case of Ron Burkholder, a naked, unarmed man killed by a member of the Los Angeles Police Department in August, 1977. The film examines this incident, the efforts to prosecute the crime, and the issues that surround prosecution of such cases in general. (April 4, 1980; 60 min.)

Producer: Richard Cohen

Third Avenue: Only the Strong Survive

A video documentary on urban survival. It focuses on six individuals along New York City's Third Avenue, a street of diverse classes and cultures that runs from Brooklyn, through Manhattan and ends in the Bronx. The cross-section of New Yorkers includes a car thief, a Bowery bum, a welfare mother, a male prostitute, a factory worker and a barber. (April 11, 1980; 60 min.)

Producers: Jon Alpert, Keiko Tsuno
Awards: Two Emmy Awards
Source: Downtown Community Television

America Lost and Found

A compilation showing how America reacted to the loss of its dreams of prosperity during the Depression years and how those dreams were rebuilt. The film examines the cultural icons of the era around which Americans rallied: Kate Smith, Popeye, F.D.R. and Eleanor Roosevelt, Henry Luce,

Paul Jacobs and the Nuclear Gang *records the journalist's investigation of the effects of low-level nuclear radiation in the Southwest over 20 years.*

Henry Fonda, Walker Evans, Dale Carnegie, *Life* magazine, Mount Rushmore, Huey Long, the Empire State Building, the 1939 World's Fair and many others. The film consists entirely of period newsreel footage, photographs and other historic materials. (April 18, 1980; 60 min.)

Director: Lance Bird
Producer: Tom Johnson
Additional funding: National Endowment for the Humanities
Contact: Direct Cinema

No Maps on My Taps

An entertaining and informative look at three black jazz tap dancers: Howard "Sandman" Sims, Chuck Green and Bunny Briggs. Each of these self-taught dancers tells how he came to be a hoofer: copying siblings or relatives, dancing on the street for spare change, competing with other dancers on the street. Rare historical film footage illustrates their careers. The three reminisce about the past and show what they are doing to keep this unique heritage from dying out. (April 25, 1980; 60 min.)

Directed and produced by: George Nierenberg
Awards: 1981 Emmy Award: Outstanding Musical Direction
Source: Direct Cinema

Alaska: Technology and Time

A prophetic look at the ongoing conflict between petroleum companies drilling for oil in Alaska's offshore waters and Alaskan residents concerned about the possible negative effects these explorations may have on the natural environment. Examines the territory surrounding Kachemak Bay and Lower Cook Inlet, an area south of Anchorage. (May 7, 1980; 60 min.)

Producer: Rick Wise

On Company Business

A three-part examination of the Central Intelligence Agency and its role in American foreign policy. Work on the film began in 1975, when Congress, reacting to the Watergate break-in, began an 18-month investigation of C.I.A. and F.B.I. activities. The film examines the C.I.A.'s history, its overt and covert activities and its power as an arm of the executive branch of the federal government in developing and carrying out foreign policy objectives. (May 9, 16 and 23, 1980; 180 min.—3 x 60 min.)

Producers: Howard Dratch, Allan Francovich
Source: MPI Home Video

Plea Bargaining—An American Way of Justice

An exploration of the practice of plea bargaining, a method used in the disposition of up to 95 percent of all felony cases nationwide. The film shows its use as an administrative remedy to pressures created by heavy caseloads, offering insight into the human dimensions of the judicial system and showing how personalities and philosophical points of view affect the quality of justice, for better or worse. Filmed in the courthouse of the 11th Circuit of Florida, serving Dade County. (May 30, 1980; 60 min.)

Producer: Robert Thurber
Source: Thurber Productions Film Library

Service Entrance

This documentary follows an 18-year-old youth named Roosevelt as he attempts to find direction in life by enlisting in the Army Reserves. Trying to escape the downward spiral on the streets, Roosevelt enlists and undergoes basic training. He has trouble with discipline and memorization of basic Army facts. His superiors are firm but supportive in helping him

deal with responsibility, but they also sense that he lacks seriousness and self-discipline. (June 6, 1980; 30 min.)

Producer: Dena Schutzer

Man of Wheat

The story of Glen Miller, a 75-year-old wheat farmer from the state of Washington whose 20,000-acre farm is one of the largest in the Northwest. The film chronicles Miller's life, in particular the 32 years he has spent farming the same land. The film is testimony to a vanishing breed: the self-made man who manages to compete with large ranches and farms owned and operated by conglomerate corporations. (June 6, 1980; 30 min.)

Director, producer: Steve Marts
Source: Pyramid Films

Taking Back Detroit

A brief history of the socialist movement in Detroit led by the Detroit Alliance for a Rational Economy (DARE), perhaps the most significant socialist organization in a major American city. The film profiles three radicals who helped found DARE in the late 1970s: Judge Justin Ravitz, City Councilman Kenneth Cockrel and Sheila Murphy, a leader of the Motor City Labor League. The film explores unionization drives, the city's economic problems and DARE's efforts to direct public funds to creating subsidized housing in city neighborhoods. (June 13, 1980; 60 min.)

Producer: Stephen Lighthill
Source: Icarus Films (educational)

Taylor Chain

The film reports on the problems of democratic process and leadership in a union local as seen during a labor dispute at a small, recently unionized chain-making factory in Indiana, the Taylor Chain plant. From the start of contract negotiations, to the decision to strike, through the seven-week strike, to its eventual settlement, the film studies conflicts within the union itself, whether in highly charged union meetings or on picket lines. (June 20, 1980; 30 min.)

Producers: Jerry Blumenthal, Gordon Quinn
Source: New Day Films

Varnette's World: A Study of a Young Artist

The artwork and personal struggles of Varnette Honeywood, a young black artist from Los Angeles. The camera follows the artist in her daily activities, integrating live action and still photography of Honeywood's paintings to capture scenes from black life in an urban ghetto. Although Honeywood is relatively unknown as an artist, the film illustrates that her situation and problems are typical of most young aspiring artists trying to survive in the contemporary art world. (June 20, 1980; 30 min.)

Director: Carroll Parrott Blue

SEASON THREE, 1980 - 1981

A Lady Named Baybie

A film about the indomitable 64-year-old Baybie Hoover and her closest friend, Virginia "Ginger" Brown. Both blind, they "pitched" their way from Wichita, Kansas, to New York City by singing religious music on the street with tin cups in hand. Settling in New York City in 1954, Baybie has preached her own interpretation of the gospel on the street and, since 1964, on the Radio Gospel Church. The film examines the unique world Hoover has created for herself—one of sound, smell and touch—and her courage and hard-won dignity in the face of discrimination and hardship. (December 17, 1980; 60 min.)

Producer: Martha Sandlin
Source: Direct Cinema

I Remember Harlem

This four-part documentary on the past, present and future of New York's Harlem community traces its history from 1600 to 1980, including interviews with such famous Harlemites as James Baldwin and Gordon Parks and rare film footage of Dr. W.E.B. DuBois, Malcolm X, Adam Clayton Powell, Jr., and others. A one-hour version of the film was broadcast February 2, 1982. (February 1 - 4, 1981; 240 min.—4 x 60 min.)

Producer: William Miles
Writer: Clayton Riley
Awards: Alfred I. DuPont-Columbia Citation in Broadcast Journalism
Source: Films for the Humanities (educational)

The Early Years: 1600 - 1930 looks at Harlem's early days: as Native American fishing village, Dutch farming community and English colony, to its growth as a wealthy New York City suburb and finally a burgeoning black neighborhood. Explores the Marcus Garvey movement and the Harlem Renaissance in the 1920s.

The Depression Years: 1930 - 1940 explores the legacy created in Harlem during the Depression: its influential music and show business tradition, the effects of the Works Progress Administration, the Father Divine movement, the numbers-game ritual and the heroic reputations of such figures as the boxer Joe Louis.

Toward Freedom: 1940 - 1965 examines Harlem's politics of protest and some of its noted political leaders, as well as the effects of World War II, the emergence of uptown gangs and the community's social growth in the 1960s.

Toward a New Day: 1965 - 1980 charts Harlem's decline and rebirth: the encouraging signs of redevelopment, the influence and stability of its churches. Several Harlemites share their predictions for its future.

Crystal City: The Brown Out

The story of the small Mexican-American town of Crystal City, Texas, and its self-sufficiency in using alternative energy sources. Crystal City's energy independence was developed following events in 1977, when its supply of natural gas was shut off after disputes with the power company over a 500 percent price increase. (February 9, 1981; 30 min.)

Producer, writer: Roberto Holguin

Hopi

A documentary exploring the split between traditional and modern members of the southwestern Hopi tribe. A small band of Hopi traditionalists tries to maintain ancient spiritual ties to a land whose vast deposits of coal, oil and uranium have made it subject to gradual appropriation over the past 100 years. (May 22, 1981; 60 min.)

Producer: Wayne Ewing

SEASON FOUR, 1981 - 1982

Pesticides and Pills: For Export Only

A two-part documentary on the sale of pesticides and medications that have been banned or restricted in the United States and other western countries to Third World countries. Part one documents how banned pesticides (DDT and many others) are shipped to developing countries where they are used on crops, many of which are exported back to developed countries—the so-called cycle of poison. Part two examines the export and

William Miles, filmmaker, interviews James Baldwin in I Remember Harlem, *a panoramic appreciation of the historic community from 1600 to 1980. Photo by Vickie Gholson.*

marketing of banned or restricted medications and drugs to Third World countries. There such drugs are sold or prescribed to patients by physicians and pharmacists often unaware of their dangerous side effects. (October 5 and 7, 1981; 120 min.—2 x 60 min.)

Producer: Robert Richter
Source: Icarus Films International

Nick Mazzuco: Biography of an Atomic Veteran

Nick Mazzuco, a U.S. Army veteran, tells of his experiences at atomic bombs test sites in the 1950s. On one occasion, while stationed in the Nevada desert in 1955, Mazucco was 2,500 yards from ground zero during a nuclear bomb blast. The film examines the U.S. government tests of the 1950s which involved more than 300,000 U.S. soldiers. (January 7, 1982; 30 min.)

Producer: Richard Schmiechen
Source: Green Mountain Post Films (educational)

Next Year Country

An exploration of the impact of widespread energy development on four rural western boom towns: Creston, Washington; Challis, Idaho; Mercer County, North Dakota, and Circle, Montana. The rush to develop their vast mineral and energy deposits, accompanied by an influx of people, large-scale strip mining and economic upheaval, is changing the face of the land and long-established ways of life. (January 31, 1982; 60 min.)

Producers: Beth Ferris, Claire Beckham, John Stern

Blood and Sand: War in the Sahara

A report on the war between the guerilla forces of the Polisario Front and the Royal Armed Forces of Morocco over control of the western Sahara. Includes interviews with officials and military leaders from both sides of the conflict and with U.S. government officials. (April 28, 1982; 60 min.)

Director, producer: Sharon Sopher
Writers: Sharon Sopher, Peter Kinoy
Source: First Run Features

Becoming American

The Hmong people of northern Laos experience culture shock when they are resettled in America. Renowned as tough and dependable guerilla fighters for the United States during the Vietnam War, the Hmong were forced from their homeland after the government fell. The film focuses on one family; after six years in a refugee camp in Thailand, they are confronted on arrival in Seattle with cultural barriers, community prejudice and economic hardship, jeopardizing the cultural identity the Hmong had kept intact for centuries. (June 4, 1982; 60 min.)

Producers: Ken Levine, Ivory Waterworth Levine
Source: New Day Films

Burden of Dreams

A documentary about the German director Werner Herzog's five-year struggle to complete the film *Fitzcarraldo*, a surreal action-adventure that takes place in the Amazon jungles. Despite deadly accidents— including torrential rains, dysentery, having their camp burned to the ground, the exit of the lead actors and the outbreak of war—Herzog finished the film. *Fitzcarraldo* is the story of a European visionary who dreams of opening an opera house in the Amazon town of Iquitos and of bringing Enrico Caruso to perform there. (June 11, 1982; 60 min.)

Producer: Les Blank
Writer: Michael Goodwin
Source: Flower Films

Trouble on Fashion Avenue

Examines the current economic problems of the New York City garment industry and their ramifications for millions of people in a variety of re-

lated industries in this country. Special attention is paid to the human effects of this economic trouble, including the demise of thousands of small businesses and the loss of hundreds of thousands of jobs. (June 18, 1982; 60 min.)

Producers: Claude Beller, Stefan Moore
Source: Cinema Guild (educational)

Vernon, Florida

A story about the residents of a small town in Washington County, Florida. Among them are a man obsessed with turkey hunting, who adorns the walls of his house with turkey feet; the town police officer, who discusses the places he sits waiting for crimes that never happen; a preacher who explains how the Lord helped him buy a used van and a parcel of land; and a couple with a jar of sand they insist is growing. (August 18, 1982; 60 min.)

Producer: Errol Morris
Writer: Seth Cagin
Source: RCA/Columbia Pictures Home Video

I Remember Beale Street

A film on the forces that established Beale Street in Memphis, Tennessee, as the legendary birthplace of the blues. It chronicles Beale Street's heyday from 1880 to the end of World War I, when it was a focal point of black culture in the South, and discusses the factors that led to its decline later in the 20th century. (November 3, 1982; 60 min.)

Producer: Reginald Brown

SEASON FIVE, 1983 - 1984

Children of Darkness

Examines the crisis in mental health care for emotionally disturbed children. Many of the seven million mentally ill children in the United States receive inadequate care; those in institutions are often subjected to intensive drug and discipline treatments without psychiatric therapy. The film shows the struggles of such children, aided by their doctors and families, to become healthy again. (May 4, 1983; 60 min.)

Produced and written by: Richard Kotuk, Ara Chekmayan

The Cancer War

An examination of the National Cancer Institute and other major institutions charged with finding a cure for cancer. It evaluates the criticism surrounding their failure to find cures for most forms of cancer and to explore fully the area of preventive medicine. The program questions whether decisions made in the past decade about the causes of cancer, its treatment and methods of diagnosis are in the best interests of cancer patients and the American public. (May 11, 1983; 60 min.)

Producers: Steven Fischler, Jane Praeger, Joel Sucher
Source: Cinema Guild (educational)

Conversations with Roy de Carava

A biographical and philosophical study of the still photographer, Roy de Carava, co-author with Langston Hughes of *Sweet Flypaper of Life*, a book documenting black life in Harlem of the 1950s, and whose work is also represented in *The Family of Man*. De Carava's "jazz" photography of John

Coltrane, Billie Holiday and others is also shown. Narrated by Alex Haley; music by Jimmy Owens. (February 22, 1984; 30 min.)

Producer, writer: Carroll Parrott Blue
Source: Icarus Films (educational)

Invisible Citizens: Japanese Americans

The evolving reaction of Japanese-Americans to the internment during World War II is shown in the lives and feelings of six individuals, representing three generations. All share a sense of pain and injustice over the events, when 120,000 Japanese-Americans were forced to abandon homes, farms and other property. Nearly 2,000 people died due to inadequate medical care, and more than 1,000 were subsequently committed to mental institutions or hospitalized with tuberculosis. (February 26, 1984; 60 min.)

Producer: Keiko Tsuno
Writer: Pat Sides
Source: Downtown Community Television

The Last Pullman Car

When the historic Pullman-Standard plant in South Chicago shut down in 1981 after 113 years in operation, Pullman workers were stunned. The last American-owned builder of passenger cars had left the business on which its worldwide fame and fortune had been built. The film documents the three-year confrontation between the Pullman workers of USWA Local 1834 who fought to save their jobs and the modern Pullman conglomerate. It questions how the American labor movement will survive this era of corporate takeovers and plant shutdowns, closing on a note of anger, not resignation. (July 6, 1984; 60 min.)

Producers: Jerry Blumenthal, Gordon Quinn
Source: Kartemquin Films

SEASON SIX, 1984 - 1985

The Work I've Done

A film on retirement and the meaning of work. It focuses on one man who is about to retire, 54-year-old Thess Campbell, and on several individuals who have already retired. The film poses a paradox: people identify who they are with what they do—so who are they when stop working? The transition to retirement is different; some feel that their life is truly at an end, while others see the beginning of a new life. (September 6, 1984; 60 min.)

Director, producer: Ken Fink
Source: Icarus Films

America and Lewis Hine

The film examines the life and work of the photographer Lewis Hine (1874 - 1940), often regarded as America's foremost social documentary photographer. For 35 years Hine photographed Ellis Island immigrants; men, women and children in the sweatshops of New York's Lower East Side and in mines, mills and factories across the country. His photographs of children at work contributed to the passage of child labor legislation. (November 8, 1984; 60 min.)

Director: Nina Rosenblum
Producers: Nina Rosenblum, Daniel V. Allentuck
Writer: Daniel V. Allentuck
Additional funding: National Endowment for the Humanities
Contact: Cinema Guild

The World of Tomorrow

The 1939 World's Fair is a symbol representing the attitudes, ideals and visions that shaped the second half of the 20th century. Jason Robards narrates the experiences of an adult remembering what it was like to visit the event as a 10-year-old child. (November 22, 1984; 60 min.)

Producers: Lance Bird, Tom Johnson
Source: Direct Cinema

Los Sures

Portraits of four Puerto Rican residents of the Williamsburg section of Brooklyn in the 1980s, exploring the endemic poverty, unemployment, drugs, juvenile delinquency and personal crises with which they live. (November 29, 1984; 60 min.)

Director, producer: Diego Echeverria
Source: Cinema Guild (educational)

Neighbors: The U.S. and Mexico

The film explores the prevailing economic realities between the United States and its third largest trading partner, Mexico, reporting on the 1982 peso devaluations, the severe economic depression that ensued and the complex interdependence of the two countries in banking, trade and immigration. (May 2, 1985; 60 min.)

Directed and produced by: Jesus Trevino, Jose Luis Ruiz
Source: Cinema Guild (educational)

The Shakers: Hands to Work, Hearts to God

The last nine surviving Shakers help recount two centuries of Shaker history—the stories of ordinary people who gave up homes, livelihoods and families to practice the celibate discipline they believed to be authentic Christianity. Rare archival material gathered from more than 40 collections details all aspects of the sect. Narrated by the historian David McCullough. (August 7, 1985; 60 min.)

Directors: Ken Burns, Amy Stechler Burns
Writers: Amy Stechler Burns, Wendy Tilghman, Tom Lewis
Source: Direct Cinema

Yo Soy

An update of the 1972 film *Yo Soy Chicano*, exploring the issues and concerns of the Mexican-American community in the United States. Profiled are Leo Montalvo, an attorney and city councilman in McAllen, Texas; Lupe Angiano, director of National Women's Employment and Education, in San Antonio, Texas; Gloria Molina, the California assemblywoman from Los Angeles; Dr. Carlos Munoz, Jr., professor of Chicano Studies at UC Berkeley; and Tommy Espinosa, co-founder and director of Chicanos por la Causa, a Phoenix-based community development group. Also appearing are San Antonio mayor Henry Cisneros and the labor leader Cesar Chavez. (September 17, 1985; 60 min.)

Directed and produced by: Jesus Trevino, Jose Luis Ruiz
Writer: Jesus Trevino
Source: Cinema Guild

Hungry for Profit

An investigation of the link between agribusiness and world hunger. Although agribusiness utilizes advanced techniques to produce more food, Third World economists contend that the net result is less food for most of the world. Large-scale cultivation of higher-value cash crops for export to industrialized countries receives priority, to the detriment of the production of staple crops for domestic consumption. Filmed in 10 countries on five continents. (June 19, 1985; 90 min.)

Producer, writer: Robert Richter

The Times of Harvey Milk

The life and violent death of one of America's first openly gay politicians. The film follows Milk from his days as a Castro Street businessman to his triumphant election to the San Francisco Board of Supervisors in 1977. A year later, Milk and San Francisco mayor George Moscone were shot and killed by Dan White, a former fireman. On-the-spot news coverage and police reports capture the moments just after the assassination when more than 40,000 people gathered in the streets of San Francisco in a silent candlelight tribute in memory of the slain leaders. Interviews with Milk's supporters, friends and foes capture the spirit of the man and his times. (November 13, 1985; 90 min.)

Director: Robert Epstein
Producers: Richard Schmiechen, Robert Epstein
Awards: Academy Award: Best Feature Documentary
Source: Pacific Arts Video (home video); Cinecom International Films

MEDIA SPECIALS

Perfect Lives (Private Parts)

Referred to as a *Ulysses* of videotapes, *Perfect Lives (Private Parts)* is dense, iconic, mythical, mystical and compelling. Written and composed by Robert Ashley, the work may be the first video opera, blending the music of three solo voices, Ashley, David Van Tieghem and Jill Kroesen; the piano of "Blue" Gene Tyranny and synchronized prerecorded orchestral tracks with video imagery created by John Sanborn. Set in a Midwestern town, the plot unfolds in seven half-hour acts, revolving around the fantastical interactions of several futuristic characters who propose to "borrow" the money in the town bank for a day. (Date of release: 1983; 210 min.—7 x 30 min.)

Director, writer: Robert Ashley
Video directors: John Sanborn, Kit Fitzgerald
Music producer: Peter Gordon
Television producer: Carlota Schoolman
A production of Haleakala (The Kitchen)
Source: Lovely Music

Jill Kroesen and David Van Tieghem in Robert Ashley's video opera, Perfect Lives (Private Parts). *Photo by Mary Ashley.*

MAJOR CO-FUNDERS
THE ARTS ON TELEVISION

Marjorie Carr Adams Charitable Trust

American Institute of Architects

Annenberg/CPB Project

AT&T Foundation

Atlantic Richfield Company

Benton Foundation

Chubb Group of Insurance Companies

Ailene B. and Pierre Claeyssens

Corporation for Public Broadcasting

Charles E. Culpeper Foundation

Charles A. Dana Foundation

Arthur Vining Davis Foundations

Exxon Corporation

Ford Foundation

General Motors Corporation

Getty Oil Company

Giorgio Armani

George Gund Foundation

Mrs. Donald Harrington

Harris Foundation

Haworth, Inc.

Robert Wood Johnson Charitable Trust

Lyndhurst Foundation

John D. and Catherine T. MacArthur Foundation

M&M/Mars Foundation

Martin Marietta Corporation

Massachusetts Council on the Arts and Humanities

Andrew W. Mellon Foundation

New York State Council on the Arts

Northwest Area Foundation

Pioneer Electronic Corporation

Polaroid Corporation

Prudential Insurance Company

Public Broadcasting Service

Rock Foundation

Rockefeller Foundation

Shell Companies Foundation

Marilyn M. Simpson Charitable Trust

L.J. Skaggs Foundation

Alfred P. Sloan Foundation

Tennessee Arts Commission

Texaco Philanthropic Foundation

Unitel

Rosalind P. Walter

Cynthia Wood

ZDF/Germany

The nation's public television stations

AWARDS

Over the past 15 years, the series supported by the Endowment and the programs presented on them have received hundreds of awards. Many of these are listed in the following pages. They are arranged alphabetically by the name of the series. Individual specials follow.

ALIVE FROM OFF CENTER

Series Awards

Chicago International Film Festival: Silver Plaque

Broadcast Designers' Association: Gold Award, First Place for Best Animated Opening

Codex

First Grand Prix International Video Dance Festival: Most Original Program

Fire, Light, Sticks

American Film Festival: Red Ribbon

Fractured Variations

American Film Festival: Blue Ribbon

From San Francisco: Dancing on the Edge

Dance on Camera Festival: Honorable Mention

Golden Gate Competition: Special Jury Award

Nine-Person Precision Ball Passing

American Film Festival: Blue Ribbon

Postcards

USA Film Festival (Dallas): Best Narrative Short

Relatives

Atlanta Film and Video Festival: Judges' Special Award

Road

Monte Carlo Film and Television Festival: Best Television Drama

Sister Suzie Cinema

Central Education Network Award

Smothering Dreams

Emmy Awards: Best Documentary; Best Camera; Best Editing

USA Film and Video Festival: First Prize

Steps

Berlin Exhibition: Prix Futura

Brazil Film Fest, Sao Paolo: First Prize

Rio Film and Video Festival: First Prize

Sticks on the Move

Bessie Award

Visual Shuffle

American Film Festival: Blue Ribbon

Women of the Calabash

American Film and Video Association: Blue Ribbon

AMERICAN MASTERS

Billie Holiday: The Long Night of Lady Day

Blues Foundation of America Award

Broadway's Dreamers: The Legacy of The Group Theatre

Emmy Award: Outstanding Informational Special

Buster Keaton: A Hard Act to Follow

Emmy Awards: Outstanding Informational Series; Outstanding Achievement in Writing

Special Peabody Award to Kevin Brownlow and David Gill

Celebrating Bird: The Triumph of Charlie Parker

American Video Conference Award

Directed by William Wyler

Chicago International Film Festival: Gold Hugo

CINE Gold Eagle

Edward R. Murrow: This Reporter

Emmy Award: Outstanding Informational Special

Eugene O'Neill: A Glory of Ghosts

Directors' Guild of America Award

Harold Clurman: A Life of Theatre

CINE Gold Eagle

National Educational Film and Video Festival: Gold Apple

James Baldwin: The Price of the Ticket

CINE Gold Eagle

John Hammond: From Bessie Smith to Bruce Springsteen

CINE Gold Eagle

Peabody Award

Lillian Gish: The Actor's Life for Me

Emmy Award: Outstanding Informational Special

Nik and Murray

Chicago International Film Festival: Gold Plaque

Houston International Film Festival: Gold Award

Preston Sturges: The Rise and Fall of an American Dreamer

Emmy Award: Outstanding Informational Programming

Private Conversations: On the Set of Death of a Salesman

Sundance Film Festival: Grand Prize

United States Film Festival: Grand Prize

The Ten-Year Lunch: The Wit and Legend of the Algonquin Round Table

Academy Award: Best Feature Documentary

Chicago International Film Festival: Silver Hugo

CINE Gold Eagle

Golden Gate Competition: Honorable Mention

Los Angeles Women in Film Festival: Lillian Gish Award

Unknown Chaplin

Emmy Award: Outstanding Informational Series

Peabody Award

Special Peabody Award to Kevin Brownlow and David Gill for their Outstanding Body of Work on the Silent Film

W. Eugene Smith: Photography Made Difficult

Emmy Award: Outstanding Individual Achievement in Informational Programming

AMERICAN PATCHWORK

The Land Where Blues Began

American Film Festival: Blue Ribbon

AMERICAN PLAYHOUSE

Series Awards

Peabody Award for Ten Years of Distinguished Broadcasting

Andre's Mother

Emmy Award: Outstanding Writing in a Limited Series or Special

Ask Me Again

Chicago International Film Festival: Silver Hugo

Houston International Film Festival: Gold Medal

The Ballad of Gregorio Cortez

Durban Film Festival: Best Actor—Edward James Olmos

United States Film Festival: Jury Award

Blue Window

Chicago International Film Festival: Silver Plaque

Break of Dawn

Nosotros: Golden Eagle Award

San Antonio Cine Festival: Special Jury Award

The Cafeteria

American Film Festival: Honorable Mention

CINE Gold Eagle

Carl Sandburg—Echoes and Silences

American Women in Radio and Television: Pinnacle Award

Directors' Guild of America: Achievement in Television Documentary

Women in Communication: Matrix Award

Cat on a Hot Tin Roof

Emmy Award: Outstanding Supporting Actress in a Limited Series or Special—Kim Stanley

City News

Athens Film Festival: Special Merit Award

for Dramatic Feature

Atlanta Independent Film Festival: Best Dramatic Film

Houston International Film Festival: Best Low-Budget Feature

Concealed Enemies

Emmy Awards: Outstanding Limited Series; Outstanding Direction in a Limited Series or Special

Displaced Person

Emmy Award: Outstanding Children's Program

El Norte

Huelva Film Festival: Colon de Oro

National Council of Christians and Jews: Imagen Award

World Film Festival: Grand Prix des Ameriques

Fifth of July

The Alliance of Gay Artists in Entertainment: Media Award

For Us, the Living

Neil Simon Award: Jury Prize

Gal Young 'Un

Chicago International Film Festival: Silver Hugo; Best First Feature

The Ghost Writer

Banff International Television Festival: Best of Festival; Best Television Feature

Go Tell It on the Mountain

American Film Festival: Blue Ribbon

CINE Gold Eagle

National Black Programming Consortium, Prized Pieces: Best Drama

San Francisco International Film Festival: Best Television Feature

The Great American Fourth of July and Other Disasters

International Film and Television Festival of New York: Silver Medal

Heartland

Berlin Film Festival: First Place Golden Bear

Christopher Award

Cowboy Hall of Fame: American Heritage Award

Neil Simon Award: Best Screenplay

United States Film Festival: First Place

The House of Ramon Iglesia

Houston International Film Festival: Silver Award

Samuel G. Engel International Television Drama Award: Best Drama

The Joy That Kills

American Film Festival: Blue Ribbon

CINE Gold Eagle

Houston International Film Festival: Bronze Award

Samuel G. Engel International Television Drama Award: First Place

USA Film Festival: First Place

The Killing Floor

Hemisfilm International Festival: Best Feature Award

International Film and Television Festival of New York: Silver Medal

National Black Consortium: First Place

United States Film Festival: Special Jury Award

USA Film Festival: Special Jury Award

Land of Little Rain

Houston International Film Festival: Gold Award

Lemon Sky

San Francisco International Film Festival: Best Television Feature

United States Film Festival: Special Jury Award

Love and Other Sorrows

Houston International Film Festival: Gold Award

The Meeting

Emmy Award: Best Technical Direction for a Mini-series or Special

Ohio State Award, Performing Arts and Humanities

Miss Lonelyhearts

Cannes Film Festival: Prix de la Jeunesse

Locarno Film Festival: Bronze Leopard

My American Cousin

Canadian Academy Genie Awards: Best Picture; Best Director; Best Actor; Best Actress; Best Original Screenplay; Best Editing

Toronto Festival of Festivals: International Critics' Award

Nightsongs

Taormina Film Festival: Critics' Special Mention

Northern Lights

Cannes Film Festival: Camera D'Or—Best First Feature

Houston Film Festival: Special Jury Award

Neil Simon Award: Best Screenplay

United States Film and Video Festival: Special Jury Award

Paper Angels

Association of Asian Pacific American Artists: Media Award

Pigeon Feathers

CINE Gold Eagle

The Prodigious Hickey

American Film and Video Festival: Blue Ribbon

Houston International Film Festival: Silver Medal for Television Special

San Francisco Film Festival: Honorable Mention

Pudd'nhead Wilson

CINE Gold Eagle

National Educational Film Festival Award

A Raisin In the Sun

Emmy Awards: Outstanding Lighting Direction; Outstanding Technical Direction/Camera; Outstanding Achievement in Editing

NAACP Image Awards: Best Drama; Best Actor—Danny Glover; Best Actress—Esther Rolle

New York International Film and Television Festival: Gold Medal; Grand Award

Ohio State Award, Performing Arts and Humanities

San Francisco International Film Festival: Best Drama

Refuge

International Conference on Television Drama: First Prize

Samuel G. Engel International Television Drama Award

The Revolt of Mother

American Film and Video Festival: Blue Ribbon

Christopher Award

Houston International Film Festival: Silver Award

The Roommate

Los Angeles International Film Festival: Grand Prix

San Francisco International Film Festival: Special Jury Award

USA Film Festival: Special Jury Award

The Silence at Bethany

Christopher Award

Smooth Talk

United States Film Festival: Grand Jury Prize

Solomon Northup's Odyssey

CINE Gold Eagle

Organization of American Historians: Erik Barnouw Award

Stand and Deliver

Christopher Award

Imagine Award

Independent Feature Project Spirit Awards: Best Feature; Best Screenplay; Best Director; Best Actor—Edward James Olmos; Best Supporting Actor—Lou Diamond Phillips; Best Supporting Actress—Rosana DeSoto

Testament

Christopher Award

The Thin Blue Line

International Documentary Association Award

Mystery Writers of America: Edgar Allan Poe Award

National Board of Review: D.W. Griffith Award

National Society of Film Critics: Best Documentary

New York Film Critics' Award: Best Documentary

The Trial of Bernhard Goetz

International Film and Television Festival of New York: Best Mini-series

San Francisco International Film Festival: Golden Gate Award, Best Television Feature

Until She Talks

American Film Festival: Blue Ribbon

Athens Film Festival: Best Short Dramatic Film

CINE Gold Eagle

Mannheim Film Festival: Best Film Made for Television

Waiting for the Moon

United States Film Festival: Best Dramatic Feature

USA Film Festival: Best Actress—Linda Hunt and Linda Bassett

Where the Spirit Lives

Le Carrousel International du Film de Rimouski: Best Actress; Best Feature Film; Public Choice Award; Humanitarian Award

Chicago International Film Festival: Silver Hugo; Gold Plaque; Silver Plaque; Certificate of Merit

Festival of the American Indian: Best Actress; Best Director; Best Film; Best Original Score

Greater Fort Lauderdale Film Festival: Critics' Choice Award

Vancouver International Film Festival: Most Popular Canadian Film Award

Who Am I This Time?

Setmana International Film Festival: Best Television Production

Working

Emmy Award: Outstanding Lighting Design for a Limited Series or Special

DANCE IN AMERICA

Series Awards

The Association of American Dance Companies Award for Excellence of a Series

Peabody Award

Agnes: The Indomitable de Mille

Chicago International Film Festival: Silver Hugo

CINE Gold Eagle

Emmy Award: Outstanding Informational Special

Balanchine, Parts One and Two

Chicago International Film Festival: Silver Plaque

International Film and Television Awards of New York: Gold Medal

Monitor Awards: Best Sound Mixer; Best Achievement in News/Documentaries; Best Editor; Best Director; Best Technical Graphics Designer

Baryshnikov by Tharp

Emmy Awards: Outstanding Achievement in Choreography; Outstanding Lighting Direction for a Limited Series; Outstanding Individual Achievement, Classical Music/Dance Programming (Directing)

Baryshnikov Dances Balanchine

Chicago International Film Festival: Gold Plaque

Bob Fosse: Steam Heat

Chicago International Film Festival: Silver Plaque

Emmy Award: Outstanding Informational Special

Ohio State Award, Performing Arts and Humanities

Choreography by Balanchine, Part Four

Emmy Award: Outstanding Classical Program in the Performing Arts

Choreography by Balanchine, Part Three

Chicago International Film Festival: Silver Plaque

Directors' Guild of America Award

Choreography by Jerome Robbins with the New York City Ballet

Chicago International Film Festival: Silver Hugo

CINE Gold Eagle

Clytemnestra

Chicago International Film Festival: Gold Hugo

Dance Theatre of Harlem in A Streetcar Named Desire

Chicago International Film Festival: Silver Hugo

Golden Prague Festival: Best Television Adaptation of a Dramatic Musical Work

Dance Theatre of Harlem

Chicago International Film Festival: Bronze Hugo

Dance Film and Video Festival: First Place

The Magic Flute

Emmy Award: Outstanding Tape Sound Mixing

The Martha Graham Dance Company

Chicago International Film Festival: Certificate of Merit

In Memory of . . . A Ballet by Jerome Robbins

Chicago International Film Festival: Silver Hugo

CINE Gold Eagle

La Sylphide

Chicago International Film Festival: Silver Plaque

Monitor Award: Best Lighting Director

Mark Morris with the Mark Morris Dance Group

American Film and Video Festival: Red Ribbon

CINE Gold Eagle

New York City Ballet: L'Enfant et Les Sortileges (The Spellbound Child)

Directors' Guild of America Award

A Night at the Joffrey

Chicago International Film Festival: Gold Plaque

IMZ: Grand Prix Video Dance, Best Video Creation (Love Songs)

International Film and Television Festival of New York: Gold Medal

Monitor Award: Best Lighting Director

Nureyev and The Joffrey Ballet in Tribute to Nijinsky

Emmy Award: Outstanding Lighting Direction

Paul Taylor: Roses & Last Look

Chicago International Film Festival: Certificate of Merit

San Francisco Ballet in Cinderella

CINE Gold Eagle

International Film and Television Festival of New York: Gold Medal

Reading Rainbow: Parents' Choice Award

San Francisco Ballet: Romeo and Juliet

Emmy Award: Best Set Design

The Search for Nijinsky's Rite of Spring

IMZ: Grand Prix Video Dance, Best Documentary

International Film and Television Festival of New York: Bronze Medal

Song for Dead Warriors

Emmy Awards: Outstanding Achievement in Choreography; Outstanding Individual Achievement, Classical Music/Dance Programming (Directing)

Monitor Award: Best Editor

The Tempest: Live with the San Francisco Ballet

Emmy Award: Outstanding Costume Design for a Special

Trailblazers of Modern Dance

Dance Film and Video Festival: First Place

GREAT PERFORMANCES

Nixon in China

Emmy Award: Outstanding Classical Program in the Performing Arts

The Orchestra

Emmy Award: Outstanding Visual Effects

THE INDEPENDENTS

The Independents: Awards

Series Awards

Likely Stories

Fourth Annual Television Movie Awards: Best Anthology Series

Ordinary People—Independent Portraits

ACE Award: Best Documentary Series

Blue Collar and Buddha

International Film and Television Festival of New York: Gold Medal

Charleen

American Film Festival: Red Ribbon

Boston Society of Film Critics: Best Feature Documentary

Close Harmony

Academy Award: Best Documentary Short

Frank: A Vietnam Vet

American Film Festival: Blue Ribbon

Leaving Home

American Film Institute: Honorable Mention

CINE Gold Eagle

Not Just Garbage

Chicago Access Community Network: Gold CAN Award

Presumed Innocent

Emmy Award

Sometimes I Run

Athens Film Festival: Second Prize

Sinking Creek Film Festival: First Prize

Young at Heart

Academy Award: Best Documentary Short

Ziveli

Chicago International Film Festival: Silver Plaque

LIVE FROM LINCOLN CENTER

Series Awards

First TV Critics' Circle Award for Achievements in Music

Sigma Alpha Iota (International Music Fraternity) Award: Outstanding Television Series (1986 and 1989)

Peabody Award

American Ballet Theatre: Swan Lake

Emmy Award: Outstanding Classical Program in the Performing Arts

American Ballet Theatre: Giselle

Emmy Award: Outstanding Classical Program in the Performing Arts

American Ballet Theatre: Romeo and Juliet

International Film and Television Festival of New York: Silver Award

Chamber Music Society of Lincoln Center with Irene Worth, Horacio Gutierrez, pianist

Emmy Award: Outstanding Special Class Program

An Evening With Danny Kaye And The New York Philharmonic

Peabody Award

Great Performers: An Evening with Placido Domingo

International Film and Television Festival of New York: Silver Award

Great Performers: Joan Sutherland, Marilyn Horne, Luciano Pavarotti

Grammy Award: London Decca Records, Best Classical Vocal Soloist Performance

Great Performers: Joan Sutherland, Marilyn Horne, Luciano Pavarotti

Emmy Award: Outstanding Achievment in Creative Technical Craft

Great Performers' Recital: Luciano Pavarotti

Emmy Award: Special Classification of Outstanding Program Achievement

Julliard at 80

Monitor Awards: Best Achievement in Broadcast Entertainment; Best Camerawork; Best Director

Mostly Mozart Festival with Itzhak Perlman

Sigma Alpha Iota Award: Outstanding Single Program

New York City Opera: The Barber of Seville

Emmy Award: Outstanding Achievement in Costume Design

New York Philharmonic: Aaron Copland's 85th Birthday

Sigma Alpha Iota Award: Outstanding Single Program

New York Philharmonic: Isaac Stern, Itzhak Perlman, Pinchas Zukerman, Zubin Mehta, conductor

Grammy Award: CBS Records Recording, Best Classical Performance, Instrumental Soloist or Soloists with Orchestra

New York Philharmonic with Leontyne Price, Zubin Mehta, conductor

Emmy Award: Outstanding Individual Performance in a Variety or Music Program—Leontyne Price, Zubin Mehta, conductor

New York Philharmonic with Luciano Pavarotti, Zubin Mehta, conductor

Emmy Award: Outstanding Achievement in Creative Technical Craft

METROPOLITAN OPERA PRESENTS

Series Awards

Chicago American Council for Better Broadcasts: Special Recognition Award

National Opera Institute: National Development Award

Peabody Award, Outstanding Radio and Television Broadcasting Services for over 43 years

Sigma Alpha Iota Award: Outstanding Production of Classical Music

Aida

Emmy Award: Outstanding Classical Program in the Performing Arts

Das Rheingold

Grammy Award: Best Classical Recording

Hansel and Gretel

Emmy Award: Outstanding Program Achievement in the Performing Arts

La Boheme (1977)

Peabody Award

La Boheme (1983)

Emmy Award: Outstanding Classical Program in the Performing Arts

The Metropolitan Opera Centennial Gala

Emmy Award: Outstanding Program Achievement in the Performing Arts

Sigma Alpha Iota Award: Outstanding Television Program

Rigoletto

Peabody Award

AWARDS **211**

The Ring of the Nibelung

Emmy Award: Outstanding Individual Achievement, Classical Music-Dance Programming

Tosca

Emmy Award: Outstanding Classical Program in the Performing Arts

MUSICAL COMEDY TONIGHT

Musical Comedy I

Peabody Award

New Television

Coffee Coloured Children

National Black Programming Consortium, Prized Pieces

NON-FICTION TELEVISION

America Lost and Found

American Film Festival: Blue Ribbon

CINE Gold Eagle

Hemisfilm/80: Winner, "Best in Time"

Hamper McBee: Raw Mash

American Film Festival: Blue Ribbon

I Remember Harlem

Alfred I. DuPont-Columbia Citation in Broadcast Journalism

American Association for State and Local History: Award of Merit

American Film Festival: Blue Ribbon

La La, Making It in L.A.

American Film Festival: Blue Ribbon

CINE Gold Eagle

A Lady Named Baybie

Christopher Award

Women in Broadcasting Award

No Maps on My Taps

American Film Festival: Blue Ribbon

Chicago International Film Festival: Bronze Hugo

Dance Video and Film Festival: Best Film Award

Emmy Award: Outstanding Musical Direction in News and Documentary

On Company Business

Berlin Film Festival: International Film Critics' Prize

Paul Jacobs and the Nuclear Gang

American Film Festival: Red Ribbon

Emmy Award: Outstanding Program Achievement

George Polk Award for Investigative Journalism

Lille International Film Festival: Special Jury Award//Baltimore Film Festival: Second Prize

Mannheim Film Festival: International Foreign Press Award; Interfilm Award

Plea Bargaining

American Film Festival: Blue Ribbon

Chicago International Film Festival: Certificate of Merit

Tampa Independent Film and Video Festival: Flori Award for Best Film

Taking Back Detroit

American Film Festival: Blue Ribbon

Chicago Film Festival: Certificate of Merit

San Francisco Film Festival: Honorable Mention

Taylor Chain

American Film Festival: Honorable Mention

Chicago International Film Festival: William Friedkin Chicago Award

Great Lakes Film and Video Festival: Second Place

International Labor Press Association: Award of Merit, Film and Broadcast Competition

Third Avenue: Only the Strong Survive

Athens International Film Festival: Honorable Mention

Emmy Awards: Outstanding Cinematography; Outstanding Editing in News or Documentary

Monitor Awards: Best Director; Best Documentary; Best Camera; Best Editing

Tokyo International Video Festival: First Prize

The Times of Harvey Milk

Academy Award: Best Feature Documentary

New York Film Critics' Circle Award: Best Documentary

Varnette's World

Chicago International Film Festival: Grand Prix

The Work I've Done

American Film Festival: Red Ribbon

P.O.V.

Series Awards

Ohio State Award, Performing Arts and Humanities

American Tongues

Peabody Award

Best Boy

Academy Award: Best Feature Documentary

D.W. Griffith Award

New York Film Critics' Award

Presidential Citation

Dark Circle

Emmy Award: Special Classification for Outstanding Individual Achievement in News and Documentary

United States Film Festival: Non-fiction Grand Prize

Days of Waiting

Academy Award: Best Documentary Short

Peabody Award

Living with AIDS

Emmy Award: Special Classification for News and Documentary Achievement

No Applause, Just Throw Money

Emmy Award: Outstanding Individual Achievement in Film Editing

Who Killed Vincent Chin?

DuPont Columbia Award

Peabody Award

SOUNDINGS

The Music of Michael Colgrass

Emmy Award, New England Regional Academy of Arts and Sciences: Outstanding Documentary

SOUTHBOUND

Fannie Bell Chapman

Bellevue Film Festival: Second Prize

Chicago Film Festival: Certificate of Merit

Columbus Film Festival: Bronze Plaque

Showdown at the Hoedown

American Film Festival: Blue Ribbon

Chicago Film Festival: Blue Ribbon

This Cat Can Play Anything

Philadelphia International Film Festival: Best TV Documentary

VISIONS

Series Awards

Peabody Award

VISIONS OF PARADISE

Grandma's Bottle Village: The Art of Tressa Prisbrey

American Film Festival: Red Ribbon

Hundred and Two Mature: The Art of Harry Lieberman

American Film Festival: Red Ribbon

Hemisfilm International Festival: Best Art and Artists Award

VOICES AND VISIONS

Emily Dickinson

American Film and Video Festival: Blue Ribbon

National Educational Film and Video Festival: Bronze Apple

Langston Hughes: The Dreamkeeper

San Francisco International Film Festival: Best Documentary

Sylvia Plath

Chicago International Film Festival: Gold Plaque

William Carlos Williams

Chicago International Film Festival: Gold Hugo

CINE Gold Eagle

WOMEN IN ART

Georgia O'Keeffe

American Film Festival: Red Ribbon

Christopher Award

Directors' Guild of America Award: Documentary Achievement

Women in Communications: Clarion Award

WONDERWORKS

Series Awards

Season One

Action for Children's Television: Achievement Award, Citation for Continued Excellence in Children's Programming

American Children's Television Festival: Alpha Award

National Television Programming for Youth: Gabriel Award

Season Two

Chicago International Festival of Children's Films: Outstanding Achievement in Developing High-quality Films for Children's Audiences

Parents' Choice Honor Television Program

Action for Children's Television Achievement Award

Television Critics' Association: Outstanding Achievement in Children's Television

TV Guide: Best Children's Program

Season Three

Action for Children's Television Achievement Award

Season Four

Action for Children's Television Achievement Award

Season Five

Houston International Film Festival: Silver Award

Season Six

Action for Children's Television Achievement Award

Houston International Film Festival: Gold Special Jury Award

National Telemedia Council: Certificate of Recognition

African Journey

Columbus International Film and Video Festival: Chris Award

International Film and Television Festival of New York: Bronze Medal

National Black Programming Consortium, Prized Pieces: International Film and Video Award

Anne of Green Gables

American Children's Television Festival: Ollie Award

Children's Film and Television Center of America: Ruby Slipper

Christopher Award

Columbus International Film Festival: President's Chris

Emmy Award: Outstanding Children's Program

Gemini Awards (ten awards)

International Film and Television Festival of New York: Gold Medal

National Educational Film and Video Festival: Gold Apple

Odyssey Institute Media Awards: First Prize

Ohio State Award, Performing Arts and Humanities

Parents' Choice Award, 1986 and 1988

Peabody Award

Prix Jeunesse

Silver Angel Award for Excellence

TV Guide: Most Popular Program

Anne of Green Gables—The Sequel

Gemini Awards: Best Actress—Megan Follows; Best Supporting Actress—Colleen Dewhurst; Best Mini-drama; Best Costume Design

Booker

American Film Festival: Honorable Mention

Banff International Festival of Films for Television: Best of Festival

Birmingham International Education Film Festival: Best of Festival

Black Filmmakers' Hall of Fame: Best of Festival

Houston International Film Festival: Silver Award

National Educational Film Festival: Best

Film, Social Science

National Television Programming for Youth: Gabriel Award

Odyssey Institute for Concerns of Children: First Prize

Odyssey Institute Media Awards Competition: First Prize

Prix Jeunesse

Youth in Film Association Award

The Box of Delights

BAFTA Awards: Best Children's Series; Best Lighting; Best Editing

The Boy Who Loved Trolls

Columbus International Film Festival: Chris Statuette

Boys and Girls

Academy Award: Outstanding Short Film

American Film Festival Award

Chicago International Film Festival Award

Caddie Woodlawn

National Educational Film and Video Festival: Gold Apple

Parents' Choice Award

The Chronicles of Narnia: The Lion, the Witch and the Wardrobe

Film Council of Greater Columbus: Bronze Plaque

International Film and Television Festival of New York: Silver Medal

Ohio State Award, Performing Arts and Humanities

Danny the Champion of the World

ACE Award: Best Programming for Children

International Film and Television Festival of New York: Gold Medal

Danny's Egg

Prix Jeunesse

The Fig Tree

International Film and Television Festival of New York: Gold Medal

Frog

Action for Children's Television Award: Achievement in Children's Television

International Festival of Television Programs for Children and Youth (Bratislava, Cz.): Prix Danube

International Film and Television Festival of New York: Gold Medal

Good Old Boy

Houston International Film Festival: Special Gold Jury Award

International Film and Television Festival of New York: Silver Award

Happily Ever After

American Film and Video Festival: Red Ribbon

Chicago International Festival of Children's Films: First Prize

Columbus International Film Festival: President's Chris

International Angel Award of Excellence

National Council for Children's Rights: Best in Media Award

The House of Dies Drear

National Black Programming Consortium, Prized Pieces: First Place

Islands

Chicago International Film Festival: Gold Plaque

Chicago International Film Festival, Intercom: Gold Award

Houston International Film Festival: Silver Award//Columbus International Film Festival: Bronze Chris

Jacob Have I Loved

International Film and Television Festival of New York: Grand Award

Women in Film Festival: Lillian Gish Award

Konrad

Youth in Film Achievement Award

A Little Princess

BAFTA Award

Chicago International Film Festival: Gold Plaque

Parents' Choice Award

Maricela

Hispanic Media Task Force: Imagen Award

The Mighty Pawns

CEBA: Award for Distinction

Chicago International Film Festival: Silver Plaque

Houston International Film Festival: Special Jury Award

Miracle at Moreaux

Columbus International Film Festival: President's Chris

Houston International Film Festival: Gold Award

International Film and Television Festival of New York: Grand Award

Samuel G. Engel International Television Award: Best Drama

Necessary Parties

International Monitor Award: Achievement in Children's Programming

Taking Care of Terrific

International Film and Television Festival of New York: Silver Medal

Two Daddies?

National Council for Children's Rights: Media Award

Walking on Air

American Film and Video Association: Red Ribbon

Media Office on Disabilities: Media Access Award

A Waltz Through the Hills

Australian Academy of Broadcast Arts and Sciences: Pater Award, Best Children's Drama

Australian Film Institute: Best Actor in a Telefeature—Ernie Dingo

Chicago International Festival of Children's Films: First Prize

Television Society of Australia: Penguin Award for Best Children's Drama

Who Has Seen the Wind?

Paris International Film Festival: Grand Prize

Words by Heart

Columbus International Film Festival: Bronze Chris

Young Charlie Chaplin

Chicago International Film Festival: Silver Plaque

SPECIALS

Alfred Stieglitz, Photographer

American Film Festival: Red Ribbon

Antonia: Portrait of a Woman

American Film Festival: Blue Ribbon

Emily Award

The Art of Gerald Gooch

CINE Gold Eagle

The Bolero

Academy Award: Live Action Short Subject

CINE Gold Eagle

Venice Film Festival: Prix Italia

Diego Rivera: I Paint What I See

Chicago International Film Festival: Gold Plaque

National Educational Film and Video Festival: Bronze Apple

Dry Wood/Hot Pepper

American Film Festival: Blue Ribbon

The Girl with the Incredible Feeling: Elizabeth Swados

American Film Festival: Red Ribbon

Baltimore Film Festival: First Prize

A Good Dissonance Like a Man

CINE Gold Eagle

Peabody Award

Mama's Pushcart: Ellen Stewart and 25 Years of La MaMa E.T.C.

National Educational Film and Video Festival: Gold Apple

Style Wars

American Film Festival: Blue Ribbon

CINE Gold Eagle

Montreal International Festival of Films on Art: Grand Prize

United States Film and Video Festival: Grand Prize

Thomas Hart Benton's "The Sources of Country Music"

Moving Image Exposition: First Prize

We Shall Overcome

Emmy Award

HOW TO OBTAIN PROGRAMS IN THIS BOOK

At least half of the programs in this book are known to be available for purchase or rental, many are not because of ownership rights and clearances. **The National Endowment for the Arts does not distribute copies of programs.** Programs are available from independent distributors, denoted as "source" in the text, and their addresses follow. This information was gathered and verified in May, 1991.

The series themselves are helpful sources of information. Here are their addresses and some basic considerations.

ALIVE FROM OFF CENTER, Twin Cities Public Television, Minnesota Telecenter, 172 East Fourth Street, St. Paul, MN 55401; 612/222-7171. Alive and KTCA/St. Paul-Minneapolis distribute many programs for audiovisual/nontheatrical use. Individual segments of programs are not available from them separately. Direct inquiries about home video distribution to the series.

American Masters, 15 West 26th Street, New York, NY 10010; 212/532-2744. Many films are unavailable in home or educational markets because they contain archival film footage and photos the rights to which are strictly controlled by their owners. In the text, those films and videos that are available give the name of the source followed by the market—home video or educational. Those followed by "Contact . . . rights holder" are not available.

American Playhouse, Public Television Playhouse, 1776 Broadway, Ninth Floor, New York, NY 10019; 212/757-4300. Programs for which no source is listed may be obtained from the produc-

tion company, whose address may be found in the list of distributors. For production alliances composed of several parties, the address for the first company listed can be found in the index.

Dance in America, Great Performances, Educational Broadcasting Corporation, WNET/Thirteen, 356 West 58th Street, New York, NY 10019; 212/560-4963. Dance in America programs produced by WNET/Thirteen are not available. The topic of distribution is currently being studied however, and it is expected that they will soon become available.

The Independents, American Community Service Network, 1525 Wilson Boulevard, Rosslyn, VA 22209; 703/276-0881.

Live From Lincoln Center, 70 Lincoln Center Plaza, New York, NY 10023-6583; 212/875-5322. Nine titles from are available on Paramount's Bel Canto home video label. One distributor of the Bel Canto series is HomeVision in Chicago.

The Metropolitan Opera Presents, The Metropolitan Opera Association, Media Department, Lincoln Center for the Performing Arts, New York, NY 10023; 212/799-3100. Thirty-one titles are available, most on both home video and laser disc formats. For information, contact the Metropolitan Opera Gift Shop, Lincoln Center, New York, NY 10023, 212/580-4090, or, the Metropolitan Opera Guild, 1865 Broadway, New York, NY 10023; 212/769-7000. Home versions of the programs may vary slightly from the broadcast original. Tapes of the Ring Cycle will be available in late 1991.

New Television, WGBH Educational Foundation, 125 Western Avenue, Boston, MA 02134; 617/492-2777.

P.O.V., The American Documentary, 330 West 58th Street, Suite 3-A, New York, NY 10019; 212/397-0970. Each season P.O.V. publishes a viewer's guide that gives the distribution and other information for the documentaries it presents. Call the Viewer Response Line (212/757-6104) to get a copy.

Trying Times, Community Television of Southern California, KCET/Los Angeles, 4401 Sunset Boulevard, Los Angeles, CA 90027; 213/666-6500.

WonderWorks, QED Communications, 4802 Fifth Avenue, Pittsburgh, PA 15213; 412/622-1300.

ADDITIONAL RESOURCES

Independent films and performing arts on film may be found in the arts, education and cultural sections of directories such as: *Bowker's Complete Video Directory* (R.R. Bowker, New Providence, NJ), *Video Log* (Trade Service Publications Company, San Diego, CA) and *The Video Sourcebook* (Gale Research International, Detroit, MI). These may be carried by the audiovisual department of local library systems or found at video stores.

Three resource books on independent film and video are: The AIVF Guide to Film and Video Distributors (FIVF/AIVF, New York, NY), The Asian American Media Reference Guide (Asian Cine Vision, New York, NY) and The Circulating Film and Video Catalog of the Museum of Modern Art (Museum of Modern Art, New York, NY).

Four organizations that may be of assistance are the following.

American Film and Video Association (AVFA) Clearinghouse, 920 Barnsdale Road, Suite 152, La Grange Park, IL 60525; 800/274-2382 (1:00 to 5:00pm, Central Time); 708/482-4200. The AVFA Clearinghouse Library provides distribution information and conducts searches for its members.

National Video Resources, 73 Spring Street, Suite 606, New York, NY 10012; 212/274-8080. A nonprofit organization that funds initiatives to make independent films available in home markets. One of its goals is to establish a toll-free phone number providing distribution information on independent works.

PBS Library, 1320 Braddock Place, Alexandria, VA 22314-1698; 703/739-5230. The library has a variety of information about the works listed in this book, including older programs.

Video Finders, 1770 North Highland Avenue, Department 721FC, Los Angeles, CA 90028; 900/860-9300; 213/668-9542. This private firm conducts searches for films and videos for a fee.

Many home video distributors only do business with retail outlets. Two sources that deal directly with individuals are Facets Video and Movies Unlimited. Their catalogs list many of the films and videos in this book.

Facets Video, 1517 West Fullerton, Chicago, IL 60614; 312/281-9075. Facets sells and rents videos through the mail. Its catalog contains some 12,000 titles, including extensive offerings in independent film and video.

Movies Unlimited, 6736 Castor Avenue, Philadelphia, PA 19149; 215/722-8398, 800/523-0823. Movies Unlimited sells home videos of feature films and many others through the mail. Its catalog lists upwards of 20,000 titles.

Many people worked with patience and persistence to compile the distribution information found in this book: Diane Dufault of American Masters; John Ligon of Alive From Off Center;

Deborah Nicholson of The Independents; Melanie Parkhurst of WonderWorks and Jan Young of American Playhouse.

Some source listings were reproduced from: Video Source Book, Vols. 1 & 2, 12th ed., 1991, edited by David J. Weiner. Copyright (c) 1990 by Gale Research, Inc. Reprinted by permission of the publisher.

INDEPENDENT DISTRIBUTORS

Note that companies named after individuals are alphabetized by the surname.

ABC Video Enterprises, 825 Seventh Avenue, Fifth Floor, New York, NY 10019; 212/887-7777

Academy Entertainment, One Pine Haven Shore Road, Shelburne, VT 05482; 802/985-2060

Adair and Armstrong, 900 23rd Street, San Francisco, CA 94107; 415/826-6500

Advocate Productions, 210 Lincoln Street, Suite 210, Boston, MA 02111; 617/426-0090

Agent Orange, 1178 Phillips, Montreal H3B 3C8, Quebec

Alaska Street Productions, Box 47, RFD-1, Dresden, ME 04342; 207/737-8679

Alive from Off Center, Twin Cities Public Television, The Minnesota TeleCenter, 172 East Fourth Street, Saint Paul, MN 55101; 612/222-1717

Alturas Films, 2533 19th Street, San Francisco, CA 94110; 415/285-3984

American Federation of the Arts, 41 East 65th Street, New York, NY 10021; 212/988-7700

American Film Foundation, 1333 Ocean Avenue, Santa Monica, CA 90401; 213/459-2116

Angelika Films, 110 Greene Street, Suite 1102, NY 10012; 212/769-1400; 212/274-1990

Antenna, 1178 Phillips, Montreal H3B 3C8, Quebec

Anthology Film Archives, 32-34 Second Avenue, New York, NY 10003; 212/505-5181

AO Productions, 23 Rue Jean Giraudoux, Paris 75116, France

Appalshop, 306 Madison Street, Whitesburg, KY 41858; 800/545-7467; 606/633-0108 (Ky.)

Atlantis Releasing, Cinevillage, 65 Heward Avenue, Toronto, Canada M4M 2T5; 416/462-0016

Austin Cable Vision, P.O. Box 2105, Austin, TX 78678, 512/448-1000, 512/448-1077

Australian Children's Foundation, 199 Grattan Street, Carlton 3053, Australia

Jane Balfour Films, Burghley House, 35 Fortress Road, London NW5 1AD England; 011-4471-267-5392

BBC Enterprises, Woodlands, 80 Wood Lane, London W12 OTT England

Beacon Films, 930 Pinter Avenue, Evanston, IL 60202; 312/328-6700, 800/323-5448

Bel Canto Video, see Paramount Home Video

Christian Blackwood Productions, 115 Bank Street, New York, NY 10014; 212/242-6260

Michael Blackwood Productions, 251 West 57th Street, No. 415, New York, NY 10019; 212/247-4710,

Blue Ridge Mountain Films, 49 Saint Marks Place, New York, NY 10003, 212/777-6187

Brandman Productions, 2062 North Vine Street, Hollywood, CA 90068; 213/463-3224

Brazos, 10341 San Pablo Avenue, El Cerrito, CA 94530; 415/525-7471

Buena Vista Home Video, see Walt Disney Home Video

Bullfrog Films, Oley, PA 19547; 800/543-FROG, 215/779-8226

Burke/Shapiro Productions, 2600 Tenth Street, Berkeley, CA 94710; 415/442-1604

California Newsreel, 630 Natoma, San Francisco, CA 94103; 415/621-6196

Camera Three Productions, 165 West Putnam Avenue, Greenwich, CT 06830; 203/661-7500

Canal Street Communications, 530 Canal Street, New York, NY 10013, 212/431-1355

Arthur Cantor Films, 2112 Broadway, Suite 400, New York, NY 10023, 212/496-5710

Caridi Entertainment, 250 West 57th Street, Suite 1216, New York, NY 10107; 212/581-2277

Carle Medical Communications, 110 West Main Street, Urbana, IL 61808; 217/384-4838

Castle Hill Productions, 1414 Avenue of the Americas, 15th Floor, New York, NY 10019; 212/888-0080

The CAT Fund (Contemporary Art Television), 955 Boylston Street, Boston, MA 02115; 617/266-5152

CBC Television, Programs and Sales, P.O. Box 500, Station A, Toronto, Ontario M5W 1E6, Canada; 416/975-3500

CBS Broadcast International, 51 West 52nd Street, 24th Floor, New York, NY 10019

CBS Music Video Enterprises, see Sony Music Video Enterprises

CBS/Fox Video, 1211 Sixth Street, New York, NY 10036; 212/819-3200; 800/222-7369

Center for New American Media, 524 Broadway, Second Floor, New York, NY 10012-4408; 212/254-4779, 212/925-5665

Center for Southern Folklore, 152 Beale Street, Memphis, TN 38103; 901/525-3655

Center for Television in the Humanities, 1264 Weatherstone Drive, Atlanta, GA 30324; 404/320-7707

Churchill Films, 12210 Nebraska Avenue, Los Angeles, CA 90025; 213/207-6600; 800/334-7830

The Ciesla Foundation, 1707 Lanier Place, N.W., Washington, DC 20009; 202/462-7528

Cinecom Entertainment Group, 1250 Broadway, New York, NY 10001, 212/239-8360

Cinema Guild, 1697 Broadway, Room 802, New York, NY 10019; 212/246-5522

Clark University, V&PA Department, 950 Main Street, Worcester, MA 01610; 508/793-7149

Clinica Estetico, 652 Broadway, No. 8-F, New York, NY 10012, 212/533-6800

Coe Film Associates, 65 East 96th Street, New York, NY 10028, 212/831-5355

Columbia Pictures Television, Studio Plaza, Suite 996, 3400 Riverside Drive, Burbank, CA 91505

Corinth Films, 34 Gansevoort Street, New York, NY 10014; 800/221-4720; 212/463-0305

Coronet/MTI, 108 Wilmont Road, Deerfield, IL 60015; 800/621-2131

Cote Blanche Feature Films, Route 3, Box 614, Cut Off, LA 70345; 504/632-4100

Council for Positive Images, 2000 L Street, N.W., Suite 202, Washington, DC 20036; 202/296-7645

Counterproductions, 161 South Main Street, Middleton, MA 01949; 508/777-9898

Crone Films, c/o Detdanske Filmstudie, Blomstervaeget 52, 2800 Kgs. Lyngby, Denmark

CrossCurrent Media, 346 Ninth Street, Second Floor, San Francisco, CA 94103; 415/552-9550

Cunningham Dance Foundation, 463 West Street, New York, NY 10014; 212/255-3130

D.L. Daffner, Ltd., 31 West 56th Street, New York, NY 10019; 212/245-4680

De Luca Films, 205 West 95th Street, No. 6B, New York, NY 10025; 212/666-6787

Deep Focus Productions, 22-D Hollywood Avenue, Hohokus, NJ 07423, 800/343-5540

Denver Center for the Performing Arts, Denver Center Productions, Denver, CO 80204; 303/893-4000

DeSoto Productions, 7559 Kimdale Lane, Los Angeles, CA 90046; 213/969-9905

Deutsche Grammophon Gesellschaft, contact The Metropolitan Opera Presents, above

Devillier and Donegan Enterprises, 1608 New Hampshire Avenue, N.W., Second Floor, Washington, DC 20009; 202/232-8200

Direct Cinema, P.O. Box 10003, Santa Monica, CA 90410; 800/525-0000, 213/396-4774

Downtown Community Television, 87 Lafayette Street, New York, NY 10013; 212/966-4510

Drew Associates, 575 Madison Avenue, Suite 1006, New York, NY 10022, 212/605-0225

Echo Pictures, 307 East 44th Street, Suite 1704, New York, NY 10017; 212/949-6079

Electronic Arts Intermix, 536 Broadway, Ninth Floor, New York, NY 10012, 212/966-4605

Ellipse, 15 Square de Vergennes, 75015 Paris, France

Embassy Entertainment, see Orion

EMK Productions, 338 North Palm Drive, Beverly Hills, CA 90210; 213/275-1770

Ergo Media, P.O. Box 2037, Tea Neck, NJ 07666; 201/692-0404

Moctesuma Esparza Productions, 3330 West Cahuenga Boulevard, No. 500, Los Angeles, CA 90068; 213/969-2896

Extension Media, University of California, 2176 Shadduck Avenue, San Francisco, CA 94704; 415/642-0460

Facets Video, 1517 West Fullerton, Chicago, IL 60614; 312/281-9075

Family Home Entertainment, c/o Lieberman International Video Entertainment, 15400 Sherman Way, Van Nuys, CA 01410; 818/908-0303

Film News Foundation, 625 Broadway, Suite 904, New York, NY 10012; 212/979-5671

Filmmakers' Library, 124 East 40th Street, Suite 901, New York, NY 10016; 212/808-4980

Films for the Humanities, P.O. Box 2053, Princeton, NJ 08543; 609/452-1128; 800/257-5126

Films, Inc., 5547 North Ravenswood Avenue, Chicago, IL 60640; 800/323-4222 312/878-2600

FilmWorld Television (Satori Entertainment), 685 Fifth Avenue, Tenth Floor, New York, NY 10036; 212/752-5050

First Run Features/Icarus Films, 153 Waverly Place, Sixth Floor, New York, NY 10014; 212/243-0600; 800/876-1710

A Flash of Green, Ltd., 227 Westminster Drive, Tallahassee, FL 32304; 904/575-2696

Flower Films, 10341 San Pablo Avenue, El Cerrito, CA 94530; 415/525-0942

FN Films, 7658 Fountain Avenue, Los Angeles, CA 90046; 213/876-3468

James Forsher Productions, 1603 North 55th Street, Seattle, WA 98103, 206/728-8290, 206/457-1357

Forty Acres and a Mule Productions, 124 DeKalb Avenue, Brooklyn, NY 11217, 718/624-3703

Fox/Lorber Associates, 419 Park Avenue South, New York, NY 10016; 212/686-6777

Fries Distribution, Fries Home Video, 6922 Hollywood Boulevard, Hollywood, CA 90028; 213/466-2266

The Galvin Company, 574 West End Avenue, New York, NY 10024; 212/580-0692

Gidney International, 35 West 90th Street, New York, NY 10024, 212/877-5748

Global Village, 454 Broome Street, New York, NY 10013, 212/966-7526

Godmother Productions, c/o Saul Zaentz Company, 2600 Tenth Street, Berkeley, CA 94710; 415/549-1528

The Great Amwell Company, Spencer Road, Austerlitz, NY 12017; 518/392-6600

Green Mountain Post Films, P.O. Box 229, Turners Falls, MA 01376; 413/863-4754

Greenberg and O'Hearn Productions, 837 West 34th Street, Chicago, IL 60608, 312/523-8620, 312/247-4038

Greenwich Film Associates, 21 Jones Street, New York, NY 10014, 212/924-4247

Hackford/Littman, 6620 Cahuenga Terrace, Los Angeles, CA 90068; 213/468-6802

Hadley Productions, 716 Tenth Avenue, New York, NY 10019; 212/765-6455

Hawaii Public Television, Culture and Arts Department, 2350 Dole Street, Honolulu, HI 96822; 808/955-7878

HBO Home Video, 1100 Avenue of the Americas, New York, NY 10036; 212/512-7400

Heartland Productions, 800 Livermore Street, Yellow Springs, OH 45387; 513/767-9357

Hemisphere Productions, c/o Nat Silver, 316 East 53rd Street, New York, NY 10022; 212/752-8200

H. Jay Holman Productions, 340 East 57th Street, New York, NY 10022; 212/753-5504

HomeVision, 5547 North Ravenswood Avenue, Chicago, IL 60640; 800/262-8600, home video; 800/323-4222, all others; ext. 43 (education), ext. 380 (all other inquiries).

HTV, Ltd., Television Center, Culverhouse Cross, Cardiff CF5 6XJ Wales; 011-44-222-590590

Icarus/Tamouz Films International, 123 West 93rd Street, No.   5-B, New York, NY 10025; 212/864-7603

Icarus Films, see First Run Features

Ideas in Motion, 141 Tenth Street, San Francisco, CA 94103, 415/863-5500

Image Entertainment, 9333 Oso Avenue, Chatsworth, CA 91311; 818/407-9100, 800/633-3475

INA (Institute National de l'Audiovisuel), 4 Avenue de L'Europe, 94366 Bry Sur-Marne Cedex, France

Independent Pictures, 111 Gorevale Avenue, Toronto, Ontario, Canada M6J 2R5; 416/363-5155

Independent Productions, 1259 Fair View Court, Ojai, CA 93023; 213/555-4205

Information Factory, 3512 Courville, Detroit, MI 48224

Interama, 301 West 53rd Street, New York, NY 10019; 212/977-4830

Intermedia Arts Minnesota, 425 Ontario Street, S.E., Minneapolis, MN 55414, 612/627-4444

International Film Exchange, Ltd., 201 West 52nd Street, New York, NY 10019; 212/582-4318

International Video Entertainment, 500 N. Ventu Park Road, P.O. Box 2520, Newbury Park, CA 91320; 805/499-5827

ITTC, 919 Third Avenue, New York, NY; 212/838-2477

Jade Films, 704 Kingman Road, Birmingham, AL 35235, 205/836-8052

Janus Films, 888 Seventh Avenue, New York, NY 10106; 212/753-7100

JCI Video, 21550 Oxnard Street, Suite 920, Woodland Hills, CA 91367; 818/593-3600, 800/223-7479

Ronald J. Kahn Productions, 87 Old Mill Road, Great Neck, NY, 11023; 516/466-8394

Karl/Lorimar Home Video, see Warner Home Video

Kartemquin Films, 1901 W. Wellington, Chicago, IL 60657

KCET/Los Angeles, 4401 Sunset Boulevard, Los Angeles, CA 90027; 213/666-6500

Keener Productions, 3177 Lindo Street, Los Angeles, CA 90068; 213/851-2167

Kent Productions, P.O. Box 340, Route 7, North, Kent, CT 06757; 203/927-4406

KERA/Dallas<196>Fort Worth, 3000 Harry Hines Boulevard, Dallas, TX 75201-1098; 214/871-1390

The Kitchen, 512 West 19th Street, New York, NY 10011, 212/255-5793

Kuiv Productions, 9 Rue Campaign Premiere, 75014 Paris, France, 011-331-432-79898

Kultur International Films, 121 Highway 36, West Long Branch, NJ 07764; 201/229-2343, 800/458-5887

Learning in Focus, 4 Chatsworth Avenue, Larchmont, NY 10538; 914/833-3390

Ruth Leon Productions, 155 West 68th Street, New York, NY 10023

Light-Saraf Films, 131 Concord Street, San Francisco, CA 94112, 415/469-0139

Lionheart Television International, 630 Fifth Avenue, Suite 2220, New York, NY 10011; 212/541-7342

The Little Sister Partnership, 221 East 49th Street, New York, NY 10017; 212/752-8930

Lorimar Home Video see Warner Home Video

Lovely Music, 105 Hudson Street, Room 200, New York, NY 10013; 212/941-8911

Felicia Lowe Productions, 398 11th Street, Suite 300, San Francisco, CA 94103, 415/626-3711

Manic Films, 13113 Rose Avenue, Los Angeles, CA 90066; 213/390-0741

Sue Marx Films, 672 Woodbridge, Detroit, MI 48226, 313/259-8505, 313/862-8429

Maysles Films, 250 West 54th Street, New York, NY 10019; 212/582-6050

MCA Home Video, MCA/Universal, 100 Universal City Plaza, Universal City, CA 91608; 818/777-1000

Merchant/Ivory Productions, 250 West 57th Street, Suite 1913A, New York, NY 10019; 212/582-8049

Metropolitan Arts, 21 Jones Street, No. 11, New York, NY 10014, 212/924-4247

Metropolitan Museum of Art, Office of Film and Television, Fifth Avenue at 82nd Street, New York, NY 10028; 212/570-3806

MGM/UA Home Video, 10000 West Washington Boulevard, Culver City, CA 90232-2728; 213/280-6000

Mirabai Films, 225 Lafayette Street, New York, NY 10012, 212/941-6188

Monterey Home Video, 5142 N. Clareton Street, Suite 270, Agoura Hills, CA 91301; 818/597-0047

Mouchette Films, 548 Fifth Street, San Francisco, CA 94107; 415/495-3934

Movies Unlimited, 6736 Castor Avenue, Philadelphia, PA 19149; 215/722-8398, 800/523-0823

MPI Home Video, 15825 Rob Roy Drive, Oak Forest, IL 60452; 312/687-7881, 800/323-0442

Museum of Modern Art, Circulating Film and Video Library, 11 West 53rd Street, New York, NY 10019; 212/708-9530

Music Project for Television, 635 Madison Avenue, New York, NY 10022; 212/877-3737

Music Vision see RCA/Columbia Pictures Home Video

Mypheduh Films, 48 Q Street, N.E., Washington, DC 20002; 202/529-0220

Mystic Fire Video, P.O. Box 9323, Dept. C-3, South Burlington, VT 05407; 800/727-8433

National Film Board of Canada, 1251 Avenue of the Americas, 16th Floor, New York, NY 10020, 212/586-5131

National Video Corporation, Liberty House, 222 Regent Street, London W1R 5DE; 01/434-9571

Nederlander Television and Film Productions, 1564 Broadway, New York, NY 10036; 212/664-0033

Nepenthe Productions, P.O. Box 1412, Ross, CA 94957; 415/456-1414

New Day Films, 121 West 27th Street, Suite 902, New York, NY 10001; 212/645-8210

New Dimensions Media, 85895 Lorane Highway, Eugene, OR 97405, 503/484-7125

New Front Films, 317 Western Drive, Point Richmond, CA 94801; 415/235-9282

New Time Films, P.O. Box 502, Village Station, New York, NY 10014; 212/206-8607

New World Entertainment, 1440 South Sepulveda Boulevard, Los Angeles, California 90025; 213/444-8100

New Yorker Films, 16 West 61st Street, New York, NY 10023; 212/247-6110

Night Owl Productions, P.O. Box 433, Vineyard Haven, Martha's Vineyard, MA 02568; 508/693-6414

Northwinds Entertainment, 1223 Wilshire Boulevard, Suite 565, Santa Monica CA 90403; 213/558-4504

Nothing But A Man Company, 81 Leighton Avenue, Yonkers, NY 10705; 914/969-0053

Amram Nowak Associates, 15 West 26th Street, New York, NY 10010; 212/686-1660

NYU Film and Video Library, Avery Fisher Center for Music and Media, 70 Washington Square South, New York, NY 10012, 212/998-5165

Oasis Pictures, 56 Shaftesbury Avenue, Toronto, Ontario M4T 1A3, Canada; 416/967-6503

One West Media, P.O. Box 5766, Santa Fe, NM 87502-5766; 505/983-8685

Orion Classics, 1325 Avenue of the Americas, New York, NY 10019; 212/632-5924

Orion Home Video, 9 West 57th Street, 15th Floor, New York, NY 10019; 212/980-1117

Pacific Arts Video, 50 North La Cienega Boulevard, Beverly Hills, CA 90211; 213/657-2233

Palm Pictures, 8920 Sunset Boulevard, Los Angeles, CA 90069; 213/276-4500

Paramount Home Video, 5555 Melrose Avenue, Los Angeles, CA 90038-3197; 213/956-5000; The Metropolitan Opera Presents, Live From Lincoln Center—800/445-3800

Past America, 12100 N.E. 16th Avenue, Miami, FL 33161; 305/893-1202

PBS Video, PBS Home Video, 1320 Braddock Place, Alexandria, VA 22314-1698; 800/424-7963; 703/739-5000

Pennebaker Associates, 21 West 86th Street, New York, NY 10024, 212/496-9195

Phoenix Films, 468 Park Avenue, New York, NY 10016, 212/684-5910; 800/221-1274

Picture Start, 221 East Cullerton, Sixth Floor, Chicago, IL 60616; 312/326-6233

Pioneer Artists/Pioneer Signature, c/o LDC America, 2265 East 220th Street, Long Beach, CA 90745; 213/835-6177; 800/322-2285; The Metropolitan Opera Presents—800/255-2550

Platform Releasing, 700 Adella Lane, Coronado, CA 92118; 619/437-8110

Port Washington Public Library, Media Port, 245 Main Street, Port Washington, NY 11050, 516/883-4400

Post Mills Productions, 309 West 29th Street, New York, NY 10001; 212/564-7131

Princeton Book Company, P.O. Box 57, Pennington, NJ 08534-0057; 609/737-8177

Prism Entertainment, 1888 Century Park East, Suite 350, Los Angeles, CA 90067; 213/277-3270

Producer Services Group, 7461 Beverly Boulevard, Penthouse, Los Angeles, CA 90036; 213/937-5020

Public Television Playhouse, 1776 Broadway, New York, NY 10019; 212/757-4300

Pyramid Films, Box 1048, Santa Monica, CA 90406; 213/828-7577; 800/421-2304

RCA/Columbia Pictures Home Video, 3500 West Olive, Burbank, CA 91506; 818/953-7900

Revcom International, Les Films Ariane, 104 Avenue des Champs Elysees, 75008 Paris, France

Rhapsody Films, P.O. Box 179, New York, NY 10014; 212/243-0152

RKB Productions, 244 West 49th Street, Room 400-A, New York, NY 10017; 212/473-3320

RKO Home Video, see Turner Entertainment

RM Associates, 250 West 57th Street, Suite 1005, New York, NY 10107; 212/262-3230

Rocky Mountain Film Center, P.O. Box 316, University of Colorado, Boulder, CO 80309-0316, 303/492-1531

Rubicon Film Productions, Ltd., 29215 Fox Hollow Road, Eugene, OR 97405; 503/686-1238

Samuel Goldwyn Company, 10203 Santa Monica Boulevard, Los Angeles, CA 90067; 213/284-9126

Sanborn, Perillo and Company, 125 Cedar Street, New York, NY 10006, 212/608-3943

School of Cinema-Television, University of Southern California Film Distribution Center, University Park, MC-2212, Los Angeles, CA 90089; 213/743-2238

Sefel Corporation, Suite 225, 11th Avenue, S.W., Calgary, Alberta T2R 1L9, Canada; 403/269-8558

Shadow Projects, 462 Broome Street, No. 2-W, New York, NY 10013, 212/925-9605

Skouras Pictures, 1040 N. Las Palmas, Hollywood, CA 90038; 213/467-3000

Sony Music Video Enterprises, P.O. Box 4450, New York, NY 10101; 212/445-4321; 800/457-0866

Sony Video Software, 1700 Broadway, New York, NY 10019; 212/757-4900; 800/832-2422

South Carolina ETV, Drawer L, Columbia, SC 29250; 803/737-3200

Sterling Educational Films, 241 East 34th Street, New York, NY 10016; 212/593-0198

Stevenson Productions, 3227 Banks Street, New Orleans, LA 70119, 504/822-7678

Stone River Multi-Media Productions, 10723 Albion Street, Thornton, CO 80233, 303/457-4762

Studio Entertainment, 386 Park Avenue South, Suite 900, New York, NY 10016; 212/679-6980, 800/247-7004

Ken Stutz Company, 2600 Tenth Street, Berkeley, CA 94710; 415/644-2200

David Sutherland Productions, P.O. Box 163, Waban, MA 02168

Tapestry International, 924 Broadway, New York, NY 10010, 212/265-1055, 212/677-6007

TCB Releasing, Ltd., Stone House, Rudge Frome, Somerset BA1 2QQ, England

Terra Nova Films, 9848 South Winchester Avenue, Chicago, IL 60643, 312/881-8491, 312/445-8894

Texture Films, see HomeVision

Thames Television International, 149 Tottenham Court Road, London W1P 9LL, England

Third World Newsreel, 335 West 38th Street, New York, NY 10018; 212/947-9277

Thurber Productions Film Library, P.O. Box 315, Franklin Lakes, NJ 07417; 201/891-8240

Timed Exposures, 79 Raymond Avenue, Poughkeepsie, NY 12601, 914/485-8489

Today Home Entertainment, 9200 Sunset Boulevard, Penthouse 9, Los Angeles, CA 90069; 213/278-6490, 800/877-8434

TRA Films, Box 1119, Point Reyes, CA 94956; 415/663-1490

Transworld Entertainment, 3330 West Cahuenga Boulevard, Suite 500, Los Angeles, CA 90068; 213/969-2800, 800/521-0107

Turner Home Entertainment, 5 Penn Plaza, 19th Floor, New York, NY 10001; 212/714-7976

Universal Pictures, 100 Universal City Plaza, Bldg. 500, Universal City, CA 91608; 818/777-3111

University of Wisconsin, South Asian Studies, Room 1238/Van Hise, Madison, WI 53706; 608/262-3012

Upstream Productions, 420 First Avenue West, Seattle, WA 98119, 206/281-9177

Vanguard Films, 135 East 65th Street, New York, NY 10021; 212/517-4333

Viacom Enterprises, 423 West 55th Street, New York, NY 10019 212/523-1142

VidAmerica, 231 East 55th Street, New York, NY 10022; 212/355-1600

Video Artists International, P.O. Box 153, Ansonia Station, New York, NY 10023; 212/799-7798; 800/338-2566

Video Data Bank, School of the Art Institute of Chicago, 37 South Wabash Avenue, Chicago, IL 60603, 312/899-5100, 312/899-5172

Video Free America, 422 Shotwell Street, San Francisco, CA 94110, 415/648-9040

The Video Project, 5332 College Avenue, Suite 101, Oakland, CA 94168; 415/655-9050

Video Repitone, Ltd., 31 Greene Street, Fifth Floor, New York, NY 10013, 212/966-6326

Video Verite Library, 22D Hollywood Avenue, Hohokus, NJ 07423; 201/652-1989

Virgin Home Entertainment/MCEG, 2400 Broadway, Suite 100, Santa Monica, CA 90404; 213/315-7800

VPI (Videfilm Producers International), 225 West 57th Street, Suite 301, New York, NY 10019; 212/581-0400

Walt Disney Home Video, 500 South Buena Vista Street, Fairmont Building 633-F, Burbank, CA 91521; 800/227-9483

Warner Brothers; Warner Home Video, 4000 Warner Boulevard, Burbank, CA 91522; 818/954-6000

Weston Woods, 389 Newtown Turnpike, Weston, CT 06883-1199; 203/226-3355, 800/243-5020

WGBH/Boston, WGBH Education Center, 125 Western Avenue, Boston, MA 02134; 617/492-2777

The Wide Net Company, c/o Southern Voices Productions, 607 Sixth Street, Brooklyn, NY 11215; 718/788-2988

Wilderness Women Productions, Box 173, Star Route, Bonner, MT 59823; 406/244-5549

Windmill Lane Productions, 4 Windmill Lane, Dublin 2, Ireland

WNET/Thirteen, 356 West 58th Street, New York, NY 10019; 212/560-2000

WNET Videotakes, P.O. Box 648, 187 Parker Avenue, Manasquan, NJ 08736; 800/338-2973

Women Make Movies, 225 Lafayette Street, Suite 211, New York, NY 10012, 212/925-0606

X-Africa Productions, 613 Cambridge Street, Cambridge, MA 02141, 617/492-1929

Zi-Fi Productions, 338-A East 13th Street, New York, NY 10003; 212/777-7850

Zworl Quern Productions, 51 West 86th Street, No. 1703, New York, NY 10024; 212/799-7645

A NOTE ON RESEARCH

Rebecca Krafft
Editor, The Arts on Television,
1976-1991

Listed in this book are 1,000-plus programs broadcast on television series funded in part by the National Endowment for the Arts' Arts on Television initiative. The first of these series began in 1976. Several dozen individual specials are also included, a few of which date from prior to 1976. In addition, approximately a dozen works funded through the Film/Video Production category were included as their subjects particularly complement those covered here. The cutoff date for inclusion in this volume was the 1989-1990 television season.

Each listing consists of a synopsis and selected credits. The original PBS airdate or initial cable transmission date follows each program description. The broadcast-feed length (rounded at times to the nearest five minutes) comes after. Of the principal personnel responsible for each program, only a few could be named—director, producer, writer and executive producer. Although their relative importance varies in television and film production, a single order of credits was adopted. Any omissions are unintentional. Four awards—Academy, ACE, Emmy and Peabody Awards—are listed in the text. These and others are found in the second appendix. Information on after-market distribution was supplied largely by series' staff. Though the main focuses of this information are the educational and home markets, distributors in other markets are named at times. We have sought to err on the side of inclusiveness.

Most photos came from press kits circulated by the series. Letters about the programs were sent by viewers to local public television stations and the series over several years. They were edited for length in some cases. The Endowment's major series co-funders are listed at the start of each series and in the first appendix. Except for the Arts Endowment's sister agency, the National Endowment for the Humanities, the numerous co-funders of individual programs were not listed for reason of space. A final editorial decision concerned the programs in chapter 10, Media Art. These were given descriptive titles.

The predominant sources for the text were the final reports submitted by grantees—written narratives, press kits or videotapes, and sometimes all three. Critical reviews and press coverage were drawn upon only after any other alternative had been exhausted. Personnel from the series reviewed pertinent text, and many gaps in information were filled by the PBS Library staff.

In seeking to complete the account, two kinds of problems were encountered. In the case of the oldest programs in this book, the written accounts were sparse, sometimes no more than a sentence. Distinguishing the producers' intentions from the results was often difficult from the documentation contained in the files, and videotapes for older shows were sometimes missing. Inquiries of the producing stations met with little success as the institutional memory about a completed series or program had been dissipated by staff turnover. The difficulty in tracing essential facts of about early programs is particularly disturbing, since, with the passage of time, many have acquired historical importance.

Documentation of more recent and ongoing series has improved markedly as advertising and marketing budgets have become widely recognized as an essential expense, and press releases are routinely composed and disseminated. Press releases, however, in describing a program attractively for public attention, were often found to omit facts important to the researcher. While the urge to package is understandable, there is much to be said for basic accounting. What is lost in superlatives is gained in verisimilitude—in directness and impact.

For the researcher, there is no substitute for a single well-written paragraph on the part of the creator of the film that gives a matter-of-fact accounting of what was attempted, what transpired and what art works are recorded. The principals appearing and the production credits, basic facts, must also be set down. Such a succinct accounting would be similar to a librarian's annotation— summarizing the plot or the approach applied to a classic theme and explicating a title where possible. Television stations, producers and filmmakers are urged—amidst all other competing pressures—to adopt a minimum standard of written documentation. Hopefully, this book will encourage such efforts in the interests of the history of the field and the record that the Arts on Television provides the future.

TITLES INDEX

DIRECTOR/PRODUCER INDEX

Producers, executive producers, directors and media artists are found in this list.

SUBJECT INDEX

FEATURE FILMS

FILM AND TELEVISION

ISBN 0-16-035926-0